Series Editor

PAOLO BERTINE

*Dean of Faculty of Modern Languages
and Professor of English Literature,
University of Turin*

Brave
New World

Aldous Huxley

Introduction,
notes and activities by

JONATHAN BENISON

Edited by Andrew Thompson

Picture source: The Huxley family (pp. II and LX); Chatto and Windus (pp. VIII, XI); Matthew Huxley (pp. XII, LXVIII).

We would be happy to receive your comments and suggestions, and give you any other information concerning our material.
info@blackcat-cideb.com
blackcat-cideb.com

CISQ CISQ CERT

TEXTBOOKS AND
TEACHING MATERIALS

The quality of the publisher's
design, production and sales processes has
been certified to the standard of
UNI EN ISO 9001

Printed in Italy by L.E.G.O. S.p.A. Lavis (TN)

CONTENTS

INTRODUCTION

The Author of *Brave New World*

Aldous Leonard Huxley ['ɔːldəs 'hʌksli] was born on 26th July 1894 near Godalming in Surrey. His father, Leonard Huxley, was a schoolmaster at the time, but shortly afterwards joined a publishing company and became assistant editor of the *Cornhill Magazine*, while his grandfather was Thomas Henry Huxley, the illustrious biologist who had been an important advocate of Charles Darwin's theory of evolution; his mother, Judith, who founded a girls' school, also had a distinguished ancestry, as she was a grand-niece of the prominent Victorian critic and poet Matthew Arnold, while his elder brother Julian (later Sir Julian), a biologist, was to become the first director general of UNESCO and one of the founders of the World Wildlife Fund. Aldous, in short, had the benefit of being born into a privileged cultural milieu.

Being a young man of remarkable intellectual abilities he was able to live up to the expectations raised by belonging to such a family. He was educated at Eton and at Balliol College, Oxford, from which he graduated with a First-Class degree in English in 1916. He had to face some sad and difficult occurrences in this early period: the death of his mother from cancer when he was only fourteen; a year of near-blindness caused by the onset of an eye disease, keratitis (irritation of the cornea), from which he was to suffer all his life (and which meant that his university reading was carried out with great difficulty, using a magnifying glass); and then, in August 1914, his brother Trevenan committed suicide at the age of twenty-four, hanging himself as a result of a personal crisis.

The years that followed also left their mark on the author of *Brave New World*: Huxley was introduced to a group of free thinking, pacifist intellectuals and through them met some of the leading literary and philosophical figures of the day, such as Bertrand Russell, the poets

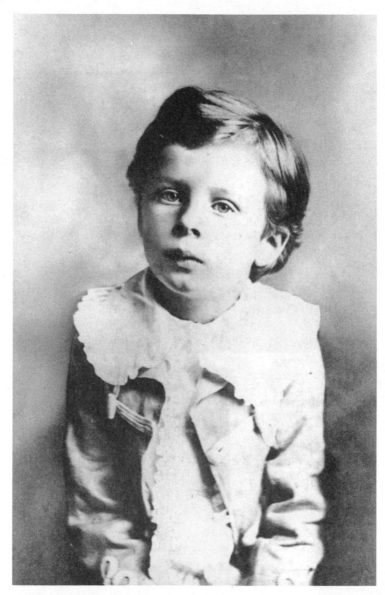

Aldous aged four

Robert Graves and T.S. Eliot, D.H. Lawrence, and Katherine Mansfield, whose husband, John Middleton Murry, helped him find openings in literary journalism. In 1919 Huxley married Maria Nys, a Belgian refugee, and began contributing reviews and articles to *The Athenaeum*, a London literary review, and drama reviews for the *Westminster Gazette*. Following the success of his novel Crome Yellow (1921),* he signed a contract with the London publishers Chatto and Windus which enabled the Huxleys (including their son Matthew, born in 1920) to spend the twenties abroad, in Italy and France, where life was less expensive and the brighter light better for Aldous's eyes. A world tour in 1925 and 1926, which took Huxley to India, the Far East and America, supplied the material for the first of his travel books, *Jesting Pilate* (1926). Following the death in 1930 of D.H. Lawrence, with whom Aldous had formed a real friendship during their sojourns in Italy in the late twenties, the Huxleys moved to the south of France, and it was here that Huxley worked on *Brave New World*.

Brave New World, the most popular of Huxley's books, was published when its author was thirty-seven years old. His first publications had been collections of his poetry, but it was his prose works that had established his reputation as a writer: the stories in *Limbo* (1920) and other collections, the regular volumes of Huxley's essays and, above all, the witty novels *Crome Yellow* (1921), *Antic Hay* (1923), *Those Barren Leaves* (1925) and *Point Counter Point* (1928), all of which are full of sparkling, clever conversation. With their lively explorations of the various attitudes to life shown by the characters and the satirical exposure of their self-deceptions, these amusing but penetrating novels reflect the scepticism typical of many intellectuals in the period after the First World War, as well as a wish to be modern, sophisticated and somewhat shocking.

---

* Huxley's books were generally first published by Chatto and Windus, London; there have been many paperback editions over the years, and at present most of them are available as paperbacks published by Mandarin Books, London.

In this respect *Brave New World* represents the culmination of the first phase of Huxley's career as a writer. It is the most disturbing of his "novels of exploration", as one critic calls them, in which he seeks "reconciliation of the absolute and the relative" (May, 1972).* His next novel, *Eyeless in Gaza* (1936), is a transitional work, while his subsequent writings (five novels, including *Ape and Essence* [New York, 1948], which offers another vision of a possible future, and several collections of essays, as well as much else), all give the impression of being the work of a man who knows exactly where he stands (on issues such as pacifism, the value of individual life, the need to expand our awareness and to learn from mystics and Eastern religious traditions), and who wants to pass on his convictions to his readers. There is an air of gloomy seriousness that derives from his deep-seated convictions regarding what he saw as the thoroughly wrong choices made by western civilisation.

The Huxleys lived in southern California from 1937; Maria Nys Huxley died in 1955 and the following year Aldous married Laura Archera, a concert violinist and practising psychotherapist. Throughout this period, up to within a few months of his death (from cancer) on November 22nd 1963 (the day President John F. Kennedy was assassinated), he continued writing and travelling to speak at universities and seminars on the subjects that concerned him most – in particular, the dangers of over-population, the threat to the individual in mass culture and the senseless destruction of the planet. His intellectual boldness and integrity was evident to the end.

Brave New World, as we have seen, belongs to an intermediate stage in Huxley's creative life, a period in which he was moving away from the cynical and critical stance he had adopted to such devastating effect in *Point Counter Point*, and was piecing together the principles that

---

* References in the *Introduction* : References to books or articles listed in the Bibliography in this volume are given in the text, as in this case, by citing the author's name and the date of the work (and the page numbers where appropriate). In all other cases details of the works referred to are given in the notes at the end of the *Introduction*.

Aldous with his son Matthew c. 1926

*Aldous, climbing in the
Sanary Back Country 1930s*

*Aldous and D. H. Lawrence at Bandol,
France, 1929*

Matthew, Maria and Aldous in the early 1930s

would underpin the committed tone of his later writings, the tone that is unmistakably present for the first time in *Ends and Means: An Enquiry into the Nature of Ideals and into the Methods Employed for their Realization*, written in 1937. Recollecting his reaction upon reading *Ends and Means* when the essay came out, John Atkins records how significant it seemed to him "that a leading and extremely intelligent but previously uncommitted writer had taken up a positive position" (Atkins, 1967: p. XXI). In fact the "new note" had already been evident in his conversation as early as 1933, and his friend and biographer Sybille Bedford remembers that those around him identified it as "something we were too shocked to recognise as hope" – "one felt a sense of grievance at the shift from a trusted intellectual position (the first reaction of readers in the coming years)" (Bedford, 1987: Vol. 1, p. 281). What emerges from these testimonies is the certainty that Huxley in 1928 was very different from Huxley in 1937. This is an important consideration when we are faced with a work written in 1931, incorporating ideas the author had made use of as early as 1921 and others which were already at an "advanced state of development" in 1929 (Meckier, 1979: p. 1), but which is prefaced with a "Foreword" written in 1946 for a new edition of the book and printed in all subsequent editions. Indeed, Huxley himself alludes to this change of outlook in the "Foreword", when he points out that whereas in 1931 he could find "amusing . . . and quite possibly true" the idea that "sanity is impossible", fifteen years later, though remaining "no less sadly certain than in the past that sanity is a rather rare phenomenon", he also says that he is "convinced that it can be achieved and would like to see more of it" (see p. 7). One can understand that in 1946, after the Second World War, and in particular after the horrors of Auschwitz and Hiroshima, when the deadly combination of modern technology and totalitarian regimes no longer appeared a matter for humorous treatment, the author would try to disassociate himself from his own earlier work and in particular from its supposed "wish to demonstrate that sanity is impossible". One can understand this change of heart without necessarily endorsing Huxley's description of his earlier self as "the amused, Pyrrhonic aesthete who was the author of this fable" (see p. 7): this is a caricature. It could be argued that it is not an adequate description even of the author of the first four novels and of some of the early essays, but as a characterisation of the writer as he was in 1931 it is surely inadequate – too condescending and too simplistic. So, what were Huxley's attitudes and beliefs at the point when he planned and wrote *Brave New World*? It would require more space than is available here to give a proper answer to that question (and my own feeling is that it would not necessarily help us appreciate and respond to the text: the implied author of Huxley's fiction is an altogether more interesting and less dogmatic person than the essay and letter writer, or the person described in the biographies).[1] Nevertheless, it may be useful to take note of at least a few significant facts about Huxley's life in an attempt to assemble a slightly more adequate set of co-ordinates in which to place the author of *Brave New World*.[2]

If we look at the pattern of his life, what emerges as the prevailing characteristic of Aldous Huxley's personality is his cultivated self-reliance. He was undoubtedly a gifted child, but if we ask how he developed into the phenomenal conversationalist of the twenties, the man who could talk knowledgeably about all sorts of subjects, who became a novelist of world renown and, later, a guru of the counter-culture movements of the sixties, then we must look for the answer in his insistence on learning from every experience, his determination to engage with whatever circumstances and possibilities life presented him with, and to turn them into occasions for extensions of the resources of the self, for self-realisation. It seems likely that the young Aldous acquired the habit of relying on himself in response to the personal calamities of his early days: the death of his mother, the sudden loss of sight, and the suicide of his brother Trev. As Sybille Bedford observes, "for any positive survival Aldous had to summon up his own resources" (Bedford, 1987: Vol.1, p. 34); she is referring here to the months of near-blindness that followed Aldous's attack of *keratitis punctata*, but the comment surely has a wider applicability.

In this respect there certainly is continuity in his life: the same self-cultivating impulse that led him to set off on a world tour in 1926 reappears in his willingness to experiment with mind-expanding drugs in the fifties. The resistance to stasis, the search for the new and valid, and the readiness to take risks that can be seen in both cases are typical of Huxley's approach to life, and it is because of this that his work will always have a special appeal to young people, to all those who have not not given up making the effort to respond to new experiences and to grow. By 1929, with the experiences of India and California behind him, he had acquired sufficient self-assurance and self-awareness to expound and defend this approach to experience. He felt able to confront the serious question of the choice of a philosophy of life, a concept of the purpose of human life, and not only to analyse alternative positions but to assert the validity of his own chosen positions, as can be seen in this passage from one of the essays in *Do What You Will* (1929):

> For what is the aspiration towards more than human knowledge but a flight from the infinite complexities and varieties of appearances? The ideas of Plato, the One of Plotinus, the Alls, the Nothings, the Gods, the Infinites, the Natures of all the mystics of whatever religions, of all the transcendental philosophers, all the pantheists – what are they but convenient and consoling substitutes for the welter of immediate experience, home-made and therefore home-like spiritual snuggeries in the alien universe? And the stoic's brutal sacrifice of the physical, instinctive and passional life, the ascetic's self-castration, the modern efficiency-monger's deprecation of all but willed and intelligent activities on the one hand, and all but purely mechanical routineering activities on the other – what are these 'high moralities' but terrified flights from the problems of social and individual life? Harmonious living is a matter of tact and sensitiveness, of judgment and balance and incessant adjustment, of being well bred and aristocratically moral by habit and instinct. . . . A cast-iron morality is not admirable; on the contrary, it is the confession of a fear of life, of an inability to deal with the facts of experience as they present themselves . . . .[3]

The tone in this passage seems to me to be close to that of the implied author of *Brave New World*, and it is not the voice of an "amused, Pyrrhonic aesthete".

The invitation to be "aristocratically moral" may in turn be linked to another characteristic which was always there, but which is not so readily recognisable in the earlier writings although it exists there in a negated form namely the sense of mission. This is not surprising given Huxley's descent:

> Aldous was born into a particular and self-conscious enclave, a class within a class, the governing upper middle – an elite, an intellectual aristocracy made up of a handful of families – Trevelyans, Macaulays, Arnolds, Wedgwoods, Darwins, Huxleys – who had produced a number of extraordinary and diversely gifted individuals whose influence . . . upon nineteenth-century England had been tremendous. Their common denominator was an intense desire to acquire, to advance and to disseminate knowledge . . . a wish to improve the lot as well as the administration of mankind, an assumption of responsibility – *l'intelligence oblige* – and a passion, no tamer word will do, for truth.
>
> (Bedford, 1987: Vol. 1, p. 19)

So much of what is most constant in Huxley's opinions and habits can be accounted for if set in this context: his apparently unquestioned conviction that inborn characteristics determine intelligence, character and lifestyle; his model of 'knowledge', which is epitomised by the *Encyclopedia Britannica*, and seems (again unquestionably) to consist of "the best that has been known and said in the world, and thus . . . the history of the human spirit",[4] as one of his ancestors famously defined culture; or his concern with exceptional individuals rather than the mass of people, as if it were assumed that they alone represent the destiny and value of humanity. This last bias is apparent throughout his work, but it is worth noting that he explicitly defended it in 1927 in an essay which has been cited as proof that "the United States is the present model for Huxley's vision of the future [in *Brave New World*]" (Firchow, 1966: p. 455). The essay, entitled "The Outlook for American

Culture, Some Reflections in a Machine Age", written after his visit to Los Angeles and other cities in the United States, begins by asserting that "speculating on the American future, we are speculating on the future of civilised man". What Huxley deplores in the American Way of Life is the way it encourages large numbers of people to "not want to be cultured" nor to be "interested in the higher life": "For these people existence on the lower, animal levels is perfectly satisfactory. Given food, drink, the company of their fellows, sexual enjoyment, and plenty of noisy distractions from without, they are happy". His attack focuses on standardisation, both mechanical and, as a result, cultural: like many other intellectuals in the period, he reacted with genuine horror and disgust at the products of the nascent mass culture industry (even though he too became a Hollywood scriptwriter in the forties). These trends seemed to conjure up the spectre of standardised man as the ideal happy consumer needed to increase profits for the manufacturers of standardised products, including cultural products:

> This tendency to raise the ordinary, worldly man to the level of the extraordinary and disinterested one seems to me entirely deplorable. The next step will be to exalt him above the extraordinary man, who will be condemned and persecuted on principle because he is not ordinary – for not to be ordinary will be regarded as a crime. In this reversal of the old values I see a real danger, a menace to all desirable progress.[5]

While it is surely correct to conclude, as Peter Firchow does, that "*Brave New World* is the fictional extension of Huxley's earlier views on the nature of American 'culture'" (Firchow, 1966: p. 456), we may also observe that in the fictional treatment the snobbish elitism of this typical passage is neatly avoided. The novel does not give the same impression of a lanky Englishman with a posh accent, an extraordinary individual with an exceptional background, feeling threatened by new forces and new values that he does not understand. On the other hand, to the extent that we can identify the working classes in Huxley's "ordinary man", it could be said that his novel adopts a more drastic solution to the problem of the ranks of Fordian industrial workers who were rivalling the bourgeoisie as consumers of cultural products: they are excluded – the Gammas, Epsilons and Deltas of *Brave New World* hardly count as men and women, and are always viewed from a safe distance as animal-like masses or vermin that by their very nature cannot enter into the foregrounded concerns of the novel.

All in all, reading Huxley's essays alongside the fiction can be a disappointing experience: the author's ideas often become more palatable when they are transposed into a fictional context. Let me give one last example of this, by quoting the final section, entitled "Probable Effects of Eugenic Reform" from Huxley's 1927 essay, "A Note on Eugenics":

> States function as smoothly as they do, because the greater part of the population is not very intelligent, dreads responsibility, and desires nothing better than to be told what to do. Provided the rulers do not interfere with its material comforts and its cherished beliefs, it is perfectly happy to let itself be ruled. The socially efficient and the intellectually gifted are precisely those who are not content to be ruled, but are ambitious either to rule or to live in an anti-social solitude. A state with a population consisting of nothing but these superior people could not hope to last for a year. The best is ever the enemy of the good. If the eugenists are in too much of an enthusiastic hurry to improve the race, they will only succeed in destroying it. [6]

Once again there is no doubt that *Brave New World* is a fictional development of thoughts of this kind, but whereas the novel implies an author who is *making use of* such ideas, in order to demonstrate the model of human life they imply, here each proposition is put forward as a given fact. The novel is speculative, and takes up the ideas as hypotheses to be tested; the essay is assertive, and sounds much more like the voice of one of the "superior people" addressing others of his class, reminding them of some of the tenets of ruling class ideology (in particular, that the underdogs enjoy being underdogs and that we "superior people" must resign ourselves to relying on such underdeveloped types to be our "subjects . . . farmers . . . bank clerks . . .

workmen [and] private soldiers"). It is disconcerting to discover that the author who had the genius to put essentially the same ideas in the mouth of his fictional World Controller had not been above advocating them himself a few years before. (C.f. Baker, 1982: p. 143 – "A significant number of Mustapha Mond's principal beliefs . . . were shared at this time by Huxley").

Literary and Cultural Background

Huxley has been described as "the 'typical' writer of his generation, and a major influence upon the young intelligentsia of his time". Indeed, "for those who . . . were growing up during the 1920's, Aldous Huxley seemed unquestionably the most stimulating and exciting writer of the day" so that "by comparison, most other contemporary writers seemed stuffy, unenlightened, and old-fashioned". Not only was Huxley "sophisticated", "agreeably shocking" and "penetrating" at the level of ideas, but in addition "his style in itself was a novelty – highly wrought yet extremely readable, deriving from unfamiliar models", such as the satirical novels of Thomas Love Peacock (1785-1866) (Brooke, 1984: p. 197). Another model was H.G. Wells, the author of scientific romances in which philosophical themes and scientific notions are brought to life and made accessible to a wide public. Wells's short stories, and novels such as *The Time Machine* (1895), *The Sleeper Awakes* (orig. 1899), in which a totalitarian future world is imagined, or *Men Like Gods* (1923), had a similarly stimulating effect on Huxley's own generation, as is recalled by George Orwell in his essay "Wells, Hitler, and the World State" (1941): "It was a wonderful thing to discover H.G. Wells. There you were, in a world of pedants, clergymen and golfers . . . and here was this marvellous man who could tell you about the inhabitants of the planets and the bottom of the sea, and who *knew* that the future was not going to be what respectable people imagined". If Huxley is recognisably part of a modern movement in literature, it is on account of a similar excitement generated by the play of ideas in his work, which are far-reaching, unorthodox, at times challengingly unpalatable. That is to say, while his fiction is not consistently experimental in the way that James Joyce's *Ulysses* (1922) is, or Virginia Woolf's *To the Lighthouse* (1927) is, it is too intellectually demanding to be considered as simply entertainment. Indeed, it is often misanthropic to a degree that is hard to accept, or rebarbartive – like the notorious opening of *Eyeless in Gaza*, when two lovers on a flat-roofed building are spattered with the blood of a dog that has fallen from a helicopter onto the roof near them – while its general tone of mockery, cynicism and critical detachment (which emerges as a comprehensive critique of contemporary trends in *Brave New World*) links it to those writers and artists we now label "modernists".

There was, in the first quarter of the century, a shared sense that the traditional, commonly used forms of expression (such as linear narrative in the novel; window-on-the-world realism in painting; conventional metrical patterns and rhyme in poetry) had become automatic, were no longer able to respond to the complexities of experience. The post-war years saw a great deal of significant innovation in all forms of artistic production. Indications of an interest in formal experimentation are to be found in *Brave New World* too: the abrupt opening which plunges the reader without preliminaries into the imagined environment was an innovation in the utopian tradition; the section in Chapter Three that juxtaposes different lines of narrative (a small-scale reutilisation of a technique more extensively exploited in *Point Counter Point* and explained and justified by the Huxley-figure in that book); the use of flashback techniques for filling in details of John's past life; the extensive use of allusions, so that really only the high-brow section of the population, who shared Huxley's cultural background, would be in a position to decode the text – as if, like T.S. Eliot in *The Waste Land* (1922), Huxley felt responsible for maintaining the integrity of a cultural heritage under threat from the popularising dynamics of mass culture.

"In the wake of the Great War the British intelligentsia had become very suspicious of the idea of progress. They had lived through a terrible war which had been fought by machines rather than men, and in which the capacity of scientific knowledge to equip men with frightful forces of destruction had been demonstrated in no uncertain terms" (Stableford, 1985: p. 158-9). It is not surprising, then, that Huxley should come to make science the object of his satire. In the twenties his work had chosen "to mock an exhausted culture whose religion and morality are spent, whose ideals have evaporated, and whose notions of romantic love have faded into animal promiscuity".[7] In the Jazz Age (with its "party craze" and Bright Young Things "jerking their bottoms in the Charleston in a vain attempt to escape the voguish 'boredom'", as Harry Blamires puts it), the conflict between the two generations (already aggravated by the war) inevitably led to battles about relations between the sexes. Conflicts of this kind, provoked by hangovers from Victorian values, had supplied Huxley with much of the subject matter for his first novels and short stories. With *Brave New World* Huxley turns his attention to the simplistic and over-optimistic expectations about science that were prevalent at the time. These, along with differing and antagonistic attitudes concerning sexual morality, represented perhaps the main intrusions of persisting nineteenth-century conceptions into post-war realities with which they were totally incapable of coming to terms. The war (but also such events as the General Strike of 1926 and the collapse of the New York Stock Exchange in 1929) had made it more difficult to believe in man's progressive elimination of suffering and increasing ability to control his conditions of life, but attitudes had been slow to adapt. Huxley's premises were rather different, since he "consistently viewed the course of modern history in terms of 'regression' (*Ends and Means*), 'degeneracy', and 'inward decay' (*Point Counter Point*)" (Baker, 1982: p. 28).

Brave New World: **Approaches to the Novel**

> *Brave New World* is one of two novels – along with George Orwell's
> *Nineteen Eighty-Four* – which seem between them to have had more
> impact on the way we think about the future than all the rest put
> together.
>
> (Stableford, 1985: p. 154)

How can we read the text with an open mind, as the kind of alert, well-informed reader it obviously hopes for, when all of us think we already know about the 'vision of the future' it contains? It is only too easy to draw up a list of highly questionable commonplaces about *Brave New World* – even from the criticism of specialists. Indeed, even from Huxley's own 1946 "Foreword": Is the story really a "fable"? Is it in fact an account of "Utopia" (see p. 6)? It is true that the word had been used in the epigraph from Berdyayev that prefaces all editions, but this passage can equally well be taken as implying that the fiction that follows will be post-utopian – no one in the World State calls it Utopia. Is it then a "dystopia"? A standard dictionary definition of dystopia is "an imaginary place where everything is as bad as it can be" (*Collins English Dictionary*): probably many people who apply this label to the novel have never actually read it! Against this prejudgment it is worth quoting Keith May's remark, in his admirable chapter on the novel: "Here is a society which fulfils what many have regarded as their best hopes for the future of mankind: war, want, and disease are things of the past; personal and social conflicts scarcely exist" (May, 1972: p. 108).

Another widespread oversimplification is that people in Huxley's imaginary state are dominated by science: it depends what is meant by "dominated". If the term is applied because of the "pattern or formula [that] emerges in this society: an irrational faith in science as the highest form of knowledge, the belief in a certain *kind* of scientific knowledge as an end in itself [that] justifies the alteration and manipulation of the species" (Aldridge, 1980: p.125), then the judgment is of dubious validity. It is not scientific knowledge that is "an end in itself" in Huxley's World State, but Stability; the World Controller explicitly states that scientific work, even if "novel and highly ingenious" cannot be tolerated if it introduces the question of "purpose" existing "somewhere outside the present human sphere" *because "so far as the present social order is concerned, [it would be] dangerous and potentially subversive"* (Chapter 12: italics added). "Every discovery in pure science is potentially subversive; even science must sometimes be treated as a possible enemy", he says. Scientific research, in other words, is subordinate to the only "goal" this society acknowledges: reproduction of the existing conditions of existence. The elect few who still think about these things are not in the grip of some irrational presupposition that science is revealing the ultimate truth: they simply do not pronounce themselves on such issues – they have called a moratorium on debates over true descriptions of reality and how to achieve them and are getting on with the business of staying alive. In this they differ from the scientists in our world, who in the thirties were developing the atom bomb: if anyone is "dominated" by science it is surely our modern world, not Huxley's postmodern one, where discussions of transcendent issues have been shelved – literally, shelved away in safes. This is very different from pretending to have answered such questions by experiments using white rats or particle accelerators. In any case, this is not the issue with which the novel is mainly concerned; as Huxley notes in the "Foreword", "the theme of *Brave New World* is not the advancement of science as such; it is the advancement of science as it affects human individuals" (p. 9). In an article published the year after the novel appeared he argued that science is "morally neutral".[8] Jenni Calder's summary seems to me much closer to the mark: the world of "*Brave New World* is presented as the logical development of a consumer and technology-orientated society, *the means are scientific and the ends are self-perpetuation*" (Calder, 1975: p. 14 – italics added; c.f. "Foreword", p. 11). Alongside which it is appropriate to quote Keith May's closing sentence: "The chief illusion which *Brave New World* shatters has less to do with an unthinking faith in scientific progress than with the assumption that truth, beauty, and happiness are reconcilable goods on the plane of ordinary, unregenerate human activity" (May, 1972: p. 117).

The most widely-held misconception, however, is that *Brave New World* is a serious attempt to predict the future. Huxley himself seems to endorse this view in his 1946 "Foreword" and in his 1958 essay *Brave New World Revisited*, but it invites a number of objections. First of all, questions of detail. If this was his intention, is it not strange that, as he points out in the "Foreword", "*Brave New World* contains no reference to nuclear fission" (p. 9)? Indeed, in that paragraph he himself admits the omission is "actually rather odd" for several reasons – another, not mentioned, is that "H.G. Wells had already described atomic bombs (using the very name) as early as 1914 in *The World Set Free*" (Firchow, 1975: p. 302). In any case, Huxley's argument at that point leads to the conclusion that the novel was not intended as a prediction of what was likely to happen in the future "in the external world"; rather its subject matter was what Huxley, in 1946, chose to describe as "the really revolutionary revolution [which] is to be achieved . . . in the souls and flesh of human beings" (p. 10). When he was working on the book in 1931 he made more modest claims:

> I am writing a novel about the future – on the horror of the Wellsian Utopia and a revolt against it. Very difficult. I have hardly enough imagination to deal with such a subject. [9]

It is true that he uses the phrase "about the future", but the rest of the sentence seems to point in a different direction, as does the answer he gave in the early sixties to the question "How did you begin *Brave New World*"?

> Well, that started out as a parody of H.G. Wells' *Men Like Gods*, but gradually it got out of hand and turned into something quite different from what I'd originally intended. As I became more and more interested in the subject, I wandered farther and farther from my original purpose. [10]

This has the ring of truth, particularly if we recall the following passage, published in 1932: "Personally, I must confess, I am more interested in what the world is now than in what it will be, or what it might be if improbable conditions were fulfilled".[11] But aside from these specific contradictory statements, there is the general impression the novel gives – in its tone and structure – of being constructed as an exploration of essentially abstract questions. In particular it involves a systematic contrast of just two alternatives whereas reality, and the real future, includes a whole range of possibilities. As an illustration, we can consider Peter Firchow's delineation of "the central problem" of the novel: "The inhabitants of the Fordian state are aware, insomuch as they are aware, of a reality which is totally 'happy'; the inhabitants of the Indian Reservation (including, for the most part, the Savage), on the other hand, are aware only of a sinister, 'unhappy' reality" (Firchow, 1966: p. 460). This, I think, is a valid and pertinent formulation, but it begs the question: why is only one simple community represented and why does it have to be "unhappy'"? One answer is that all those who disagreed with the principles of the World State were systematically exterminated and the remaining Reservations only exist on sufferance in places "which, owing to unfavourable climatic or geological conditions, or poverty of natural resources, [have] not been worth the expense of civilizing", as we are told in Chapter 11 (p. 172): their inhabitants are not likely to be happy. Nevertheless, a truer answer is surely this: the alternatives are reduced to two because *Brave New World* is a fundamentally unrealistic and schematic text.[12] It abstracts from the messy contingencies of empirical reality and focuses on what Huxley saw as the essential issues, which are best described as philosophical. In this respect *Brave New World* can be seen as a further extension of the same contrasts that had always informed Huxley's fiction: "Behind the world of narrow, self-centred characters who inhabit a Huxley novel and behind the Wellsian utopia wherein every person has imbalance or one-sidedness built into him on a Fordian assembly line, stands the forgotten world of Shakespeare", who "remains for Huxley the incarnation of the ideal, complete artist who sees the multiplicity of life".[13] This is a novel that carefully isolates and develops the "continual contrast between a total, imaginative view of life and the one-sided, incomplete, chiefly functional existences led by the inhabitants of a brave new world" (*ibid.*);

its construction foregrounds issues such as this and their implications are explored with great liveliness and wit. Surely it is asking too much to expect the same novel to carry out the quite different task of assessing the multifarious processes at work in the external world and extrapolating from them a likely scenario for the future. That would have required an entirely different outlook and reading programme: it would have led to an essay in futurology, like *Brave New World Revisited*, which would now have merely historical interest.

Instead what we have is very much a work of imaginative fiction, and it is the reader's imaginative experience of the concrete *feel* of the projected system (that is, the experience of it as a human situation) and the reader's ability to be constantly asking the right sort of questions that determines the value of the encounter with the text. No summary of the book's themes or of critics' comments can substitute this engagement with what the fiction offers, and to get the most out of it every reader must simply read the book as receptively as possible (making use of the information provided in the notes in this edition), trying to make sense of the choices that lie behind the various situations and techniques embodied in the text. Brian Aldiss, voicing what must be a widely felt response, observes that "Huxley shows us a world that indeed does have its insidious attractions", a world, moreover, that "we can believe in".[14] It is because we come to believe in it that we take seriously the questions it poses, concerning the value of the individual in a highly organised society, and whether people really want to be happy or whether they need some further goal in life, and in particular, what happens to human beings if, as the epigraph puts it, "utopias can be achieved". Is life still worth living if our hopes and expectations are perfectly matched by what is on offer to us? Indeed, can human beings exist at all without aspirations involving obstacles that have to be overcome? Inevitably the text also obliges you to ask yourself whose side (if anyone's) you are on: Bernard's or Lenina's, John's or that of Mustapha Mond? (Some readers may agree with Brian Stableford that the latter, "the defender of the world, comes off better than he is usually given credit for" [Stableford, 1985: p. 254]).

The remainder of this introduction will assess the merits of the approaches to the book that have most frequently been adopted by critics. *Brave New World* can be examined in various frameworks, notably the contexts of popular fiction and the novel, the satirical or utopian traditions, the author's life and works, the socio-cultural context, or that of modernism; each of these contexts in turn is likely to privilege particular forms of reading, calling in turn for different instruments, criteria, aims and standards of assessment. Here it is impossible to do more than suggest the range of such readings. What needs emphasising is that the great success of *Brave New World* is that it can be taken up in so many frameworks and can manage to acquit itself with honours in virtually all of these different contexts and reading patterns.

I   A Novel of Prediction: *Brave New World* as Futurology

This is undoubtedly the most common way of interpreting the novel and, as we have seen, it was endorsed by Huxley himself in his 1946 "Foreword", which stated clearly enough: "*Brave New World* is a book about the future and, whatever its artistic or philosophical qualities, a book about the future can interest us only if its prophecies look as if they might conceivably come true". The problem with this sort of claim is that it focuses attention on questions that have nothing to do with the literary qualities of the book and, worse still, it implies that if the predictions look as if they cannot possibly come true, the book will not interest us. Probably Huxley adopted this line of argument in the "Foreword" because he had shifted his priorities over the intervening period (as mentioned above) and found himself having to defend a novel he would now, fifteen years later, write quite differently and with changed objectives in mind. He is uneasy about the fact that the novel tests just two alternatives and rejects both of them without offering any other solution. The emphasis the later Huxley puts on the extrapolative aspect of the fiction is, therefore, part of an attempt to justify *Brave New World* as a coherent, instructive text; however, it is perhaps more accurate to set it in the context of the author's development as the work which marks the point when, as Roberto Bertinetti argues, "the writer realises the pointlessness of indiscriminate satire (the pillorying of the upper classes in his previous fiction)" (Bertinetti, 1983: p. 47) and turns to other genres and traditions in an attempt to pursue his objectives by other means. *Brave New World* is thus seen as a work that surpasses the "generalised satire" that had characterised his fiction up to that point while at the same time extending it to its limits. The future setting was one of the means used to this end.

It is probably best to see Huxley's Fordian future as "a *caricature* of what could be" (Kessler, 1957: p. 571). It seems to fit the evidence better to think of the dating ("A.F. 632") and the mentions of past wars and so forth as markers whose function in the text is mainly that of indicating to the reader that the human situations presented exist on a continuum with those of the reader's empirical experience. This is important because it is only on this basis that the novel can offer a simulacrum of life in which moral judgments are pertinent. It has a marvellously effective opening section and from the very first sentence the reader is faced with the vividly imagined reality of a new world, something that cannot be responded to on the basis of the process of recognition at work when we read stories set in world like our own. As we go on reading the text this immediate impact is filled out with what we learn of the attitudes and conceptions of the various characters concerning the past and present of this surprising model of a new world order. Rather than spending time asking if the World State would work, we should take note of Huxley's skill in brushing aside the question by the classic technique of capturing the reader's attention with a series of sharply defined snapshots combined with suggestive snippets of information aimed at reassuring us that it would be possible, if time permitted, to show us how they fit into the whole new order of things.

Treating *Brave New World* as prediction would oblige us to give great importance to features that are, if not entirely absent then at least in a subordinate position in its structure, for the focus of the novel is certainly not on the processes through which today's society will have developed into the World State. On the other hand, it is true all the same that these processes can be reconstructed, in part, from what is said (in Chapter 3 in particular), and this shows that the author of *Brave New World* intended his fictional world to be taken as representing, in simplified form, one possible future permutation of aspects of the present. At the very least it represents a reality not discontinuous with our own, so that the links with the present are not simply arbitrary.

Another problem that arises if *Brave New World* is read as prophetic is the issue of whether the model of society described is supposed to be accepted as actually possible or not: could human beings live in such a state? This question hinges on a factor accurately pinpointed by Jenni Calder, who notes that while "human nature has always responded to the suggestion that it can be improved" in Huxley's novel (as in George Orwell's *Nineteen Eighty-Four*) "there is the suggestion that it might voluntarily co-operate in its debasement" (Calder, 1975: pp. 35-36). This indeed is the crux of the matter. For what we are presented with is not a portrait of human beings as we know them, but as "almost sub-human" – as Huxley himself later described them [15]: they have, as it were, opted out of being human beings. In order to accept Huxley's Fordian state as a possible future we have to believe that human beings, en masse, would take such a step.

But this premise comes into contradiction with an essential dimension of the experience of reading *Brave New World*, which is the reader's recognition of residual elements of human nature that are still at work in Alphas and Betas at least, and that allow us to identify, to some extent, with the characters in the storyworld. It is indeed hard to conceive of the characters as humans without assuming, for example, that they too will have some sort of innate resistance to simply accepting the fact of death or the transitoriness of emotional attachments. Huxley knows this and makes use of it, for example when Henry adopts a "melancholy" tone as he reflects on the source of the gases emitted from the Crematorium – "some human being finally and definitively disappearing" (p. 92); or when Lenina remembers spending a "cheap week-end in New York" (p. 104) with someone; or when so integrated a character as the Director, recollecting Linda's accident, admits that "it upset [him] very much at the time. *More than it ought to have done*", adding, "I actually dream about it sometimes, . . . Dream of being woken up by that peal of thunder and finding her gone; dream of searching and searching for her under the trees" (p. 113). And why does Huxley, in the closing paragraphs of Chapter 11 and elsewhere, go to the trouble of constructing a conspicuous parallelism between the actions of John, the Savage from a 'primitive' tribal community, and Lenina the factory worker (who has been aptly likened to a "well-groomed and polished American career woman"[16])? Surely the 'textural' message, as distinct from the textual message, is *plus ça change, plus c'est la même chose*: human nature does not change, so, as Harold Watts puts it, "what man is in 1932 is a persisting element in what man has become in After Ford 632" (Watts, 1969: p. 79).[17] Keith May points out, quite rightly, that this persistence of old patterns of behaviour is an essential part of the parody, at the expense of futuristic fiction like Wells's *Men Like Gods*, that permeates *Brave New World*, and which "consists not only in a portrait of a spiritual decline from the standards of the twentieth century but also, and perhaps mainly, in the fact that people, in spite of momentous changes in environment, often behave in thoroughly familiar ways. Whereas in Wells's imagination the distant future, or a contemporary world in a different dimension from ours, always belongs to radically different beings (god-like Utopians, bestial Morlocks, ennervated Eloi [in *The Time Machine*]), Huxley's characters manifest all the usual vanities and selfishnesses" (May, 1972: p. 104). This kind of parody must have come naturally to Huxley, who began his essay "Fashions in Love", in *Do What You Will*, by declaring: "Human nature does not change, or, at any rate, history is too short for any changes to be perceptible".

More damagingly, considered as a view of our future, the society pictured in *Brave New World* may be criticised for introducing a range of false problems that have prevented rather than aided recognition of the real changes already under way.[18] It could be said, in particular, that Aldous Huxley did a disservice to public debate over the issue of genetic engineering. His popular novel certainly brought it to the attention of large numbers of people, but in treating the question of improvement and manipulation of the gene pool as if it were a matter of deciding freely on our wishes for the human race it unfortunately played some part in leading astray, or even closing, debate on this crucially important issue: in the public mind genetic engineering was stigmatised and equated with playing God (as if decisions about these technologies were likely to be based on whim or on abstract ideals). Actually it seems more likely that if scientists use these techniques it will be because they are obliged to, in an effort to help us live in a significantly changed environment, a world transformed by such gifts of misapplied science and technology as the greenhouse effect, which may one day require all our children to have the skin pigments and other features possessed by Negroid types. At present genetic engineering has not developed the techniques that would be needed to enable our offspring to withstand conditions on a planet with a seriously injured ozone layer; fortunately its help is not necessary, not yet at least. In today's world it is in most cases no more than a procedure like many others that are used to improve the quality of life (it plays a part, for example, in predicting hereditary illnesses); most people seem to agree that so long as these procedures are applied to individuals and do not involve changes to future generations, the ethical questions connected with genetic engineering are those we are familiar with in medicine in general. Debate over the crucially important question of who decides what is permissible in the field of genetic engineering and how it can be kept under control is undoubtedly long overdue,[19] but this is true of virtually all the far-reaching changes associated with the spread of new technologies – has the general public ever been asked, for example, whether it wants computerised systems throughout society? Global issues of vital concern to the future of humanity as a whole – ecological issues, over-population, the threat of nuclear war, the need to avoid reliance on non-renewable resources, and so on – seem to be intractable in the context of the present-day capitalist world system. But it is in this context, and through the inadequate forums that exist for international dialogue and co-operation, that these issues will have to be tackled. Huxley's premises in *Brave New World* are completely different: there is a World State, the question of the general good can be at the top of the decision-makers' agenda. In the real world of the twentieth century this is unlikely to happen; when the issue of the social role of genetic engineering is finally given the serious consideration it calls for, debate will not take place at the elevated, abstract levels envisaged in *Brave New World*, that much is certain.

Lastly, Huxley wilfully leaves out of account the question of atomic energy and was unable, not surprisingly, to foresee the future role of computers and robots. On the other hand, his descriptions of the "feelies" and of high-tech riot police in action are triumphs of imaginative foresight. At the same time, however, there are many little details that do not ring true, as, for example, when Bernard has to go and find a telephone (in Chapter 11) – these should remind us that Huxley is not interested in convincing us of the authenticity of this future in the way that many science fiction writers want to. Paradoxically, then, it is as a novel of the future that *Brave New World* has come to seem most behind the times.

II A Novel of the Present: *Brave New World* as Critique

> "*Brave New World* . . . is a *reductio ad absurdum* of the sociopolitical outlook prevalent since 1758, when Procrustean efforts to fit man to rationalist philosophy accelerated."
>
> (Meckier, 1979: p. 19)

In *Brave New World* Huxley wanted, above all, to confront us with a world in which we were brought face to face with the consequences of not safeguarding the specifically human capacity for reflection and moral judgment. In 1931 he felt that such a world would need to demonstrate just two contrasting ways in which mankind could exist inauthentically, not actualising the potential acquired through millennia of evolutionary and historical development. One of the two inadequate modes of existence Huxley chose to focus upon involves reliance on rigid, pre-Enlightenment systems of thought and morality (like John the Savage's), while the other involves regression to a state of moral and intellectual imbecility (induced by sleep-teaching and so on). The reader is expected to accept the first option as a hangover from the past, although the persistence of such primitive communities is not properly explained, since it is not really clear why the Reservations have not been suppressed. The second option represents a form of what Immanuel Kant called "self-incurred tutelage", which Kant saw as an obstacle to enlightenment.[20] In Huxley's novel it emerges as the direct consequence of allowing liberalism and democracy to be smashed by the instruments of war; it could not be clearer that *Brave New World* was written in response to what Huxley saw as dangerous tendencies existing in the present. Not surprisingly, Orwell's *Nineteen Eighty-Four*, written immediately after witnessing the effects of nazism and Stalinism, also centres on a critique of the willing "acceptance of subservience": "Orwell and Huxley both show how easy it is for human nature, even in spite of itself, to be enwrapped by the system. The insidious attractions of power are not just for those who want to wield it, but also for those who want to feel its influence" (Calder, 1975: p. 34).

Huxley's main concern, in other words, was not with predicting the future, but with satirising the complacent hypocrisy he witnessed around him. He was saying: "If you believe in enlightenment as a project, if you want us to continue to have the chance to be creatures distinguished by the capacity to reach autonomous decisions using our faculty for reason and for moral judgment, then you must watch out for the effects of the tremendously powerful forces we have at our disposal now which, *if we let them*, can rob us of our hard-won abilities by conning us into accepting Success and Efficiency as ready-made substitutes for Reason and the interminable struggle against 'self-incurred tutelage'." It is not that this particular society *must* follow ours as time unfolds; rather, it represents, in parody form, the inner truth of our condition as soon as we accept what Martin Kessler calls "an operational philosophy" with "no objective beyond the purely pragmatic one of effectiveness" (Kessler, 1957: p. 570). Modern science, as Kant perceived, depends upon a commitment to conditions set by reason in contradiction to what our immediate perception prompts us to believe – reason is "legislative of experience" and requires us not simply to surrender to what seem to be the brute facts;[21] no such impulse can be allowed to survive in the World State (which has no properly problem-seeking scientific activity but only science as a rule-book containing the know-how needed for developing technologies). The predominant consideration is not whether a hypothesis may lead to new discoveries or whether a theory corresponds best to the available facts, but simply whether or not it serves the purpose of reproducing and strengthening the given system: all that matters is whether it has this kind of immediate application. The goals set by the system have become the ultimate criteria. Huxley saw this as a dangerous tendency; he argued against it in his essay *Ends and Means* (1937), and returns to the issue in his 1946 "Foreword" to *Brave New World*, with the contention that "at present and still more in the Brave New World", we live "as though man were to be adapted and enslaved" (p. 8) to science and technology instead of using them as instruments in the service of human goals. What *Brave New World* offers is a situation that allows the author to show the self-conception of humanity implied in such a position (and to expose the emptiness of its self-satisfaction by means of satire).

It is as a novel of the present that the great German philosopher, Theodor Adorno, interprets the text, but he takes Huxley's book to task for "its failure to contemplate a praxis which would explode the infamous continuum" that leads from the self-regulating "open-air prison" of today's society to that of the "totalitarian world-state" ("Aldous Huxley and Utopia" [1942]: see note 16). Huxley, says Adorno, laments "the inexorable decline of culture", but the conception of historical processes that underlies his novel involves an "empty schematism", opposing the individual, who has access to and may defend "the eternal sunshine of the heavenly realm of ideas", to "the pressure of domination" that stands over against the individual and that brings about "the liquidation of everything that is not assimilated" to the one-dimensional logic of the society of controlled consumption. But these are two sides of the same system: Huxley fails to consider the unpredictability of history because he gives no consideration to the possibility that men and women will become aware of this trap and will act collectively to change the conditions of their existence (see also Runcini, 1968). According to Adorno, "The inevitable character of the negative utopia arises from projecting the limitations imposed by the relations of production (the enthronement of the productive apparatus for the sake of profit) as properties of the human and technical forces *per se*". Moreover, argues Adorno, Huxley seems to have unlimited faith in the ability of science and technology to achieve their aims and even to succeed, with the help of brainwashing techniques, in adapting people to fit this new reality, as though "something like an intrinsically non-self-contradictory total subject of technological reason" were possible. (In *Brave New World Revisited* Huxley contends that "if indoctrination is given in the right way at the proper stage of nervous exhaustion, it will work" [edition cited in note 15, pp. 103-4]; this remains open to doubt, while his claim that after listening to charismatic preachers like John Wesley, the famous eighteenth-century Methodist, people "emerged . . . with new and generally better behaviour patterns ineradicably implanted in their minds and nervous systems" [p. 103], is surely an exaggeration.) In other words, if "the fiction of the future bows before the omnipotence of the present" as Adorno says, this happens because it has falsely simplified the range of possibilities contained in the present and because it chooses to play down the internal contradictions of all the elements involved.

Adorno concludes that in *Brave New World*, "Huxley construes humanity and reification as rigid opposites, in accordance with the tradition of the novel, which has as its object the conflict of human beings with rigidified conditions". This habit of thinking in terms of rigid dichotomies is very apparent, for example, in this passage from Huxley's essay "One and Many", published in 1929 in *Do What You Will*: "We are members of a very highly organised society, in which it pays to be either a man who understands and unremittingly wills, or else a kind of obedient automaton. Inevitably, for the more complicated the social machine, the more inhumanly and mechanically simple becomes the task of the subordinate individual, the more inhumanly difficult that of the commanding organizer. Those who wish to lead a quiet life in our modern world must be like Babbitt [the weak, conformist petit-bourgeois businessman in Sinclair Lewis's 1922 novel *Babbitt*] – unquestioningly a cog. Those who are ambitious to lead a (by current standards) successful life must be like [Henry] Ford, determined and very consciously intelligent"(edition cited in note 11, p. 35).

Undoubtedly, however, the novel does offer accurate pictures of many features of life in the advanced industrialised societies of the recent past and, to some extent, of the present. As a critique of certain aspects of this contemporary context, *Brave New World* has to be read as a novel of exaggeration of present tendencies or outlooks: it can very well be labelled an "anti-utopian satire" (Meckier, 1979: p. 7) since, by and large, its treatment of these contemporary elements is satirical and is directed against what Huxley saw as their unrealistic, utopian core. It has several targets: most obviously, the principles of what has come to be called Fordism, but also the philosophy and practices of behaviourism and the ethics implied in Freudian psychoanalysis, and, more generally, all philosophies or lifestyles that purport to provide an adequate basis for human existence without reference to ultimate purposes – what Huxley in the "Foreword" calls "man's Final End" (p. 9). It is not possible in this introduction to deal adequately with all of these areas of critique (see the endnote for some bibliographical indications [22]), but space must be found for at least a brief discussion of the reasons why Huxley – rather brilliantly – gave such a key role to the founder of the Ford Motor Company.

Henry Ford is famous above all for having introduced automated assembly-line methods in car manufacturing: his watchwords were standardisation, efficiency and control and his aim was to make large quantities of consumer goods available at low cost to the mass of people.[23] In 1908, when the first Model T Fords came off the production line at a rate of 27 a day, they cost $825 each; by 1923, when the enormous River Rouge plant was functioning, they were being produced at a rate of more than 2,000 a day and each one cost just $395. In Ford's terms these statistics are a record of success and the story of how it was achieved is a fascinating one. From the start the Model T made use of a standard design and uniform parts that could be made by unskilled workers operating single-purpose machine tools, but the real breakthrough came with the installation, in 1913, of the moving assembly-line (an idea Ford borrowed from the huge slaughter-houses of the Midwest, in which animal carcasses were 'disassembled' as they were carried along on an endlessly moving chain in front of the workers), as a result of which he was able to control the speed at which the workers worked. These methods are parodied in the Hatchery described in first chapter of Huxley's novel, where workers stand side by side carrying out unrelated tasks at a speed dictated by the moving production line, just as in the 'rationalised' automated plants pioneered by Ford.

But despite the many similarities and parallels of this sort that can be found in *Brave New World*, the significance of Fordism needs to be seen, not in these details, but in the vision of a new kind of man and a new lifestyle that it seemed to announce.[23] In an essay entitled "The Puritan", published more or less contemporaneously in *Music at Night*, Huxley had this to say:

> Fordism demands that we should sacrifice the animal man (and along with the animal large portions of the thinking, spiritual man) not indeed to God, but to the Machine. There is no place in the factory, or in that larger factory which is the modern industrialized world, for animals on the one hand, or for artists, mystics, or even, finally, individuals on the other. Of all the ascetic religions Fordism is that which demands the cruellest mutilations of the human psyche – demands the cruellest mutilations and offers the smallest spiritual returns.
>
> (*Music at Night, and Other Essays* [London, 1931], p. 180; as cited in Bowering, 1968: p. 99)

Huxley treats the Fordian factory as a synecdoche for a whole world organised to match the needs of a phantasm, a sub-human mutant:

> For nothing could be more chimerical than the notion that Man is the same thing as the Economic Man and that the problems of life, Man's life, can be solved by any merely economic arrangements. To suppose that the equalization of income could solve these problems is only slightly less absurd than to suppose that they could be solved by the universal installation of sanitary plumbing or the distribution of Ford cars to every member of the human species.
>
> ("Revolutions", *Do What You Will* [edition cited in note 11]. p. 224)

By the time Huxley wrote *Brave New World*, a short time later, he had apparently decided that even if the five-dollar, eight-hour day (introduced by Ford in 1914) and the efforts of the "Ford Sociological Department" to create a uniform workforce could not succeed, other more effective technological means would eventually be found. It is perhaps surprising to discover that Antonio Gramsci had also come to see in Fordism a phenomenon of potentially greater significance than it had first seemed to be:

> In America rationalisation of work and prohibition are undoubtedly connected. The enquiries conducted by the industrialists into the workers' private lives and the inspection services created by some firms to control the 'morality' of their workers are necessities of the new methods of work. People who laugh at these initiatives (failures though they were) and see in them only a hypocritical manifestation of 'puritanism' thereby deny themselves any possibility of understanding the importance, significance and objective import of the American phenomenon, which is also the biggest collective effort to date to create, with unprecedented speed, and with a consciousness of purpose unmatched in history, a new type of worker and of man.
>
> (Gramsci, *Prison Notebooks*, p. 302)

It was no doubt a similar intuition, that a "new type of man" (Gramsci, p. 297) was being trialled in the Fordian system, that made Huxley give the new phenomenon such a central role in the book he was working on at precisely the same time that Gramsci, in prison near Bari, was filling his fifth notebook with a lengthy discussion of "Americanism and Fordism". Neither of them would have been surprised to find that a recent study of "the condition of postmodernity" also gives pride of place to Fordism, and reaches the conclusion that "Postwar Fordism has to be seen . . . less as a mere system of mass production and more as a total way of life. Mass production meant standardization of product as well as mass consumption; and that meant a whole new aesthetic and a commodification of culture . . ." (Harvey, 1990: p. 135).

III   *Brave New World* as Satire

The word "satire" refers to the aim of a text, namely to call into question the given conceptions concerning some aspect of life (a set of ideas or some behaviour) and, very often, to ridicule the pretensions of those associated with it. Satire may be achieved by any of several techniques, especially those of irony, parody, and exaggeration. Huxley's novel has been described as "doubly satiric" (Schmerl, 1962: p. 331):

> On the one hand, it satirises the world of 1932, or rather the world of the decade just completed: the mindlesness and synthetic emotions of the movies and popular music, the compulsive pursuit of pleasure or of what passes for it, the vulgarity ranging from bathroom fixtures to religious cults. (. . .) On the other hand, *Brave New World*'s fantastic historiography satirises the limited visions of possible futures entertained by serious thinkers such as Huxley's grandfather.
> (Schmerl, 1962: p. 331)

It can be seen as a satire which has as its object the vacuous charms of a certain kind of easily-acquired happiness and the naivety of a certain kind of facile optimistic spirit. It is also satirical in relation to features and patterns of life familiar from the contemporary world. To appreciate its satirical thrust the reader has to read the text as a series of witty, ironic contrasts and distortions: the "feelies" exaggerate the same lust for thrills and excitement that led to Hollywood blockbusters; the sleep-taught maxims are simply today's advertising slogans one stage further on; the refusal to mend things follows directly from the mass production of poor quality goods which break and have to be thrown away – the planned obsolescence of consumer goods that led towards today's 'throwaway culture'; and so on.

As pointed out above, Huxley once described *Brave New World* as a novel "on the horror of a Wellsian Utopia and a revolt against it". He probably had in mind above all H.G. Wells's *A Modern Utopia* (1905) and *Men Like Gods* (1923). The latter presents a picture of how the world may be in a thousand years' time, provided people allow progress to go on. Wells's future men and women all live long lives and are physically perfect thanks to eugenics and careful birth-control; a perfect system of education has done away with the need for government institutions and has eliminated crime and madness. These god-like men and women are able to acquire knowledge and put into practice what they learn. *Brave New World* is a satire of what Huxley saw as blinkered optimism of this kind: in Huxley' s world a similar utopian dream is realised but in such a way as to devalue it and make it seem worthless. As Brian Stableford puts it, "these men are not like gods, and only a few of them are much like men. The rest are slaves, not to a system of economic exploitation, but to an efficient technology of direct social control" (Stableford, 1985: p. 255).

All of the scientific and technological aspects of the novel involve satire in fact. It is clear that in *Brave New World* the principal technique involves conceding to the opponents everything they appear to want, so that they incriminate themselves. For example, J.B. Watson, the American psychologist who took up Pavlov's theories and applied his procedures to the study of human behaviour, made the following claim in his influential book *Behaviorism* (1919): "Give me a dozen healthy infants, well-formed and my own specified world to bring them up in and I'll guarantee to take any one at random and train him to become any type of specialist I might select . . . regardless of his talents, penchants, tendencies, abilities, vocations, and race of his ancestors" (quoted in Firchow, 1975: p. 311). As I pointed out before, Huxley seems willing to admit that the scientists can do what they boast they are able to do, but he gives them the benefit of the doubt only so that he can question whether the world will be a better place as a result.

Similar comments might be made with regard to the relationship between *Brave New World* and the ideas of the British biologist J.B.S. Haldane, particularly those expounded in "Daedalus; or, Science and the Future", "A Paper Read to The Heretics, Cambridge on February 4th, 1923" (as it says on the title page of the published version). Huxley knew Haldane at university and in the years just after, so it is not surprising to find an anticipation of some of Haldane's ideas, in particular that of ectogenesis (i.e. test-tube babies), in Huxley's first novel, *Crome Yellow*. A character in the novel, Scogan, describes a scientific utopia: "An impersonal generation will take the place of Nature's hideous system. In vast state incubators, rows upon rows of gravid bottles will supply the world with the population it requires. The family system will disappear; society, sapped at its very base, will have to find new foundations; and Eros, beautifully and irresponsibly free, will flit like a gay butterfly from flower to flower in a sunlit world"(Chapter 5). The ironical tone is already noticeable.

It is not difficult to see that in *Brave New World* Huxley returned to this sort of undermining of the enthusiasm that runs through *Daedalus*, and in order to demonstrate this it will be sufficient to quote from Haldane's essay. The following passages are taken from the section that he presents as having been written by an undergraduate 150 years in the future (introduced as "extracts from an essay on the influence of biology on history during the 20th century"):[24]

> If reproduction is once completely separated from sexual love mankind will be free in an altogether new sense. [. . .] In the future perhaps it may be possible by selective breeding to change character as quickly as institutions. I can foresee the election placards of 300 years hence, if such quaint political methods survive, which is perhaps improbable, 'Vote for Smith and more musicians', 'Vote for

> O'Leary and more girls', or perhaps finally 'Vote for Macpherson
> and a prehensile tail for your great-grandchildren'. We can already
> alter animal species to an enormous extent, and it seems only a
> question of time before we shall be able to apply the same principles
> to our own. [pp. 68-69]
> We already know however that many of our spiritual faculties can
> only be manifested if certain glands, notably the thyroid and sex-
> glands, are functioning properly . . . . As our knowledge of this
> subject increases we may be able, for example, to control our
> passions by some more direct method than fasting and flagellation,
> to stimulate our imagination by some reagent with less after-effects
> than alcohol, to deal with perverted instincts by physiology rather
> than prison. [pp. 70-71]
> The abolition of disease will make death a physiological event like
> sleep [. . .] at the end of a completed life's work . . . our
> contemporaries will rarely leave us sorrowing for long. [pp. 73-74]

The echoes of these speculations that find their way into Huxley's novel
have a hollow, mocking ring to them that differs completely from
Haldane's hearty enthusiasm.

The other target of Huxley's satire is the *be happy* lifestyle he had
seen in America: the way of life that assumes that life is simply a matter
of having fun, and that everyone can and should be participating in an
endless 'good time'. Huxley's visit to Los Angeles, recorded in *Jesting
Pilate* (1926), sensitised him to the lures and risks of the anti-intellectual,
self-indulgent, high-consumption way of life: it offered constant
superficial amusement, but seemed purposeless. For him California
girls may be "plumply ravishing", may feed hopes of "pneumatic bliss",
but "to judge by their faces", they are "curiously uniform, unindividual
and blank" (quoted in Firchow, 1966: p. 455). Presumably Huxley
thought they all aspired to the condition of Lenina!

IV *Brave New World* as Utopian Fiction

> "The Utopian writer does not want to be impossible. He is not a
> realist, no, but he is serious. His 'If only – if only you would' is
> wistful . . .".
> (H.G. Wells, "Utopias" [a radio talk transmitted in 1939]).[25]

Brave New World is clearly an anti-utopia. The epigraph Huxley chose
from Berdyayev sets the tone, suggesting that soon "intellectuals and
educated people will be thinking of ways of avoiding utopias and of
returning to a freer, less 'perfect', non-utopian society". Compared with
E.M. Forster's classic dystopia, "The Machine Stops" (1909),[26] which
was also written, according to its author, as "a reaction to one of the
earlier heavens of H.G. Wells", Huxley's anti-utopia is more radical:
whereas Forster imagines an underground world with everyone totally
reliant on a mighty Machine that, of course, breaks down, causing most
of them to die, Huxley is willing to grant that a System that works may
emerge from the ruins of today's world, a System that will not fail to
deliver the goods, but he is willing to concede this possibility because
he wants to demonstrate that the whole principle of utopia as goal
needs to be rejected anyway, on other grounds.

The inhabitants of an efficient utopia would indeed be happy – this
much can be admitted, the technologies of social control described in
Brave New World are plausible and convincing enough – but, and this is
Huxley's objection, for the very same reason they would no longer be
human (World Controllers apart [27]), at least not as we, the twentieth-
century readers, are human. In other words, while Huxley maintains
that utopias are credible only to the extent that they incorporate what
Steven Rose labels as "proposals to modify human behaviour", he
draws our attention to the fact that, far from being the solution, this
condition reveals their fundamental incoherence:

> If it is asked who is right in the Savage-Mustapha Mond controversy,
> then the answer is surely that Mustapha Mond is. There is no logical
> objection to the behaviourist position which he puts forward. If the
> inhabitants of his society are happy, then they are happy and there is

> nothing more to be said. If we were in their place we would be happy too, nor would we know whether we were missing anything or not. But if we ask whether proposals to modify human behaviour are a valid part of utopian designs, the answer must be no. The whole purpose of a fictional utopia is to depict a society sufficiently appealing to persuade us to construct a real one on similar lines. But in order to decide whether it is appealing we have to be able to tell from the author's description of it whether we should be happy living there. This is the stumbling block as far as behavioural engineering is concerned. No possible effort of the imagination can help us to decide whether we should be happy living in a society peopled entirely by reconditioned versions of our former selves, since we cannot, by definition, put ourselves in their place to judge.
> (Rose, 1974: p. 67)

Impulses that cannot be satisfied are a problem for any utopia, since their existence would falsify its claim to be a utopia. In this sense Huxley's utopia is designed to be 'the utopia to end all utopias' because it works directly on the source of the impulses, totally re-moulding human beings themselves and, in the process, nipping unrealisable desires in the bud: it pre-empts the threat that all utopias are subject to, but at the same time it does away with the dissatisfied creatures who wanted it in the first place and thus remains essentially senseless.

In short, the trouble with *Brave New World*'s 'utopia', as Huxley leads us to see, is that it does not allow you to be unhappy (see the last page of Chapter 17). For it is only for human beings who experience misery that the whole notion of utopia can be meaningful and have a powerful appeal. Mustapha Mond sounds enthusiastic as he points out, "People are happy; they get what they want, and they never want what they can't get" (Chapter 16), but his subsequent list of their advantages is mainly a list of exclusions; theirs is a happiness achieved by reducing the range of their experience. This presumably is why the Savage Reservations are maintained – so as to remind people that their world is, in fact, merely one possible solution to the problem of organising social life and human goals, and more appealing than the only apparent alternative.[28] Nevertheless, few of them visit the Reservations; for most of the people most of the time, there is simply no yardstick of comparison. The price to be paid for achieving the ultimate utopia is that it is unable to understand itself as utopia: in the World State the idea of utopia is dead, or at least moribund.

The only justification of this utopian society, then, is its own self-perpetuation. Huxley showed extraordinary foresight in making this sort of critique, and it remains challenging today because it relates to a fundamental and unresolved dilemma in the modern world, which can be expressed as the question "If God is dead, what is to take his place?". What Grand Narratives can continue to make sense of mankind's place in time and space? At the time Huxley was writing, this deeper, more troubling issue was usually pushed into the background, and most people, in a practical, ameliorationist spirit, focused their attention on programmes for dealing with contemporary problems, as if this activity were a sufficient end in itself, or they projected the premises and logic of their own frame of reference onto all spheres of life and convinced themselves that the definition of the "Final End principle" ("Foreword", p. 8) produced by such reductionist procedures was the only possible one and therefore axiomatically true. Huxley regularly attacks both these ways of negating the complexity and recalcitrance of lived experience: both the hard-nosed Henry-Ford-style absorption in practical business (or, for that matter, the life-without-heavy-baggage hedonism epitomised by Lucy Tantamount in *Point Counter Point* [29]) and the one-sided utopian idealising he associated with scientism, Marxism, rationalism, behaviourism and all such 'isms'. Rampion, the D.H. Lawrence figure in *Point Counter Point*, gives memorable expression to the misgivings Huxley shared at the over-extension of a partial viewpoint and its imposition on others as if it constituted the whole truth: after complaining that the intellectuals, men of science and business men live "one-sidedly", and that the "fruits" of their choices are not only "the external apparatus of modern industrial life" but also "an inward decay . . . infantilism and degeneracy and all sorts of madness and primitive reversion", he continues, "After all, the only truth that can be of any interest to us, or that we can know, is a human truth. And to discover that, you must look for it with the whole being, not with a specialized part of it. What the scientists are trying to get at is non-human truth". And this, he declares, is "utterly irrelevant to ordinary human living"; all it leads to is the "reduction of human beings to absolute imbecility and absolute subservience to their machines" (Chapter 34).

In the early part of the century it was widely assumed among thinking people that some sort of elite would have to take charge of directing society – the candidates ranged from military men, to politicians, philosophers, scientists, through to a vanguard of the common people. As Harold Watts puts it: "These – not deity – can be expected to shape the destiny of future generations. Such superior persons must decide what man should become and then – by conditioning, by the ruthless imposition of adjustment to the 'right' kind of social structure – see that all men become what, in the minds of intelligent planners, they ought to be" (Watts, 1969: p. 78). These were what Watts calls "the commonplaces of progressive hopes for mankind" at the time, and Huxley's response is to reject the framework as a whole: he is not interested in showing that one kind of utopian aspiration is better than another or that any given utopia cannot work (judged by its own standards), but in raising doubts about the desirability of all such supposedly final solutions. On the other hand, the fact that Huxley went on to describe his own utopia in *Island* (1962) might be taken as proof that Huxley was not unsympathetic to other, truer forms of utopianism. Franco Ferrini has expressed very well the difference between the genuine utopian spirit and the travesty of it that forms the parody of *Brave New World* (which, on this view, is closer to science fiction):

> The real utopia is never a programme for the future (as in the classic models of social utopias constituted by Plato's Utopia ot Campanella's City of the Sun), which is to say an image of the future constructed on the basis of elements of the past and the present, considered as points of departure for a historical process continuing into the future but dominated by the same laws that were operative at those departure points . . . It is, rather, the fruit of an unsuppressible

veneration for the freedom represented by the future, as an
unconditioned space of possibility . . .
Science fiction, on the other hand, in building on certain aspects still
in the larval stage in the present, and in assigning them to a
drastically changed future, rather than being directed towards this
form of utopia, towards this unconditioned space of possibility,
prefers to concentrate its efforts on a parodic function. The images
that arise from this parodying are images of a negative utopia (if the
utopian view points at the atemporal, that of parody focuses on the
shortcomings of the past and present – turned around and re-set in a
future where they reveal themselves to be shortcomings . . .).[30]

Huxley's adoption of this parodic mode in *Brave New World* is not,
therefore, necessarily anti-utopian; rather it is evidence of his refusal to
play the game of selling panaceas. In other words, it may be construed as
a preliminary discrediting of the presumptuous, ungrounded optimism
of those who can see only passing setbacks that can always be put right
by various 'technological fixes'. Scepticism like Huxley's could be the
indispensable first condition for a genuine revitalisation of radical
utopianism at a time when all such visionary impulses have been
systematically excluded from the decisions that, little by little, are
determining the shape of the future social order we may all, someday,
find that we have been fitted into. In any case, even in a society able to
resist or contain change as well as Huxley's World State, little islands of
utopian hope can still be found if we look for them: in the imagination,
as exemplified by John's hopes and cherished memories of "a paradise of
goodness and loveliness", the "beautiful Other Place" (p. 210) that
human beings are prone to dreaming of; in the world-transforming
fervour that John suddenly responds to in Miranda's words in *The
Tempest* – "'O brave new world!' Miranda was proclaiming the
possibility of loveliness, the possibility of transforming even the
nightmare into something fine and noble. 'O brave new world!' It was a
challenge, a command" (p. 218); and, of course, in the literal islands –
"an island. That's to say . . . a place where he'll meet the most interesting
set of men and women to be found anywhere in the world" (p. 233).

V *Brave New World* as a Novel

Ultimately it is necessary to bring together these various approaches and to combine them in a coherent reading of the text, a novel which involves the use of a utopian society set in the future as a way of reflecting on and satirising aspects of the present. Any analysis of these features of the novel will have to look closely at the narrative and stylistic techniques through which these effects are achieved. Indeed, its formal techniques are so resourceful that *Brave New World* can also be approached as a kind of *performance*, constantly drawing attention to its own dazzling display of erudition and cultural knowledge, to its skilful reworking of classics of English literature, from Shakespeare to Gray to Dickens,[31] and to its highly self-conscious procedures (notably that of the contrapuntal method we find in Chapter 3, which was probably inspired by the use of jumpcuts in the cinema). Attention to these aspects will go a long way towards explaining the pleasure the novel provides.

Lastly, it should not be forgotten that it is a narrative. The two parallel strands, one centred on Bernard and the other on John the Savage, are, admittedly, quite rudimentary, but they do serve the purpose of connecting the various episodes together and of supplying the reader with a point of view inside the world of the text. John's part of the plot is a sort of compressed *Bildungsroman* (a novel of character-formation) like Goethe' s *Wilhelm Meister* or Charles Dickens's *David Copperfield*; his education is crammed down his throat (literally, in the end, when he succumbs to *soma*) and he chokes on it, especially on the word "science", which "Shakespeare and the old men of the pueblo had never mentioned" (Chapter 16; see Bertinetti, 1983: pp. 54-5). It is interesting to discover that Huxley's revisions of the manuscript were largely concerned with improving this closing narrative sequence:

> At a comparatively late stage of the composition, Huxley rearranged his script to enliven what threatened to become a dull confrontation scene and to add greater clarity and force to his presentation of the Savage. Most important, Huxley interjected the Park Lane Hospital

sequences (Chapters XIV-XV) between Lenina's abortive seduction of John and John's appearance before Mustapha Mond. The Park Lane Hospital additions bring Huxley's trio of rebels into open defiance of their society. By this significant move, Huxley discovered at once a means of adding substantial drama to his narrative's crisis point and a way of lending greater credibility to his final presentation of John's motivations. (Watt, 1978: p. 378)

The main signficance of that hospital chapter . . . is that the reasons for John's revolt and subsequent suicide shift from his outrage over the massed twins to which humanity has been reduced to his sense of loss and guilt over his mother's death. (. . . .) John is much less of a hero than an unsettled and misguided fanatic who comes to embody an untenable alternative to the brave new world. (ibid., pp. 381, 382)

John at the end of the narrative, unsettled by the death of his mother and aware of his insignificance as an opponent of the entire world system, retreats into his own past and seeks an individual solution: "foregoing whatever remnants of sophistication he had acquired, he turns to the Indian mode – becomes a Penitente – isolating himself in a deserted air lighthouse where he 'purifies' the body" (Aldridge, 1980: p.131). But even this private salvation is denied him; his primitive ritual is taken up by the new-worlders and John's identity is destroyed as he gets sucked into the homogenizing spiral of a culture that swallows up everything it encounters, reshaping reality in accordance with its own priorities and preconceptions: "What neater or more logical resolution of the thesis-antithesis between . . . future London and a primitive world than this synthesis in an orgy of devolution?" (Aldridge, 1980: p. 131).

The novel forms a carefully-structured whole. Huxley did not let himself get distracted by the possibilities the narrative element offered for a more sensational, adventure-based treatment of the central idea. Consider, in this connection, the comment made by Kingsley Amis in his history of the science fiction of social critique: "if we can imagine *Brave New World* rewritten by [a science-fiction writer like] . . . Frederick Pohl, we could expect (as well as a little more narrative from time to time) an early scene showing a group of technicians working out a scheme for secretly subjecting all the Beta, Gamma, Delta, and Epsilon embryos to Alpha conditioning, just as a start".[32] The possibility for this kind of organised revolt does seem to be there – a sub-theme of the novel indeed is the old question *Quis custodiet custodes?* But Huxley's novel is not an adventure story. It is an exercise in philosophical speculation, and most readers and critics seem to agree that Huxley got the balance just about right between all the elements we have looked at. He used the narrative element to give a sense of finality to the last pages while at the same time leaving all the issues unresolved. Life at Malpais drifts on under the burning sun; the World Controller puts his books back in the safe; Helmholtz arrives in the Falklands just as Lenina's shift starts one morning; Bernard is forgotten, but unnoticed in the shadows of the Fordian monolith, a group of technicians is secretly plotting . . . .

1. c.f. John Atkins' comment (Atkins, 1967): "The novels appear to be written by someone of immense experience, soemone who is a little jaded by what the world can offer. On the other hand, his essays, though brilliantly perceptive in places, do not seem to come from the same olympian mind" (p. 100). "What Huxley tells us in his essays is the fruit of ratiocination. The real Huxleyan desires are those that find expression in the novels, which increasingly emphasise all that is rotten, diseased, demoralised" (p. 99).

2. For the reasons given, I would also suggest it is best to read the novel before reading the "Foreword".

3. Aldous Huxley, "Spinoza's Worm", in *Do What You Will*, Collected Edition (London: Chatto and Windus, 1970, pp.69-70).

4. Matthew Arnold, Preface to *Literature and Dogma* (1873).

5. Aldous Huxley, "The Outlook for American Culture, Some

Reflections in a Machine Age", *Harper's Magazine*, Vol.155 (August, 1927), p. 270. The previous quotations were from pages 265 and 267; all these quotations are taken from Firchow's article (Firchow, 1966). Huxley reiterates these views in his essay "Silence is Golden", where his "disgust" at the "talkies" (films with sound) leads him to invoke "the immemorial decencies of human life" against such signs of their "inward decay" and "corruption" as "urbanization and democracy and the apotheosis of the Average Man", the "repulsive philosophy and ethic of the young Good Timer", "creation-saving machinery and the thought-saving, time-killing press" and "Taylorized work and mechanized amusement" (in *Do What You Will* [1929], Collected Edition, Chatto and Windus, London, 1970, pp. 60-61). Huxley was not always prone to such jeremiads against the "spiritual climate" of the day: this dates from the period when he was very much under the influence of D.H. Lawrence's irrational anti-modernism.

6. Aldous Huxley, "A Note on Eugenics" in *Proper Studies* (London: Chatto and Windus, 1927), p. 282. The subsequent list of social roles is taken from p.280.

7. Harry Blamires, *Twentieth-Century English Literature* (New York: Schocken Books, 1982), p. 120.

8. Aldous Huxley, "Economists, Scientists, and Humanists", in *Science in the Changing World*, edited by Mary Adams (New York: The Century Company, 1933), p. 222. (As cited in Firchow, 1966: p. 456).

9. *The Letters of Aldous Huxley*, edited by Grover Smith (London: Chatto and Windus, 1969), p. 348. (Letter of 18 May, 1931 to Mrs Roberts).

10. Aldous Huxley, in an interview with George Wickes and Ray Frazer, in *Writers at Work: The 'Paris Review' Interviews*, Second Series, edited by George Plimpton (London: Secker and Warburg, 1963), p. 165.

11. Aldous Huxley, *Texts and Pretexts* [1932] (London: Chatto and Windus, 1959), p. 6. There is a comparable passage in his essay "Spinoza's Worm" in *Do What You Will* [1929] (London: Chatto and Windus, 1970), pp. 71-72: "My own feeling, whenever I see a book about the Future, is one of boredom and exasperation. What on earth is the point of troubling one's head with speculations about what men may, but almost certainly will not, be like in A.D. 20,000? (. . .) Let us think about the present, not the future. If we don't, there will very soon be no future to think about".

12. Actually, of course, there is a third possibility, the islands to which inventive minds and rebels are banished: these represent the real utopia, perhaps, but we are told almost nothing about them. Huxley refers to them in his "Foreword" as places where "the possibility of sanity" is "already actualized, to some extent" (p. 7).

13. Jerome Meckier, "Shakespeare and Aldous Huxley", *Shakespeare Quarterly*, Vol. 22 (1971), pp. 131-32. For more information about Huxley's use of Shakespeare in *Brave New World*, see Robert H. Wilson, "*Brave New World* as Shakespeare Criticism", *Shakespeare*

Association Bulletin, Vol. 21 (July,1946), pp. 91-107.

14. Brian W. Aldiss (with David Wingrove), *Trillion Year Spree: The History of Science Fiction* (London: Gollancz, 1986; rpt. London: Paladin Books, 1988), p. 229.

15. Aldous Huxley, *Brave New World Revisited* [1958] (London: Grafton Books, 1983), p. 29. (Chapter 2, first paragraph).

16. Theodor Adorno, "Aldous Huxley and Utopia"[1942], in *Prisms*, translated by S. and S. Weber (London: Spearman, 1967), p. 105. (This is the English translation of the essay cited in the Bibliography.)

17. I have taken the terminology in this sentence from Walter Nash, *Designs in Prose* (London: Longman,1980): "By the *textual plane* we shall understand that level of composition at which the writer is concerned with the cohesion and continuity [coherence] of his text, while the phrase *textural plane*, or the adjective *textural*, will refer to the colouring and fleshing of the text with imagery, metaphor, dominant motifs, figures of speech, powerfully evocative language, and all the resources of address and persuasion. These 'planes' are essentially interlocked . . ." (p. 46).

18. Comments of the same kind could be made about the other major instrument of social control, social conditioning. This is a complicated issue; there is a very interesting discussion in G. Kateb, *Utopia and Its Enemies* (London: Collier-Macmillan, 1963), Chapter 6; see also the excellent essay by Steven Rose (Rose, 1974).

19. c.f. Jean Chesneaux, *Brave Modern World : The Prospects for Survival* [orig. *Modernité-monde*, 1989], trans. Diana Johnstone et al. (London: Thames and Hudson, 1992: "The reality of BRAVE MODERN WORLD would converge with the fantasies of *Brave New World*. . . . Modern eugenics is *normative*, it appeals to the 'modern' values of efficiency, conformity, improved performance. Thanks to highly sophisticated techniques, it can eliminate deviants and all those who risk being a burden to society in whatever way. Thanks to the remarkable progress made in human genetic engineering, it is now apparently possible to create beings with higher psychic capacities and a higher biological profile . . . in the sense of being more profitable and efficient. Under this racism of rationality, laboratory tests are already being carried out to define the meaning of a 'genetically consistent worker' . . ." (p. 103).

20. See Immanuel Kant, "What Is Enlightenment?" [1784], in *Foundations of the Metaphysics of Morals*, trans. and ed. Lewis White Beck (Chicago: University of Chicago Press, 1950): "Enlightenment is man's release from his self-incurred tutelage. Tutelage is man's inability to make use of his understanding without direction from another. Self-incurred is this tutelage when its cause lies not in lack of reason but in lack of resolution and courage to use it without direction from another. Sapere aude! 'Have courage to use your own

reason!' – that is the motto of enlightenment". [As reproduced in *The Portable Age of Reason Reader*, ed. Crane Brinton (Harmondsworth: Penguin Books, 1977), p. 298.]

21. William Barrett, *The Illusion of Technique: A Search for Meaning in a Technological Civilization* (Garden City, NY: Anchor Press/Doubleday, 1978), p. 181.

22. Consult the following books and articles for more detailed information about *Brave New World* in relation to: *behaviourism* – Firchow, 1975; Hacker (see note 27); *Freudian psychoanalysis* – Firchow, 1975; *rationalism* – Meckier, 1979 (discussses the significance of Claude Helvètius' ideas about education and conditioning); *D.H. Lawrence* – Firchow, 1984 (the relevant chapter was first published as "Wells and Lawrence in Huxley's *Brave New World*", *Journal of Modern Literature*, Vol. 5 [1976], pp.260-78; *romanticism* – Baker, 1982; Zamiatin – Macey, 1986; Edward James Brown, *Brave New World, 1984, and We: An Essay on Utopia: Zamyatin and English Literature*, Ardis Essays series, no.4 (Ann Arbor: Ardis, 1976).

23. My discussion of Fordism is based on the following works (further references are given in the text): Henry Ford, *My Life and Work* (Garden City, N.Y.: Garden City Publishing Co., 1922); Henry Ford, *My Philosophy of Industry, An Authorized Interview* (New York: Coward-McCann Inc., 1929); Carroll Pursell, *White Heat: People and Technology* (London: BBC Books, 1994) and programme 4 of the television series which it accompanied, first broadcast in 1994; Firchow, 1984; David Harvey, *The Condition of Postmodernity: An Enquiry into the Origins of Cultural Change* (Oxford: Blackwell, 1990); Antonio Gramsci, "Americanism and Fordism" in *Selections from the Prison Notebooks*, ed. and trans. Q. Hoare and G. Nowell Smith (London: Lawrence and Wishart, 1971), pp. 277-318.

24. J.B.S. Haldane, *Daedalus or Science and the Future* (London: Kegan Paul, Trench, Trubner and Co., Ltd, 1924), pp. 56-57. Further page references will be given in the text. This book is not easy to obtain, so it is worth mentioning the excellent recent Italian translation, with accompanying essays: "Dedalo o scienza e futuro", translated by Fiorella Conti Pasquino, in Saverio Avveduto/John B. S. Haldane, *Dedalo rivisitato* (Palermo: Sellerio, 1989).

25. H.G. Wells, "Utopias", *Science-Fiction Studies*, Vol. 9, Pt. 2 (July 1982), p. 118.

26. Edward Morgan Forster, *La macchina si ferma*, [bilingual edition, with Italian text on facing pages] (Milano: Editrice Nord, 1985). On the distinction between "dystopia" and "anti-utopia" see: John Huntington, "Utopian and Anti-Utopian Logic: H.G. Wells and His Successors", *Science-Fiction Studies*, Vol. 9, Pt. 2 (July 1982), pp. 122-46; Lyman Tower Sargent, "The Three Faces of Utopianism Revisited", *Utopian Studies*, Vol. 5, Pt. 1 (1994), pp. 1-37.

27. This exception is of crucial importance of course, since it introduces

the question of power, which Huxley chooses to push into the background. It can be convincingly argued, in fact, that the most serious objection to any society based on social conditioning is precisely the problem that it will necessarily require a basic social division into controllers and controlled: this problem is political not technological. See, above all, Firchow, 1984, Chapter 4: "The Politics of Anti-Utopia" and the article by Andrew Hacker, "Dostoevsky's Disciples: Man and Sheep in Political Theory", *Journal of Politics*, Vol. 17 (1955), pp. 590-613, which discusses *Brave New World* at some length; also Rose, 1974; Kateb's book (see note 18); and Carl R. Rogers and B.F. Skinner, "Some Issues Concerning the Control of Human Behavior: A Symposium", *Science*, Vol. 124, No. 3231 (30 Nov. 1956), pp. 1057-1066.

28. James D. Mulvihill, " A Source for Huxley's 'Savage Reservation'", *Notes and Queries*, Vol. 229 (1984), pp. 83-4, argues that "Huxley may have got the basic idea for his Savage Reservation from a largely forgotten work by Havelock Ellis entitled *The Nineteenth Century: a Dialogue in Utopia* [London: Grant Richard, 1900]", set in the future but including an account of "'a piece of ancient life carried into the present' (p. 21) known as the 'Lancashire Enclosure'. Like the Savage Reservation, this curious survival of the past is surrounded by a wall and is of interest primarily to scientists (p. 23)".

29. "'Living modernly's living quickly,' she went on. 'You can't cart a wagon-load of ideals and romanticisms about with you these days. When you travel by aeroplane, you must leave your heavy baggage behind. The good old-fashioned soul was all right when people lived slowly. But it's too ponderous nowadays. There's no room for it in the aeroplane.'" "'If you like speed, if you want to cover the ground, you can't have luggage. The thing is to know what you want and to be ready to pay for it.'" (*Point Counter Point*, Chapter 15)

30. Franco Ferrini, *Il ghetto letterario* (Roma: Armando Editore, 1976), p.150. Laurence Brander makes another distinction, between two "Utopian traditions in English writing": that of "optimistic idealism" (including Wells) and "the satirical tradition", from Swift to Huxley and Orwell (Brander, 1969: p.62). See also Norbert Elias, "Utopie scientifiche e utopie letterarie per il futuro", *Intersezioni*, Vol. 4, No. 1 (April 1984), pp. 5-24; Krishan Kumar, *Utopia and Anti-Utopia in Modern Times* (Oxford: Blackwell, 1987); M. Keith Booker, *The Dystopian Impulse in Modern Literature: Fiction as Social Criticism* (Westport, Conn. and London: Greenwood Press, 1994).

31. On the relationship with Charles Dickens, see especially: Jerome Meckier, "Boffin and Podsnap in Utopia", *The Dickensian*, Vol. 77, Pt. 3 (Autumn 1981), pp. 154-61.

32. Kingsley Amis, *New Maps of Hell: A Survey of Science Fiction* (London: Gollancz, 1961), p. 78.

SELECT BIBLIOGRAPHY

Bibliographical

CLARESON, Thomas D. and Carolyn S. Andrews, "Aldous Huxley: A Bibliography 1960-1964", *Extrapolation: A Journal of Science Fiction and Fantasy*, Vol. 6 (1964), pp. 2-21.

DAVIS, Dennis D., "Aldous Huxley: A Bibliography 1965-1973", *Bulletin of Bibliography*, [Westwood, MA], Vol. 31 (1974), pp. 67-70.

ESCHELBACH, Claire J., *Aldous Huxley: A Bibliography 1916-1959* (London: Cambridge University Press, 1961).

ESCHELBACH, Claire J. and Joyce S. Marthaler, "Aldous Huxley: A Bibliography, 1914-1964 (A Supplementary Listing)", *Bulletin of Bibliography*, [Westwood, MA], Vol. 28 (1971), pp. 114-17

Biographical

BEDFORD, Sybille, *Aldous Huxley: A Biography*, 2 vols. (London: Chatto and Windus / Collins, 1973; Quartet, 1979; Paladin, 1987).

HUXLEY, Laura A., *This Timeless Moment: A Personal View of Aldous Huxley* (London: Hogarth, 1969).

Concerning Huxley as a Writer

ATKINS, John A., *Aldous Huxley: A Literary Study* (London: Calder, 1956; Revised ed. 1967).

BAKER, Robert S., *The Dark Historic Page: Social Satire and Historicism in the Novels of Aldous Huxley, 1921-1939* (Madison: University of Wisconsin Press, 1982).

BOWERING, Peter, *Aldous Huxley: A Study of the Major Novels* (London: Athlone Press, 1968).

BRANDER, Lawrence, *Aldous Huxley: A Critical Study* (London: Hart-Davis, 1970).

BROOKE, Jocelyn, *Aldous Huxley* (London: Longman, 1954; revised edition, 1972).

— "Aldous Huxley", in *British Writers*, Vol. 7, ed. Ian Scott-Kilvert (New York: Scribner's Sons, 1984), pp.197-208.

FERNS, C.S., *Aldous Huxley: Novelist* (London: Athlone Press, 1980).

FIRCHOW, Peter, *Aldous Huxley, Satirist and Novelist* (Minneapolis: University of Minnesota Press; London: Oxford University Press, 1972).

HUXLEY, Julian (ed.), *Aldous Huxley, 1894-1963: A Memorial Volume* (London: Chatto and Windus, 1965).

KUEHN, Robert E. (ed.), *Aldous Huxley: A Collection of Critical Essays*, 20th-Century Views series (Englewood Cliffs, NJ: Prentice-Hall, 1974).

MAY, Keith, *Aldous Huxley*, Novelists and Their World series (London: Elek, 1972).

MECKIER, Jerome, *Aldous Huxley: Satire and Structure* (London: Chatto and Windus, 1969).

NANCE, Guinevera, *Aldous Huxley* (New York: Continuum, 1988).

THODY, Philip, *Aldous Huxley: A Biographical Introduction* (London: Studio Vista, 1973).

WATT, Donald J. (ed.), *Aldous Huxley: The Critical Heritage* (London: Routledge and Kegan Paul, 1975).

WATTS, Harold H., *Aldous Huxley* (New York: Twayne Publishers, 1969).

WOODCOCK, George, *Dawn and the Darkest Hour: A Study of Aldous Huxley* (London: Faber, 1972).

Concerning *Brave New World* and Literary Utopias

ALDRIDGE, Alexandra, "*Brave New World* and the Mechanist/Vitalist Controversy", *Comparative Literature Studies*, Vol. 17 (1980), pp. 116-32.

CALDER, Jenni, *Huxley and Orwell: Brave New World and Nineteen Eighty-Four* (London: Arnold, 1976).

DEERY, June, "Technology and Gender in Aldous Huxley's Alternative (?) Worlds", *Extrapolation*, Vol. 33, Pt. 3 (Fall 1992), pp. 258-73.

FIRCHOW, Peter, "The Satire of Huxley's *Brave New World*", *Modern Fiction Studies*, Vol. 12 (Winter 1966-7), pp. 451-60.

— "Science and Conscience in Huxley's *Brave New World*", *Contemporary Literature*, Vol. 16, No. 3 (Summer 1975), pp. 301-316.

— *The End of Utopia: A Study of Aldous Huxley's "Brave New World"* (Lewisburg: Bucknell University Press; London: Associated University Presses, 1984).

GRUSHOW, Ira, "*Brave New World* and *The Tempest*", *College English*, Vol. 24 (1962), pp. 42-45.

HARTOUNI, Valerie, "*Brave New World* in the Discourses of Reproductive and Genetic Technologies" in Jane Bennett and William Chaloupka (eds.), *In the Nature of Things: Language, Politics, and the Environment* (Minneapolis: University of Minnesota Press, 1993), pp. 85-110.

HILLEGAS, Mark R., *The Future as Nightmare: H. G. Wells and the Anti-utopians* (New York: Oxford University Press, 1967 and Carbondale and Edwardsville: Southern Illinois University Press, 1974).

KESSLER, Martin, "Power and the Perfect State: A Study in Disillusionment as Reflected in Orwell's *Nineteen Eighty-Four* and Huxley's *Brave New World*", *Political Science Quarterly*, Vol. 72 (1957), pp. 565-577.

LARSEN, Peter M., "Synthetic Myths in Aldous Huxley's *Brave New World*: A Note", *English Studies* [Lisse, Netherlands], Vol. 62, Pt. 6 (Dec. 1981), pp. 506-08.

MACEY, Samuel L., "The Role of Clocks and Time in Dystopias: Zamyatin's *We* and Huxley's *Brave New World*", in Makoto Ueda (ed.), *Explorations: Essays in Comparative Literature* (Lanham, MD: UPs of America, 1986), pp. 24-43.

MADDEN, Deanna, "Women in Dystopia: Mysogyny in *Brave New World*, *1984*, and *A Clockwork Orange*," in Anne Katherine Ackley (ed.), *Misogyny in Literature: An Essay Collection* (New York: Garland, 1992), pp. 289-313.

MATTER, William W., "The Utopian Tradition and Aldous Huxley", *Science-Fiction Studies*, Vol. 2 (1975), pp. 146-51.

— "On *Brave New World*", in *No Place Else: Explorations in Utopian and Dystopian Fiction*, eds. Eric S. Rabkin et al. (Carbondale: Southern Illinois University Press, 1983), pp. 94-109.

MECKIER, Jerome, "A Neglected Huxley 'Preface': His Earliest Synopsis of *Brave New World*", *Twentieth Century Literature*, Vol. 25 (1979), pp. 1-20.

MILLICHAP, Joseph A., "Huxley's *Brave New World*, Chapter V", *The Explicator*, Vol. 32, No. 1 (Sept. 1973), Item 1 [2 pp].

ROSE, Steven, "The Fear of Utopia", *Essays in Criticism*, Vol. 24 (1974), pp. 55-70.

SCHMERL, Rudolf B., "The Two Future Worlds of Aldous Huxley", *P.M.L.A.*, Vol. 77 (1962), pp. 328-34.

SEXTON, James, "Aldous Huxley's Bokanovsky", *Science-Fiction Studies*, Vol.16, Pt.1 (March 1989), pp. 85-89.

— "*Brave New World* and the Rationalization of Industry", *English Studies in Canada*, Vol. 12, Pt. 4 (Dec. 1986), pp. 424-39.

STABLEFORD, Brian, *Scientific Romance in Britain 1890-1950* (London: Fourth Estate, 1985).

THIEL, Berthold, *Aldous Huxley's Brave New World* (Amsterdam: Gruner, 1980). [346 pp]

WATT, Donald, "The Manuscript Revisions of *Brave New World*", *Journal of English and Germanic Philology*, Vol.77 (1978), pp. 367-82.

WESTLAKE, J.H.J., "Aldous Huxley's '*Brave New World*' and George Orwell's 'Nineteen Eighty-Four': A Comparative Study", *Die Neueren Sprachen*, n.s. Vol. 21 [=71] (1972), pp. 94-102.

Some Contributions in Italian

ADORNO, Theodor, "Aldous Huxley e l'utopia" [1942], in T. Adorno, *Prismi: Saggi sulla critica della cultura* (Turin: Einaudi, 1972), pp. 89-114.

BERTINETTI, Roberto, "Il suicidio della cultura. Divagazioni su *Brave New World* di A. Huxley", in R. Bertinetti, A. Deidda, M. Domenichelli, *L'infondazione di Babele: l'antiutopia* (Milano: Franco Angeli, 1983), pp. 17-58.

BIANCHI, Ruggero, "I parametri della controutopia", in *Utopia e fantascienza* (Turin: Giappichelli, 1975).

BONICELLI, Elena, "Libertà dell'utopia, utopia della libertà in Aldous Huxley", *Rivista di letterature moderne e comparate*, Vol. 26, No. 4 (Dec. 1973), pp. 307-314.

FORTUNATI, Vita, *La letteratura utopica inglese* (Ravenna: Longo, 1978).

GUARDAMAGNA, Daniela, *Analisi dell'incubo: l'utopia negativa da Swift alla fantascienza* (Roma: Bulzoni, 1980).

— *La narrativa di Aldous Huxley* (Bari: Adriatica, 1989).

MANFERLOTTI, Stefano, *Anti-utopia: Huxley Orwell Burgess* (Palermo: Sellerio, 1984).

— *Invito alla lettura di Aldous Huxley* (Milan: Mursia, 1987).

RUNCINI, Romolo, "Il `mondo nuovo' di A. Huxley", in his *Illusione e paura nel mondo borghese da Dickens a Orwell* (Bari: Laterza, 1968), pp. 293-307.

— "Aldous Huxley", in *I contemporanei: Letteratura inglese*, Vol. 1, eds. Vita Amoruso and Francesco Binni (Roma: Lucarini, 1977), pp. 641-666.

SPINA, Giorgio, *Utopia e Satira nella fantascienza inglese* (Genoa: Tilgher, 1974).

Aldous and his cat, California 1952

CHRONOLOGY

1894   Aldous Leonard Huxley is born on 26th July near
Godalming, in Surrey, the third son of Leonard and Julia
Huxley. His father is a schoolmaster at the time, but
shortly afterwards will join a publishing company and
become assistant editor of the *Cornhill Magazine*. (He will
also publish a biography of Aldous' illustrious
grandfather, Thomas Henry Huxley, the biologist and
promoter of Charles Darwin's theory of evolution). His
mother, Julia Huxley, also has a distinguished ancestry,
as she is a grand-niece of the prominent Victorian critic
and poet Matthew Arnold.

1903-08   Attends Hillside Preparatory School near Godalming.

1908   Is sent to Eton public school. His mother dies of cancer in
November: it is a devastating and unexpected blow.

1911   Suffers a serious illness of the eyes, diagnosed as
keratitis punctata (irritation of the cornea). He leaves
Eton and is almost blind for eighteen months; teaches
himself Braille. For years afterwards all his reading is
done with the aid of a magnifying glass, with great
difficulty.

1912   At the age of 17, he writes his first novel (now lost).

1913   Enters Balliol College, Oxford; he later graduates with a
First-Class degree in English in 1916.

1914   War against Germany is declared in August; Aldous is
unfit for military service. His brother, Trevenan, commits
suicide at the age of twenty-four, hanging himself as a
result of a personal crisis.

1915   Some of his verse is published. He is introduced to a
                    group of free-thinking, pacifist intellectuals who
                    frequent the Manor House at Garsington owned by Lady
                    Ottoline Morrell, including the leading literary and
                    philosophical figures of the day, such as Betrand Russell,
                    the poets Robert Graves and T.S. Eliot, Katherine
                    Mansfield and her husband, John Middleton Murry
                    (who helps him find openings in literary journalism).
                    There Aldous meets his future wife, Maria Nys, a
                    Belgian refugee, and D.H. Lawrence, who will later
                    become a very close friend of the Huxleys.

1916   He tries again to enlist in the army to fight in the First
                    World War, but is still rejected for health reasons.
                    Publishes more poetry, including his first volume of
                    verse *The Burning Wheel*. Works for six months on the
                    farm at Garsington.

1917   Works in the War Office for a few months then becomes
                    a schoolmaster at Eton. Writing poetry and short stories.

1919   Resigns his post as teacher at Eton. Goes to Belgium,
                    where he becomes officially engaged to Maria Nys in
                    April; they marry in July and the couple live in London,
                    where Aldous has an editorial job with *The Athenæum*, a
                    literary review. The young couple are not rich, and
                    Aldous works hard as a journalist and reviewer over the
                    next few years, publishing no less than 171 pieces of
                    journalism in 1919, including 37 articles, most of them
                    written for *The Athenæum* under the pseudonym of
                    "Autolycus".

1920   Publishes *Limbo*, a volume of short stories, and *Leda and
                    Other Poems*. The Huxleys' first son, Matthew, is born in
                    April and Aldous takes on additional work as drama
                    critic on the *Westminster Gazette*.

1921   Most of the year in Italy (Florence, Rome, Forte dei
                Marmi). Writes and publishes his first novel, *Crome
                Yellow*: it is a success.

1922   Publishes *Mortal Coils* (short stories).

1923   Signs the first of his three-year contracts with the
                publishers Chatto and Windus, this one for £500 a year
                and requiring him to produce two narrative works every
                year, one of them a novel. This enables the Huxleys to
                spend the twenties abroad, in Italy and France, where
                life is less expensive and the brighter light is better for
                Aldous' eyes. Publishes his second novel, *Antic Hay*, and
                the essays of *On the Margin*.

1924   Living in Florence (the sudden move to Italy in mid-
                1923 was Maria's desperate means of extricating Aldous
                from the passionate affair he had entered into, in
                London, with a captivating and wayward young
                woman, Nancy Cunard). *Little Mexican* (short stories)
                published.

1925   His third novel, *Those Barren Leaves*, further establishes
                his reputation, and is followed shortly afterwards by the
                travel book, *Along the Road*. In August he and Maria
                leave on an 11-month journey round the world (India,
                Malaysia, Indonesia, Hong Kong, Japan, USA), as
                recounted in *Jesting Pilate*, published in October 1926,
                four months after their return to England.

1926   *Two or Three Graces* (short stories) published in May. In
                October, in Italy, he starts writing *Point Counter Point*
                and then works on the essays in *Proper Studies*
                (published in 1927). The Huxleys meet D.H. Lawrence
                again, in Florence: the old acquaintance becomes a
                friendship, and they stay with each other many times
                over the next few years.

1928   The Huxleys rent a house near Paris, where they live
                until April 1930. The novel *Point Counter Point* is
                published to critical and popular acclaim on both sides
                of the Atlantic, and translations into several languages
                soon follow. The Huxleys are financially much better off
                from now on.

1929   Publication of *Do What You Will*, a collection of essays.
                Long motoring tour in Spain.

1930   The couple attend Lawrence at his deathbed, in Venice,
                in March. They move into the small house they have
                bought at Sanary, near Toulon, in the south of France.
                Brief Candles (short stories) and *Vulgarity in Literature*
                (essays) published.

1931   *The World of Light*, Aldous' first play, has a brief and not
                very successful run in London. He works on *Brave New
                World*, written (according to Sybille Bedford) between
                May and August. Publishes *The Cicadas and Other Poems*
                and *Music at Night* (essays).

1932   *Brave New World* is published in February, and sells well:
                by March 31st he has received earnings from 10,000
                copies in 7/6 editions (nearly £900). Travels in France,
                Belgium (where the Huxleys dine with the King and
                Queen in Brussels) and Germany. Completes his edition
                of *The Letters of D.H. Lawrence* and an anthology of
                favourite passages, *Texts and Pretexts*.

1933   Travels in West Indies, Guatemala and southern Mexico,
                which form the basis of *Beyond the Mexique Bay* (1934).

1935   Joins the Reverend Dick Sheppard's Peace Pledge Union,
                and gives his first public talk on pacifism and
                internationalism.

1936   Publishes the novel *Eyeless in Gaza* as well as a book of
                essays, *The Olive Tree*, and a Peace Pamphlet, *What Are*

You Going To Do About It? The Case for Constructive Peace.
Travels in Belgium and the Netherlands.

1937   With Aldous' friend, Gerald Heard, the family sail to
        New York and they travel in the United States. Writes
        and publishes *Ends and Means: An Enquiry into the Nature
        of Ideals*, and, with Heard, lectures on peace at various
        places in the U.S.

1938   Transfer of residence to southern California. Becomes
        involved with the Vedanta movement of California and
        Swami Prabhavananda; begins working on scripts for
        films of classic English novels for Metro-Goldwyn-
        Mayer (and later also for Twentieth Century Fox). Starts
        to follow the unorthodox methods of Dr W.H. Bates for
        improving his sight and is soon making rapid progress,
        as described later in *The Art of Seeing* (1942).

1939   Meets Christopher Isherwood and completes the comic
        fantasy novel, *After Many a Summer Dies the Swan*.

1941   Publishes *Grey Eminence*, a biographical study of Father
        Joseph, Cardinal Richelieu's advisor.

1944   The novel *Time Must Have a Stop* (started in 1941) is
        published; Aldous learns to drive.

1945   Now a convinced advocate of the value of mystical
        experience, he publishes *The Perennial Philosophy*, a
        commentary on the writings of various mystics. Works
        on Walt Disney's film of *Alice in Wonderland*.

1948   Stage version of his short story "The Gioconda Smile"
        (1922) has a successful 9-month run in London, and a
        French version is later staged in Paris; his film version of
        it, *A Woman's Vengeance*, is also released. Publishes the
        novel *Ape and Essence*, set in California after an atomic
        Third World War. Travel in Europe. Aldous' health is
        not good.

1949   Gathering material for a biographical study of Maine de
            Biran.

1950   *Themes and Variations,* a collection of essays, is published.
            Travels in France, Italy and England. A production of
            The Gioconda Smile has a 5-week run on Broadway.

1952   Publishes *The Devils of Loudun,* a psychological study of a
            case of demonic possession in France in the seventeenth
            century.

1953   Begins his association with Dr. Humphrey Osmond,
            under whose guidance he experiments with the
            hallucinogenic drug mescalin; he writes about the
            experiment in *The Doors of Perception* (1954), a work
            which is destined to make of him a guru of the
            psychedelic generation of the sixties.

1954   Travels in France, Egypt, Israel, Lebanon, Cyprus,
            Greece, Italy and England. Lectures at universities in the
            USA.

1955   Death of Maria Huxley. Publication of a novel: *The
            Genius and the Goddess.*

1956   Aldous marries Laura Archera, a concert violinist and
            practising psycho-therapist. Publishes *Heaven and Hell,*
            once again dealing with experiences induced by
            psychedelic drugs (this time lysergic acid, LSD), as well
            as a volume of essays, *Adonis and the Alphabet.*

1958   *Brave New World Revisited* is published. He resumes work
            on his utopian novel *Island,* begun in 1956. Travels with
            Laura in Peru, Brazil, Italy, and France. He gives lectures
            in Turin, Milan, Rome and Naples.

1959   Gives a course of lectures at the University of California
                on "The Human Situation". Receives the "Award of
                Merit for the Novel" from the American Academy of
                Arts and Letters.

1960-63   In the last years of his life he continues to travel
                (returning to Europe in 1962 and 1963), gives numerous
                lectures all over the USA and attends several conferences
                (in Brussels, Rome, Stockholm and elsewhere).

1960   Diagnosis of cancer of the tongue, followed by
                apparently successful radium treatment.

1961   His house in Los Angeles is totally destroyed by fire: his
                books and manuscripts are all lost.

1962   His novel *Island*, the manuscript of which escaped the
                fire, is finally published. In July he undergoes an
                operation and receives cobalt treatment.

1963   In Rome for a conference of the United Nations Food and
                Agricultural Organisation in March, he has an audience
                with Pope John XXIII. His essay *Literature and Science* is
                published in September. Repeated treatment has not
                been successful, and after a period of declining health,
                Aldous Huxley dies, in Los Angeles, on 22nd November
                (the same day that President John F. Kennedy is
                assassinated). In December a service is held in London,
                at which memorial speeches are made by prominent
                figures, including his eldest brother, the biologist Julian
                Huxley (the first director general of UNESCO and one of
                the founders of the WWF) and the poet Stephen Spender,
                with music performed by the violinist, Yehudi Menuhin,
                a friend and fellow admirer of Krishnamurti.

Aldous and Maria in Siena, 1948

PHONETIC SYMBOLS

Vowels

[ɪ]	*as in*	s**ix**
[i]	"	happ**y**
[iː]	"	s**ee**
[e]	"	r**e**d
[æ]	"	h**a**t
[ɑː]	"	c**ar**
[ɒ]	"	d**o**g
[ɔː]	"	d**oor**
[ʊ]	"	p**u**t
[uː]	"	f**oo**d
[ʌ]	"	c**u**p
[ə]	"	**a**bout
[ɜː]	"	g**ir**l

Diphthongs

[eɪ]	*as in*	m**a**de
[aɪ]	"	f**i**ve
[aʊ]	"	h**ou**se
[ɔɪ]	"	b**oy**
[əʊ]	"	h**o**me
[ɪə]	"	b**eer**
[eə]	"	h**air**
[ʊə]	"	p**oor**

Consonants

[b]	*as in*	**b**ed
[k]	"	**c**at
[tʃ]	"	**ch**ur**ch**
[d]	"	**d**ay
[f]	"	**f**oot
[g]	"	**g**ood
[dʒ]	"	pa**ge**
[h]	"	**h**ow
[j]	"	**y**es
[l]	"	**l**eg
[m]	"	**m**u**m**
[n]	"	**n**i**n**e
[ŋ]	"	si**ng**
[p]	"	**p**en
[r]	"	**r**ed
[s]	"	**s**oon
[z]	"	**z**oo
[ʃ]	"	**sh**ow
[ʒ]	"	mea**s**ure
[t]	"	**t**ea
[θ]	"	**th**in
[ð]	"	**th**is
[v]	"	**v**oice
[w]	"	**w**ine

['] represents primary stress in the syllable which follows

[ˌ] represents secondary stress in the syllable which follows

[r] indicates that the final "r" is only pronounced before a
word beginning with a vowel sound (British English).
In American English, the "r" is usually pronounced
before both consonants and vowel sounds.

Brave New World *

---

* *Brave New World* : the title is taken from Shakespeare's play The Tempest (1611). The word "brave" here means "excellent", "fine": it was commonly used, in Shakespeare's day, "as a general epithet of admiration or praise" (as the Oxford English Dictionary puts it) "to express the superabundance of any valuable quality in men or things". Huxley uses the word ironically of course.

These symbols indicate the beginning and the end of the extracts recorded.

Les utopies apparaissent comme bien plus réalisables qu'on ne le croyait autrefois. Et nous nous trouvons actuellement devant une question bien autrement angoissante: Comment éviter leur réalisation définitive? . . . Les utopies sont réalisables. La vie marche vers les utopies. Et peut-être un siècle nouveau commence-t-il, un siècle où les intellectuels et la classe cultivée rêveront aux moyens d'éviter les utopies et de retourner à une société non utopique, moins 'parfaite' et plus libre.[1]

NICOLAS BERDIAEFF [2]

1. "Utopias now appear to be much more realizable than they were once thought to be. And we find ourselves faced with a truly disturbing question: How can they be prevented from taking shape definitively? . . . Utopias can be achieved. Life moves towards utopias. And it could be that a new era is beginning, an era in which the intellectuals and educated people will be thinking of ways of avoiding utopias and of returning to a freer, less 'perfect', non-utopian society." The quotation comes from his book *Un nouveau moyen age*, which Huxley had reviewed a short time before. (English edition: *The End of Our Time* [1933]).

2. *Berdiaeff* : Nikolai Aleksandrovich Berdiaeff [birÆdjaj f] (1874-1948) was a Russian philosopher; his thinking, which developed on the basis of nineteeth-century Russian lay theology and Western mysticism, offered an influential critique of both capitalism and Marxism. (He had been expelled from Russia in 1922 as anti-Communist.)

Foreword

CHRONIC remorse, as all the moralists are agreed, is a most undesirable sentiment. If you have behaved badly, repent, make what amends you can and address yourself to the task of behaving better next time. On no account brood over [1] your wrongdoing. Rolling in the muck [2] is not the best way of getting clean.

Art also has its morality, and many of the rules of this morality are the same as, or at least analogous to, the rules of ordinary ethics. Remorse, for example, is as undesirable in relation to our bad art as it is in relation to our bad behaviour. The badness should be hunted out, acknowledged and, if possible, avoided in the future. To pore over the literary shortcomings of twenty years ago, to attempt to patch a faulty work into the perfection it missed at its first execution, to spend one's middle age in trying to mend the artistic sins committed and bequeathed by that different person who was oneself in youth – all this is surely vain and futile. And that is why this new *Brave New World* is the same as the old one. Its defects as a

1. *brood over* : persist in thinking about and regretting.
2. *Rolling in the muck* : immersing oneself in dirt (as pigs do)

work of art are considerable; but in order to correct them I should have to rewrite the book – and in the process of rewriting, as an older, other person, I should probably get rid not only of some of the faults of the story, but also of such merits as it originally possessed. And so, resisting the temptation to wallow in artistic remorse, I prefer to leave both well and ill alone and to think about something else.

In the meantime, however, it seems worth while at least to mention the most serious defect in the story, which is this. The Savage is offered only two alternatives, an insane life in Utopia,[1] or the life of a primitive in an Indian village, a life more human in some respects, but in others hardly less queer and abnormal. At the time the book was written this idea, that human beings are given free will in order to choose between insanity on the one hand and lunacy on the other, was one that I found amusing and regarded as quite possibly true. For the sake, however, of dramatic effect, the Savage is often permitted to speak more rationally than his upbringing among the practitioners of a religion that is half fertility cult and half *Penitente* [2] ferocity would actually warrant. Even his acquaintance with Shakespeare would not in reality justify such utterances. And at the close, of course, he is made to retreat from sanity; his native *Penitente*-ism reasserts its authority and he ends in maniacal self-torture and despairing suicide. 'And so they died miserably ever after'[3] – much to the

---

1. *Utopia* [juːˈtəʊpɪə]: an imaginary ideal state. Nowadays we would probably say "in a utopia", but the word also acts as the name of the originary "Ideal Nowhere-Land", the island pictured in Sir Thomas More's *Utopia* (1516). In More's book, a traveller, Raphael Hythloday, describes the perfect social and political conditions he encounters in Utopia, and through the contrast between these and the actually existing conditions, More is able to criticize the England of his time.

2. *Penitente* : see p. 173, note 1.

3. *'And . . . miserably ever after'* : the traditional ending of a fairy-tale is "And so they lived happily ever after".

reassurance of the amused, Pyrrhonic [1] aesthete [2] who was the author of the fable.

To-day I feel no wish to demonstrate that sanity is impossible. On the contrary, though I remain no less sadly certain than in the past that sanity is a rather rare phenomenon, I am convinced that it can be achieved and would like to see more of it. For having said so in several recent books and, above all, for having compiled an anthology [3] of what the sane have said about sanity and all the means whereby it can be achieved, I have been told by an eminent academic critic that I am a sad symptom of the failure of an intellectual class in time of crisis. The implication being, I suppose, that the professor and his colleagues are hilarious symptoms of success. The benefactors of humanity deserve due honour and commemoration. Let us build a Pantheon for professors. It should be located among the ruins of one of the gutted cities of Europe or Japan, and over the entrance to the ossuary I would inscribe, in letters six or seven feet high, the simple words: SACRED TO THE MEMORY OF THE WORLD'S EDUCATORS. SI MONUMENTUM REQUIRIS CIRCUMSPICE.[4]

But to return to the future . . . If I were now to rewrite the book, I would offer the Savage a third alternative. Between the utopian and the primitive horns of his dilemma [5] would lie the possibility of sanity – a possibility already actualized, to some extent, in a community of exiles and refugees from the Brave

---

1. *Pyrrhonic* : highly sceptical, in the manner of Pyrrho of Elis, a Greek sceptic philosopher who lived around 300 B.C.

2. *aesthete* [iːs'θiːt]: someone with a great devotion to the beautiful and little interest in practical everyday matters.

3. *anthology* : *The Perennial Philosophy* (New York, 1945).

4. SI . . . CIRCUMSPICE : "If you want to see his monument, look around you". This is the epitaph of the architect Sir Christopher Wren (1632-1723); it is inscribed over a door in St. Paul's cathedral, London, Wren's greatest achievement.

5. *horns of his dilemma* : the two alternatives, both undesirable, of the over-advanced and under-developed societies. (Facing some intellectual options is like confronting an angry bull: if you escape one horn you will surely be a victim of the other.)

New World, living within the borders of the Reservation. In this community economics would be decentralist and Henry-Georgian,[1] politics Kropotkinesque [2] and co-operative. Science and technology would be used as though, like the Sabbath, they had been made for man, not (as at present and still more so in the Brave New World) as though man were to be adapted and enslaved to them. Religion would be the conscious and intelligent pursuit of man's Final End, the unitive knowledge of the immanent Tao [3] or Logos, the transcendent Godhead or Brahman.[4] And the prevailing philosophy of life would be a kind of Higher Utilitarianism,[5] in which the Greatest Happiness principle would be secondary to the Final End principle – the

1. *Henry-Georgian* : the underlying principle of the economic theories of Henry George (1839-97), as expressed in his widely-read book *Progress and Poverty* (1879), was that everyone should have equal opportunities; to end the monopolization of the land by the rich he advocated the substitution of all taxes by a Single Tax on land values.

2. *Kropotkinesque* : Prince Piotr Alexeivich Kropotkin (1842-1921), a Russian anarchist, wanted to see capitalist society replaced by spontaneously formed groups cooperating and assisting each other on a voluntary basis; he did not see competition as being intrinsic to human society, and was opposed to Darwin's views on the struggle for survival and Marx's notion of class struggle.

3. *Tao* : the key notion in the Eastern religion of Taoism; Tao is the universal principle of existence, the harmonious whole of eternal being and eternal not-being. It translates as "the way".

4. *Brahman* : in Hinduism, Brahman is permanent Being; it is transcendent (beyond the gods) but it is also the fluid essence of life, present in the wheel of existence; the human soul (Atman), in knowing itself is also Brahman, and attains Nirvana, complete understanding.

5. *Utilitarianism* : an ethical theory; in the psychological utilitarianism associated with Jeremy Bentham (1748-1832) and John Stuart Mill (1806-73), it is argued that, as the achievement of happiness is the ultimate aim of all human action, this is the only thing good as an end, so that conduct is morally right if it achieves the greatest happiness of the greatest number of people; Huxley wants to subordinate this measure (good = pleasing) to a "higher" principle (good = final transcendent /immanent truth).

first question to be asked and answered in every contingency of life being: 'How will this thought or action contribute to, or interfere with, the achievement, by me and the greatest possible number of other individuals, of man's Final End?'

Brought up among the primitives, the Savage (in this hypothetical new version of the book) would not be transported to Utopia until he had had an opportunity of learning something at first hand about the nature of a society composed of freely cooperating individuals devoted to the pursuit of sanity. Thus altered, Brave New World would possess an artistic and (if it is permissible to use so large a word in connection with a work of fiction) a philosophical completeness, which in its present form it evidently lacks.

But *Brave New World* is a book about the future and, whatever its artistic or philosophical qualities, a book about the future can interest us only if its prophecies look as though they might conceivably come true. From our present vantage point, fifteen years further down the inclined plane of modern history, how plausible do its prognostications seem? What has happened in the painful interval to confirm or invalidate the forecasts of 1931?

One vast and obvious failure of foresight is immediately apparent. *Brave New World* contains no reference to nuclear fission. That it does not is actually rather odd; for the possibilities of atomic energy had been a popular topic of conversation for years before the book was written. My old friend, Robert Nichols, had even written a successful play about the subject, and I recall that I myself had casually mentioned it in a novel published in the late twenties. So it seems, as I say, very odd that the rockets and helicopters of the seventh century of Our Ford should not have been powered by disintegrating nuclei. The oversight may not be excusable; but at least it can be easily explained. The theme of *Brave New World* is not the advancement of science as such; it is the advancement of science as it affects human individuals. The triumphs of physics, chemistry and engineering are tacitly taken for granted. The only scientific advances to be specifically described are those involving the application to human beings of the results of future research in biology, physiology and psychology. It is only by means of the sciences of life that the quality of life can be radically changed. The sciences of matter can be applied in such a way that they will destroy life or make the living of it impossibly complex and uncomfortable; but, unless used as instruments by the biologists and psychologists, they can do nothing to modify the natural forms and expressions of life itself. The release of atomic energy marks a great revolution in human history, but not (unless we blow ourselves to bits and so put an end to history) the final and most searching revolution.

This really revolutionary revolution is to be achieved, not in the external world, but in the souls and flesh of human beings. Living as he did in a revolutionary period, the Marquis de Sade [1] very naturally made use of this theory of revolutions in order to rationalize his peculiar brand of insanity. Robespierre [2] had achieved the most superficial kind of revolution, the political. Going a little deeper, Babeuf [3] had attempted the economic revolution. Sade regarded himself as the apostle of the truly revolutionary revolution, beyond mere politics and economics – the revolution of individual men, women and children, whose bodies were henceforward to become the common sexual property of all and whose minds were to be purged of all the natural decencies, all the laboriously acquired inhibitions of traditional civilization. Between Sadism and the really

---

1. *Marquis de Sade* : French writer (1740-1814), notorious for his life of debauchery and for works like *Justine* (1797), which describes acts of sadism, a perversion in which the loved one is tortured.

2. *Robespierre* : Maximilien Marie Isidore de Robespierre (1758-94), a prominent Jacobin, played a leading role in the French Revolution, becoming the most prominent member of the Committee of Public Safety which ruled France during the Reign of Terror.

3. *Babeuf* : François Noel, or "Gracchus", Babeuf (1760-97), French revolutionist and journalist, executed after leading a communist attack against the Directory in 1796; "Babouvism", in which practical proposals were made for creating socialist egalitarianism, reemerged in the 1848 Revolution and the 1870 Paris Commune.

revolutionary revolution there is, of course, no necessary or inevitable connection. Sade was a lunatic and the more or less conscious goal of his revolution was universal chaos and destruction. The people who govern the Brave New World may not be sane (in what may be called the absolute sense of that word); but they are not mad men, and their aim is not anarchy but social stability. It is in order to achieve stability that they carry out, by scientific means, the ultimate, personal, really revolutionary revolution.

But meanwhile we are in the first phase of what is perhaps the penultimate revolution. Its next phase may be atomic warfare, in which case we do not have to bother with prophecies about the future. But it is conceivable that we may have enough sense, if not to stop fighting altogether, at least to behave as rationally as did our eighteenth-century ancestors. The unimaginable horrors of the Thirty Years War [1] actually taught men a lesson, and for more than a hundred years the politicians and generals of Europe consciously resisted the temptation to use their military resources to the limits of destructiveness or (in the majority of conflicts) to go on fighting until the enemy was totally annihilated. They were aggressors, of course, greedy for profit and glory; but they were also conservatives, determined at all costs to keep their world intact, as a going concern.[2] For the last thirty years there have been no conservatives; there have only been nationalistic radicals of the right and nationalistic radicals of the left. The last conservative statesman was the fifth Marquess of Lansdowne;[3] and when he wrote a letter to The

1. *Thirty Years War* : a series of wars fought in Germany between 1618 and 1648 mainly for religious reasons; many atrocities were committed, with armies pillaging and burning everywhere.

2. *as a going concern* : as an enterprise which will continue to pay for itself (the language of business).

3. *fifth Marquess of Lansdowne* : Henry Petty-Fitzmaurice (1845-1927), foreign secretary before World War I, cabinet minister 1915-16. Lansdowne's letter was eventually published in the *Daily Telegraph* in November 1917, when Russia was out of the war, following the Bolshevik coup.

Times, suggesting that the First World War should be concluded with a compromise, as most of the wars of the eighteenth century had been, the editor of that once conservative journal refused to print it. The nationalistic radicals had their way, with the consequences that we all know – Bolshevism, Fascism, inflation, depression, Hitler, the Second World War, the ruin of Europe and all but universal famine.

Assuming, then, that we are capable of learning as much from Hiroshima [1] as our forefathers learned from Magdeburg,[2] we may look forward to a period, not indeed of peace, but of limited and only partially ruinous warfare. During that period it may be assumed that nuclear energy will be harnessed to industrial uses. The result, pretty obviously, will be a series of economic and social changes unprecedented in rapidity and completeness. All the existing patterns of human life will be disrupted and new patterns will have to be improvised to conform with the nonhuman fact of atomic power. Procrustes [3] in modern dress, the nuclear scientist will prepare the bed on which mankind must lie; and if mankind doesn't fit – well, that will be just too bad for mankind. There will have to be some

1. *Hiroshima* : a Japanese city considered to be of military importance; the Americans dropped on it the first atomic bomb used in war, on August 6th, 1945, causing at least 80,000 deaths and injuring 70,000 (not to mention the terrible long-term consequences).

2. *Magdeburg* : German town; it was burned down in 1188, and, after resisting a seige in the Thirty Years War it was taken by a storm in 1631, sacked and almost entirely burned to the ground and nearly all of its 40,000 inhabitants brutally killed. During the Second World War, as a Krupp armaments factory was situated there, it was once again 90% destroyed, this time by bombing.

3. *Procrustes* [prəʊ'krʌstiːz]: according to a Greek legend, Procrustes the robber would offer his guests a bed which was either too long or too short for them, and would tie them down and stretch them or cut their legs until they fitted it.

stretchings and a bit of amputation – the same sort of stretchings and amputations as have been going on ever since applied science really got into its stride, only this time they will be a good deal more drastic than in the past. These far from painless operations will be directed by highly centralized totalitarian governments. Inevitably so; for the immediate future is likely to resemble the immediate past, and in the immediate past rapid technological changes, taking place in a mass-producing economy and among a population predominantly propertyless, have always tended to produce economic and social confusion. To deal with confusion, power has been centralized and government control increased. It is probable that all the world's governments will be more or less completely totalitarian even before the harnessing of atomic energy; that they will be totalitarian during and after the harnessing seems almost certain. Only a large-scale popular movement toward decentralization and self-help can arrest the present tendency toward statism. At present there is no sign that such a movement will take place.

There is, of course, no reason why the new totalitarianism should resemble the old. Government by clubs and firing squads, by artificial famine, mass imprisonment and mass deportation, is not merely inhumane (nobody cares much about that nowadays); it is demonstrably inefficient – and in an age of advanced technology, inefficiency is the sin against the Holy Ghost. A really efficient totalitarian state would be one in which the all-powerful executive of political bosses and their army of managers control a population of slaves who do not have to be coerced, because they love their servitude. To make them love it is the task assigned, in present-day totalitarian states, to ministries of propaganda, newspaper editors and schoolteachers. But their methods are still crude and unscientific. The old Jesuits' boast that, if they were given the schooling of the child, they could answer for the man's religious opinions, was a product of wishful thinking. And the modern pedagogue is probably rather less efficient at conditioning his pupils' reflexes than were the reverend fathers who educated Voltaire.[1] The greatest triumphs of propaganda have been accomplished, not by doing something, but by refraining from doing. Great is the truth, but still greater, from a practical point of view, is silence about truth. By simply not mentioning certain subjects, by lowering what Mr Churchill [2] calls an 'iron curtain'[3] between the masses and such facts or arguments as the local political bosses regard as undesirable, totalitarian propagandists have influenced opinion much more effectively than they could have done by the most eloquent denunciations, the most compelling of logical rebuttals. But silence is not enough. If persecution, liquidation and other symptoms of social friction are to be avoided, the positive sides of propaganda must be made as effective as the negative. The most important Manhattan Projects [4] of the future will be vast government-

1. *Voltaire* : French philosopher of the Enlightenment. François-Marie Arouet (1694-1778) assumed the name Voltaire in 1718. The "reverend fathers" who educated him were Jesuits, the Roman Catholic order whose highly organized, efficient system of instruction was employed in more than 600 institutions during the 17th and 18th Centuries; they claimed to be able to shape a person's character if the child was given to them at a young age.

2. *Mr Churchill* : Sir Winston Leonard Spencer Churchill (1874-1965), British Prime Minister during the Second World War.

3. *'iron curtain'* ['aən 'kɜːtn]: Churchill's recent use of this expression had given it currency; it normally refers to the impenetrable barrier raised around themselves by the Soviet Union and the Eastern European countries in its sphere of influence, to shield themselves from the non-socialist countries in Europe.

4. *Manhattan Projects* : the Manhattan Project was a task force of engineers and physicists (including R. Oppenheimer and E. Fermi) set up by the U.S. War Department in June 1942 to advance the work of developing the atomic bomb.

sponsored enquiries into what the politicians and the participating scientists will call 'the problem of happiness' – in other words, the problem of making people love their servitude. Without economic security, the love of servitude cannot possibly come into existence; for the sake of brevity, I assume that the all-powerful executive and its managers will succeed in solving the problem of permanent security. But security tends very quickly to be taken for granted. Its achievement is merely a superficial, external revolution. The love of servitude cannot be established except as the result of a deep, personal revolution in human minds and bodies. To bring about that revolution we require, among others, the following discoveries and inventions. First, a greatly improved technique of suggestion – through infant conditioning and, later, with the aid of drugs, such as scopolamine.[1] Second, a fully developed science of human differences, enabling government managers to assign any given individual to his or her proper place in the social and economic hierarchy. (Round pegs in square holes tend to have dangerous thoughts about the social system and to infect others with their discontents.) Third (since reality, however utopian, is something from which people feel the need of taking pretty frequent holidays), a substitute for alcohol and the other narcotics, something at once less harmful and more pleasure-giving than gin or heroin. And fourth (but this would be a long-term project, which would take generations of totalitarian control to bring to a successful conclusion), a foolproof system of eugenics,[2] designed to standardize the human product and so to facilitate the task of the managers. In *Brave New World* this standardization of the human product has been pushed to fantastic, though not

1. *scopolamine* [skɑ'pɑləmiːn]: an alkaloid that can have sedative or narcotic effects.
2. *eugenics* [juː'dʒenɪks]: the methods of the science of race improvement; that is, selective breeding and (now) genetic engineering to produce only first-rate human beings.

perhaps impossible, extremes. Technically and ideologically we are still a long way from bottled babies and Bokanovsky groups of semi-morons. But by A.F. 600, who knows what may not be happening? Meanwhile the other characteristic features of that happier and more stable world – the equivalents of soma and hypnopëdia and the scientific caste system – are probably not more than three or four generations away. Nor does the sexual promiscuity of *Brave New World* seem so very distant. There are already certain American cities in which the number of divorces is equal to the number of marriages. In a few years, no doubt, marriage licences will be sold like dog licences, good for a period of twelve months, with no law against changing dogs or keeping more than one animal at a time. As political and economic freedom diminishes, sexual freedom tends compensatingly to increase. And the dictator (unless he needs cannon fodder [1] and families with which to colonize empty or conquered territories) will do well to encourage that freedom. In conjunction with the freedom to daydream under the influence of dope [2] and movies and the radio, it will help to reconcile his subjects to the servitude which is their fate.

All things considered, it looks as though Utopia were far closer to us than anyone, only fifteen years ago, could have imagined. Then, I projected it six hundred years into the future. To-day it seems quite possible that the horror may be upon us within a single century. That is, if we refrain from blowing ourselves to smithereens [3] in the interval. Indeed, unless we

1. *cannon fodder* : "fodder" is the word for the large stocks of food, such as hay, needed by farm animals; soldiers are treated like fodder when war strategy permits large numbers of them to die in battle, as if they were simply food for the cannons.
2. *dope* : narcotic drugs (like marijuana, heroin or amphetamines).
3. *blowing ourselves to smithereens* : making our world explode into tiny fragments (an idiom).

choose to decentralize and to use applied science, not as the end to which human beings are to be made the means, but as the means to producing a race of free individuals, we have only two alternatives to choose from: either a number of national, militarized totalitarianisms, having as their root the terror of the atomic bomb and as their consequence the destruction of civilization (or, if the warfare is limited, the perpetuation of militarism); or else one supra-national totalitarianism, called into existence by the social chaos resulting from rapid technological progress in general and the atom revolution in particular, and developing, under the need for efficiency and stability, into the welfare-tyranny [1] of Utopia. You pays your money and you takes your choice.[2]

1946

1. *welfare-tyranny* : a coercive, oppressive form of Welfare State.
2. *You pays ... your choice* : a catchphrase or saying based on the cry of market stallholders to prospective customers. The "s" on the verbs is typical of Cockney speech. (First appeared in print in 1846; less common nowadays).

Chapter I

A SQUAT grey building of only thirty-four storeys. Over the main entrance the words, CENTRAL LONDON HATCHERY [1] AND CONDITIONING CENTRE, and, in a shield, the World State's motto, COMMUNITY, IDENTITY, STABILITY. [2]

The enormous room on the ground floor faced towards the north. Cold for [3] all the summer beyond the panes, for all the tropical heat of the room itself, a harsh thin light glared through the windows, hungrily seeking some draped lay figure, [4] some

1. HATCHERY ['hætʃəri]: place where eggs (usually of fish) are hatched, that is, made to produce young ones.
2. COMMUNITY, IDENTITY, STABILITY : this three-word motto imitates that of the French Revolution, "Freedom, Equality, Brotherhood".
3. for : despite.
4. lay figure : model of the human body used by artists (sometimes lay-figure).

pallid shape of academic goose-flesh,[1] but finding only the glass and nickel and bleakly shining porcelain of a laboratory. Wintriness responded to wintriness. The overalls of the workers were white, their hands gloved with a pale corpse-coloured rubber. The light was frozen, dead, a ghost. Only from the yellow barrels of the microscopes did it borrow a certain rich and living substance, lying along the polished tubes like butter, streak after luscious streak in long recession down the work tables.

'And this,' said the Director opening the door, 'is the Fertilizing Room.'

Bent over their instruments, three hundred Fertilizers were plunged, as the Director of Hatcheries and Conditioning entered the room, in the scarcely breathing silence, the absent-minded, soliloquizing hum or whistle, of absorbed concentration. A troop of newly arrived students, very young, pink and callow,[2] followed nervously, rather abjectly, at the Director's heels. Each of them carried a note-book, in which, whenever the great man spoke, he desperately scribbled. Straight from the horse's mouth.[3] It was a rare privilege. The D.H.C. for Central London always made a point of personally conducting his new students round the various departments.

'Just to give you a general idea,' he would explain to them. For of course some sort of general idea they must have, if they were to do their work intelligently – though as little of one, if they were to be good and happy members of society, as possible. For particulars, as every one knows, make for virtue and happiness; generalities are intellectually necessary evils.

---

1. *goose-flesh* ['guːsfleʃ]: when the skin forms pimples, with the hairs erect, as a result of cold or fear – in this case caused by the coldness of the light. The room is not an artist's studio or a place of study, as someone might at first suppose.

2. *callow* ['kæləʊ]: inexperienced (literally, unbearded).

3. *Straight from the horse's mouth* : used of tips or information obtained directly from someone immediately involved and therefore well-informed. (Originally a horse-racing expression.)

Not philosophers, but fret-sawyers [1] and stamp collectors compose the backbone of society.[2]

'To-morrow,' he would add, smiling at them with a slightly menacing geniality, 'you'll be settling down to serious work. You won't have time for generalities. Meanwhile . . .'

Meanwhile, it was a privilege. Straight from the horse's mouth into the note-book. The boys scribbled like mad.

Tall and rather thin but upright, the Director advanced into the room. He had a long chin and big, rather prominent teeth, just covered, when he was not talking, by his full, floridly curved lips. Old, young? Thirty? fifty? fifty-five? It was hard to say. And anyhow the question didn't arise; in this year of stability, A.F. 632,[3] it didn't occur to you to ask it.

'I shall begin at the beginning,' said the D.H.C., and the more zealous students recorded his intention in their note-books: *Begin at the beginning*. 'These,' he waved his hand, 'are the incubators.' And opening an insulated door he showed them racks upon racks of numbered test-tubes. 'The week's supply of ova. Kept,' he explained, 'at blood heat; whereas the male gametes,' and here he opened another door, 'they have to be kept at thirty-five instead of thirty-seven. Full blood heat sterilizes.' Rams wrapped in thermogene beget no lambs.[4]

---

1. *fret-sawyers* ['fretˌsɔːjəz]: skilled craftsmen who use a narrow-bladed saw for cutting fine, decorative designs in wood.

2. *backbone of society* : supporting structure sustaining the society.

3. *A.F. 632* : the year of Our Ford 632 (i.e. 2540 A.D.). "Ford" refers to Henry Ford (1863-1947), the U.S. industrialist and pioneer of the moving assembly line. As we learn in Chapter Three, in the World State time is measured from 1908, when the famous Ford Model T ("Tin Lizzie") motor-car was introduced; this was a standardized car, cheap enough to be bought by masses of people.

4. *Rams wrapped in thermogene beget no lambs* : if male sheep are encased in a heat-generating material their reproductive potential is removed. "Beget" [bɪˈget] sounds archaic here: the result is a parody of an Old Testament proverb. "Thermogen" (the proprietary name for an "orange wool") is also exploited for comic effect in Huxley's 1928 novel *Point Counter Point*, Chapter 18.

Still leaning against the incubators he gave them, while the pencils scurried illegibly across the pages, a brief description of the modern fertilizing process; spoke first, of course, of its surgical introduction – 'the operation undergone voluntarily for the good of Society, not to mention the fact that it carries a bonus [1] amounting to six months' salary'; continued with some account of the technique for preserving the excised ovary alive and actively developing; passed on to a consideration of optimum temperature, salinity, viscosity; referred to the liquor in which the detached and ripened eggs were kept; and, leading his charges to the work tables, actually showed them how this liquor was drawn off from the test-tubes; how it was let out drop by drop on to the specially warmed slides of the microscopes; how the eggs which it contained were inspected for abnormalities, counted and transferred to a porous receptacle; how (and he now took them to watch the operation) this receptacle was immersed in a warm bouillon containing free-swimming spermatozoa – at a minimum concentration of one hundred thousand per cubic centimetre, he insisted; and how, after ten minutes, the container was lifted out of the liquor and its contents re-examined; how, if any of the eggs remained unfertilized, it was again immersed, and, if necessary, yet again; how the fertilized ova went back to the incubators; where the Alphas and Betas [2] remained until definitely bottled; while the

1. *it carries a bonus* ['bəʊnəs]: women are offered a financial incentive to submit to an operation in which an ovary is removed.

2. *Alphas and Betas* : the population of the World State is divided into classes or castes, clearly separated by physical appearance and intellectual capacity. Each one is labelled with a letter of the Greek alphabet, ranging from Alpha-Double-Plus, through Beta, Gamma, Delta, down to Epsilon, and the mindless Epsilon-Minus Semi-Morons. The first two categories do the jobs requiring thought (administration, management, research); the other castes are quite distinct from them, and do routine work.

Gammas, Deltas and Epsilons were brought out again, after only thirty-six hours, to undergo Bokanovsky's Process.[1]

'Bokanovsky's Process,' repeated the Director, and the students underlined the words in their little note-books.

One egg, one embryo, one adult – normality. But a bokanovskified egg will bud, will proliferate, will divide. From eight to ninety-six buds, and every bud will grow into a perfectly formed embryo, and every embryo into a full-sized adult. Making ninety-six human beings grow where only one grew before. Progress.

'Essentially,' the D.H.C concluded, 'bokanovskification consists of a series of arrests of development. We check [2] the normal growth and, paradoxically enough, the egg responds by budding.'[3]

Responds by budding. The pencils were busy.

He pointed. On a very slowly moving band a rack-full of test-tubes was entering a large metal box, another rack-full was emerging. Machinery faintly purred. It took eight minutes for the tubes to go through, he told them. Eight minutes of hard X-rays being about as much as an egg can stand. A few died; of the rest, the least susceptible divided into two; most put out four buds; some eight; all were returned to the incubators, where the buds began to develop; then, after two days, were suddenly chilled, chilled and checked. Two, four, eight, the buds in their

1. *Bokanovsky's Process* : an ingenious technique (invented by Huxley) thanks to which a single fertilized human ovum is made to produce large numbers of identical twins. The next paragraph explains the process. The name is that of a Russian revolutionary, Ivan Vasil'evich Bokhanovsky (1848-1917), but probably Huxley intended rather the French politician Maurice Bokanowski (1879-1928), who advocated the rationalization of industry as a means of securing stability, and was concerned with counteracting the falling birth rate in France.

2. *check* : hold back, restrain, prevent the progress of. (It has the same meaning in the next paragraph.)

3. *budding* ['bʌdɪŋ]: process in which small protuberances (like the buds on trees that develop into flowers) form on the eggs, each one a potential embryo.

turn budded; and having budded were dosed almost to death with alcohol; consequently burgeoned [1] again and having budded – bud out of bud out of bud were thereafter – further arrest being generally fatal – left to develop in peace. By which time the original egg was in a fair way to becoming anything from eight to ninety-six embryos – a prodigious improvement, you will agree, on nature. Identical twins – but not in piddling [2] twos and threes as in the old viviparous days,[3] when an egg would sometimes accidentally divide; actually by dozens, by scores at a time.

'Scores,' the Director repeated and flung out his arms, as though he were distributing largesse. 'Scores.'

But one of the students was fool enough to ask where the advantage lay.

'My good boy!' The Director wheeled sharply round on him. 'Can't you see? Can't you see?' He raised a hand; his expression was solemn. ' Bokanovsky's Process is one of the major instruments of social stability!'

Major instruments of social stability.

Standard men and women; in uniform batches. The whole of a small factory staffed with the products of a single bokanovskified egg.

'Ninety-six identical twins working ninety-six identical machines!' The voice was almost tremulous with enthusiasm. 'You really know where you are. For the first time in history.' He quoted the planetary motto. 'Community, Identity, Stability.' Grand words. 'If we could bokanovskify indefinitely the whole problem would be solved.'

---

1. *burgeoned* ['bɜːdʒənd]: put out shoots (in literary/poetic language).
2. *piddling* : insignificant, not deserving of attention.
3. *viviparous* [vɪ'vɪpərəs] *days* : the earlier period when women had given birth to babies. The offspring of viviparous animals (mammals for example) develop in the mother's body before being born.

Solved by standard Gammas, unvarying Deltas, uniform Epsilons. Millions of identical twins. The principle of mass production at last applied to biology.

'But, alas,' the Director shook his head, 'we can't bokanovskify indefinitely.'

Ninety-six seemed to be the limit; seventy-two a good average. From the same ovary and with gametes of the same male to manufacture as many batches of identical twins as possible – that was the best (sadly a second best) that they could do. And even that was difficult.

'For in nature it takes thirty years for two hundred eggs to reach maturity. But our business is to stabilize the population at this moment, here and now. Dribbling out twins over a quarter of a century – what would be the use of that?'

Obviously, no use at all. But Podsnap's Technique [1] had immensely accelerated the process of ripening. They could make sure of at least a hundred and fifty mature eggs within two years. Fertilize and bokanovskify – in other words, multiply by seventy-two and you get an average of nearly eleven thousand brothers and sisters in a hundred and fifty batches of identical twins, all within two years of the same age.

'And in exceptional cases we can make one ovary yield us over fifteen thousand adult individuals.'

1. *Podsnap's Technique* : this procedure, for making the ova produced in the ovary mature much more quickly, is also a fictional invention. The name recalls that of Mr Podsnap in Charles Dickens's novel *Our Mutual Friend* (1864-5); it is used to indicate someone complacent and self-satisfied, whose optimism is really the result of ignoring unpleasant facts.

Beckoning to a fair-haired, ruddy young man who happened to be passing at the moment, 'Mr Foster',[1] he called. The ruddy young man approached. 'Can you tell us the record for a single ovary, Mr Foster?'

'Sixteen thousand and twelve in this Centre,' Mr Foster replied without hesitation. He spoke very quickly, had a vivacious blue eye, and took an evident pleasure in quoting figures. 'Sixteen thousand and twelve; in one hundred and eighty-nine batches of identicals. But of course they've done much better,' he rattled on, 'in some of the tropical Centres. Singapore has often produced over sixteen thousand five hundred; and Mombasa [2] has actually touched the seventeen thousand mark. But then they have unfair advantages. You should see the way a negro ovary responds to pituitary! It's quite astonishing, when you're used to working with European material. Still,' he added, with a laugh (but the light of combat was in his eyes and the lift of his chin was challenging), 'still, we mean to beat them if we can. I'm working on a wonderful Delta-Minus ovary at this moment. Only just eighteen months old. Over twelve thousand seven hundred children already, either decanted [3] or in embryo. And still going strong. We'll beat them yet.'

1. *Mr Foster* : names in the World State tend to be significant; many are formed from names and surnames of important nineteenth and early twentieth-century figures associated with socialist or utopian thought and politics, with scientific and technological discoveries important to the World State, or with mass production. In this case, the reference is to Sir Michael Foster (1836-1907), who succeeded Thomas H. Huxley, the author's distinguished grandfather, as Professor of Physiology at the Royal Institution in London. He also acts as a kind of foster-parent (an adoptive parent); his first name, as we find out later, is Henry, in commemoration of Henry Ford.

2. *Mombasa* : the main port in Kenya, in east Africa (a British crown colony when Huxley wrote this).

3. *decanted* : after the gestation period in bottles, the fully-formed babies are turned out of the bottles (decanted). The "Decanting Rate", mentioned a little further on, corresponds to what we call "birth rate".

'That's the spirit I like!' cried the Director, and clapped Mr Foster on the shoulder. 'Come along with us and give these boys the benefit of your expert knowledge.'

Mr Foster smiled modestly. 'With pleasure.' They went.

In the Bottling Room all was harmonious bustle and ordered activity. Flaps of fresh sow's peritoneum [1] ready cut to the proper size came shooting up in little lifts from the Organ Store in the sub-basement. Whizz and then, click![2] the lift-hatches flew open; the Bottle-Liner had only to reach out a hand, take the flap, insert, smooth-down, and before the lined bottle had had time to travel out of reach along the endless band, whizz, click! another flap of peritoneum had shot up from the depths, ready to be slipped into yet another bottle, the next of that slow interminable procession on the band.

Next to the Liners stood the Matriculators. The procession advanced; one by one the eggs were transferred from their test-tubes to the larger containers; deftly the peritoneal lining was slit, the morula [3] dropped into place, the saline solution poured in . . . and already the bottle had passed, and it was the turn of the labellers. Heredity, date of fertilization, membership of Bokanovsky Group – details were transferred from test-tube to bottle. No longer anonymous, but named, identified, the procession marched slowly on; on through an opening in the wall, slowly on into the Social Predestination Room.

'Eighty-eight cubic metres of card-index,' said Mr Foster with relish, as they entered.

'Containing *all* the relevant information,' added the Director.

'Brought up to date every morning.'

'And co-ordinated every afternoon.'

---

1. *peritoneum* [ˌperɪtə'niːəm]: the membrane lining the walls of the abdominal cavity, in this case of a female pig (sow [sau]). A piece (flap) of it is used to cover the inside of each bottle, which acts as an artificial uterus.

2. *Whizz and then, click!* : onomatopoeic words imitating the noise of the lift and of the lift-doors opening.

3. *morula* ['mɔːrjuːlə]: solid round mass of cells formed early on in the development of the human embryo.

'On the basis of which they make their calculations.'

'So many individuals, of such and such quality,' said Mr Foster.

'Distributed in such and such quantities.'

'The optimum Decanting Rate at any given moment.'

'Unforeseen wastages promptly made good.'

'Promptly,' repeated Mr Foster. 'If you knew the amount of overtime I had to put in after the last Japanese earthquake!' He laughed good-humouredly and shook his head.

'The Predestinators send in their figures to the Fertilizers.'

'Who give them the embryos they ask for.'

'And the bottles come in here to be predestinated in detail.'

'After which they are sent down to the Embryo Store.'

'Where we now proceed ourselves.'

And opening a door Mr Foster led the way down a staircase into the basement.

The temperature was still tropical. They descended into a thickening twilight. Two doors and a passage with a double turn ensured the cellar against any possible infiltration of the day.

'Embryos are like photograph film,' said Mr Foster waggishly [1], as he pushed open the second door. 'They can only stand red light.'

And in effect the sultry darkness into which the students now followed him was visible and crimson, like the darkness of closed eyes on a summer's afternoon. The bulging flanks of row on receding row and tier above tier [2] of bottles glinted with innumerable rubies, and among the rubies [3] moved the dim red spectres of men and women with purple eyes and all the symptoms of lupus.[4] The hum and rattle of machinery faintly stirred the air.

1. *waggishly* : jokingly, like a playfully witty person (a wag).
2. *tier above tier* [tɪər]: parallel rows, one higher than another.
3. *rubies* ['ruːbɪːz]: the ruby is a red jewel. Here, a metaphor for the reflection of the red lights.
4. *lupus* ['luːpəs]: tuberculosis of the skin.

'Give them a few figures, Mr Foster,' said the Director, who was tired of talking.

Mr Foster was only too happy to give them a few figures.

Two hundred and twenty metres long, two hundred wide, ten high. He pointed upwards. Like chickens drinking, the students lifted their eyes towards the distant ceiling.

Three tiers of racks: ground-floor level, first gallery, second gallery.

The spidery steelwork of gallery above gallery faded away in all directions into the dark. Near them three red ghosts were busily unloading demijohns [1] from a moving staircase.

The escalator from the Social Predestination Room.

Each bottle could be placed on one of fifteen racks, each rack, though you couldn't see it, was a conveyor travelling at the rate of thirty-three and a third centimetres an hour. Two hundred and sixty-seven days at eight metres a day. Two thousand one hundred and thirty-six metres in all. One circuit of the cellar at ground level, one on the first gallery, half on the second, and on the two hundred and sixty-seventh morning, daylight in the Decanting Room. Independent existence – so called.

'But in the interval,' Mr Foster concluded, 'we've managed to do a lot to them. Oh, a very great deal.' His laugh was knowing and triumphant.

'That's the spirit I like,' said the Director once more. 'Let's walk round. You tell them everything, Mr Foster.'

Mr Foster duly [2] told them.

Told them of the growing embryo on its bed of peritoneum. Made them taste the rich blood-surrogate on which it fed. Explained why it had to be stimulated with placentin and thyroxin.[3] Told them

1. *demijohns* : large bottles (derives from the Italian, 'damigiana').
2. *duly* ['djuːli]: in the way requested, at the right time (from "due").
3. *placentin and thyroxin* [θaɪˈrɒksɪn]: substances affecting the body's growth produced by the placenta and the thyroid gland.

of the *corpus luteum* [1] extract. Showed them the jets through which at every twelfth metre from zero to 2040 it was automatically injected. Spoke of those gradually increasing doses of pituitary administered during the final ninety-six metres of their course. Described the artificial maternal circulation installed on every bottle at metres 112; showed them the reservoir of blood-surrogate, the centrifugal pump that kept the liquid moving over the placenta and drove it through the synthetic lung and waste-product filter. Referred to the embryo's trouble-some tendency to anæmia, to the massive doses of hog's stomach extract and fœtal foal's liver with which, in consequence, it had to be supplied.

Showed them the simple mechanism by means of which, during the last two metres out of every eight, all the embryos were simultaneously shaken into familiarity with movement. Hinted at the gravity of the so-called 'trauma of decanting,'[2] and enumerated the precautions taken to minimize, by a suitable training of the bottled embryo, that dangerous shock. Told them of the tests for sex carried out in the neighbourhood of metre 200. Explained the system of labelling – a T for the males, a circle for the females and for those who were destined to become freemartins [3] a question mark, black on a white ground.

'For of course,' said Mr Foster, 'in the vast majority of cases, fertility is merely a nuisance. One fertile ovary in twelve hundred – that would really be quite sufficient for our purposes. But we want to have a good choice. And of course one must

1. *corpus luteum* : a yellowish body that develops in the ovary after discharge of the ovum; it degenerates after a few days unless fertilization takes place. The "extract" is presumably the hormone progesterone, which prepares the uterus to receive an embryo.

2. *'trauma of decanting'* : compare this with the "birth-trauma" ['trɔːmə], with its sudden physiological changes and abrupt separation from the mother, that Sigmund Freud saw as the origin and model of all forms of anxiety.

3. *freemartins* : here this means women made sterile (unable to reproduce). (Normally used of an animal born as a sterile twin.)

always leave an enormous margin of safety. So we allow as many as thirty per cent. of the female embryos to develop normally. The others get a dose of male sex-hormone every twenty-four metres for the rest of the course. Result: they're decanted as freemartins – structurally quite normal (except,' he had to admit, 'that they *do* have just the slightest tendency to grow beards), but sterile. Guaranteed sterile. Which brings us at last,' continued Mr Foster, 'out of the realm of mere slavish imitation of nature into the much more interesting world of human invention.'

He rubbed his hands. For, of course, they didn't content themselves with merely hatching out embryos: any cow could do that.

'We also predestine and condition. We decant our babies as socialized human beings, as Alphas or Epsilons, as future sewage workers or future . . .' He was going to say 'future World Controllers,' but correcting himself, said 'future Directors of Hatcheries' instead.

The D.H.C. acknowledged the compliment with a smile.

They were passing Metre 320 on Rack 11. A young Beta-Minus mechanic was busy with screw-driver and spanner on the blood-surrogate pump of a passing bottle. The hum of the electric motor deepened by fractions of a tone as he turned the nuts. Down, down . . . A final twist, a glance at the revolution counter, and he was done. He moved two paces down the line and began the same process on the next pump.

'Reducing the number of revolutions per minute,' Mr Foster explained. 'The surrogate goes round slower; therefore passes through the lung at longer intervals; therefore gives the embryo less oxygen. Nothing like oxygen-shortage for keeping an embryo below par.'[1] Again he rubbed his hands.

---

1. *below par* : at less than the standard level. (An expression commonly used in golf, where "par" is the number of strokes set for any hole.)

'But why do you want to keep the embryo below par?' asked an ingenuous student.

'Ass!' said the Director, breaking a long silence. 'Hasn't it occurred to you that an Epsilon embryo must have an Epsilon environment as well as an Epsilon heredity?'

It evidently hadn't occurred to him. He was covered with confusion.

'The lower the caste,' said Mr Foster, 'the shorter the oxygen.' The first organ affected was the brain. After that the skeleton. At seventy per cent of normal oxygen you got dwarfs. At less than seventy, eyeless monsters.

'Who are no use at all,' concluded Mr Foster.

Whereas (his voice became confidential and eager), if they could discover a technique for shortening the period of maturation, what a triumph, what a benefaction to Society!

'Consider the horse.'[1]

They considered it.

Mature at six; the elephant at ten. While at thirteen a man is not yet sexually mature; and is only fully grown at twenty. Hence, of course, that fruit of delayed development, the human intelligence.

'But in Epsilons,' said Mr Foster very justly, 'we don't need human intelligence.'

Didn't need and didn't get it. But though the Epsilon mind was mature at ten, the Epsilon body was not fit to work till eighteen. Long years of superfluous and wasted immaturity. If the physical development could be speeded up till it was as quick, say, as a cow's, what an enormous saving to the Community!

'Enormous!' murmured the students. Mr Foster's enthusiasm was infectious.

---

1. *'Consider the horse'* : Huxley is deliberately reminding us of the famous opening chapters of Charles Dickens's novel *Hard Times* (1854), which provide a model for BNW's opening. *Hard Times* starts with a visit by Mr Thomas Gradgrind to the model school he owns, in which he explains how things should be done; at one point he demands of a pupil a definition of a horse.

He became rather technical; spoke of the abnormal endocrine [1] co-ordination which made men grow so slowly; postulated a germinal mutation to account for it. Could the effects of this germinal mutation [2] be undone? Could the individual Epsilon embryo be made to revert, by a suitable technique, to the normality of dogs and cows? That was the problem. And it was all but [3] solved.

Pilkington,[4] at Mombasa, had produced individuals who were sexually mature at four and full grown at six and a half. A scientific triumph. But socially useless. Six-year-old men and women were too stupid to do even Epsilon work. And the process was an all-or-nothing one; either you failed to modify at all, or else you modified the whole way. They were still trying to find the ideal compromise between adults of twenty and adults of six. So far without success. Mr Foster sighed and shook his head.

Their wanderings through the crimson twilight had brought them to the neighbourhood of Metre 170 on Rack 9. From this point onwards Rack 9 was enclosed and the bottles performed the remainder of their journey in a kind of tunnel, interrupted here and there by openings two or three metres wide.

'Heat conditioning,' said Mr Foster.

Hot tunnels alternated with cool tunnels. Coolness was wedded to discomfort in the form of hard X-rays. By the time they were decanted the embryos had a horror of cold. They were predestined to emigrate to the tropics,[5] to be miners and acetate silk spinners and steel workers. Later on their minds would be made to endorse the judgment of their bodies. 'We condition

---

1. *endocrine* : that is, of the glands that do not have ducts, such as the pituitary or the thyroid.

2. *germinal mutation* : a mutation at an early stage.

3. *all but* : very nearly, almost completely.

4. *Pilkington* : the Pilkington glass company was associated with the recently developed and marketed "vita-glass", a scientifically advanced material which is specifically mentioned in Chapter 11.

5. *emigrate to the tropics* : the hot countries presumably still rely on the advanced technologies of those that became industrialized earlier, but given the realization of a "World State" they cannot, of course, be described as "developing".

them to thrive on heat',[1] concluded Mr Foster. 'Our colleagues upstairs will teach them to love it.'

'And that,' put in the Director sententiously, 'that is the secret of happiness and virtue – liking what you've *got* to do. All conditioning aims at that: making people like their unescapable social destiny.'

In a gap between two tunnels, a nurse was delicately probing with a long fine syringe into the gelatinous contents of a passing bottle. The students and their guides stood watching her for a few moments in silence.

'Well, Lenina',[2] said Mr Foster, when at last she withdrew the syringe and straightened herself up.

The girl turned with a start. One could see that, for all the lupus and the purple eyes,[3] she was uncommonly pretty.

'Henry!' Her smile flashed redly at him – a row of coral teeth.

'Charming, charming,' murmured the Director, and, giving her two or three little pats, received in exchange a rather deferential smile for himself.

'What are you giving them?' asked Mr Foster, making his tone very professional.

'Oh, the usual typhoid and sleeping sickness.'

'Tropical workers start being inoculated at metre 150,' Mr Foster explained to the students. 'The embryos still have gills.[4]

1. *thrive* [θraɪv] *on heat* : this would normally mean to grow strong and healthy with the aid of heat, but here (ironically) it means only that the bodies are conditioned to be more comfortable with heat than with cold. In the world State, "to thrive" can only be defined negatively – as the absence of any desire for alternative conditions: it is not a matter of positively liking heat as such, but simply of disliking what comes with the cold.

2. *Lenina* : a name modelled on that of Lenin (Vladimir Ilich Ulyanov [1870-1924]), one of the leaders of the 1917 Russian Revolution.

3. *for all the lupus and purple eyes* : despite the effects of the red lighting.

4. *still have gills* [gɪlz]: they have not developed lungs for internal respiration. The gill is the organ with which a fish breathes underwater: Mr Foster refers here to the embryos, metaphorically, as fish and later he mentions their "tails".

We immunize the fish against the future man's diseases.' Then, turning back to Lenina, 'Ten to five on the roof this afternoon,' he said, 'as usual.'

'Charming,' said the Director once more, and, with a final pat, moved away after the others.

On Rack 10 rows of next generation's chemical workers were being trained in the toleration of lead, caustic soda, tar, chlorine. The first of a batch of two hundred and fifty embryonic rocket-plane engineers was just passing the eleven hundredth metre mark on Rack 3. A special mechanism kept their containers in constant rotation. 'To improve their sense of balance,' Mr Foster explained. 'Doing repairs on the outside of a rocket in mid air is a ticklish [1] job. We slacken off [2] the circulation when they're right way up, so that they're half starved, and double the flow of surrogate when they're upside down. They learn to associate topsy-turvydom [3] with well-being; in fact, they're only truly happy when they're standing on their heads.'

'And now,' Mr Foster went on, 'I'd like to show you some very interesting conditioning for Alpha-Plus Intellectuals. We have a big batch of them on Rack 5. First Gallery level,' he called to two boys who had started to go down to the ground floor.

'They're round about metre 900,' he explained. 'You can't really do any useful intellectual conditioning till the fœtuses have lost their tails. Follow me.'

But the Director had looked at his watch. 'Ten to three,' he said. 'No time for the intellectual embryos, I'm afraid. We must go up to the Nurseries [4] before the children have finished their afternoon sleep.'

Mr Foster was disappointed. 'At least one glance at the Decanting Room,' he pleaded.

'Very well, then.' The Director smiled indulgently. 'Just one glance.'

---

1. *ticklish* ['tɪklɪʃ]: precarious, requiring careful attention because it can easily go wrong.
2. *slacken off* : reduce the speed of, decrease.
3. *topsy-turvydom* [ˌtɒpsi'tɜːvɪdəm]: the condition of being upside-down.
4. *Nurseries* : rooms in which babies and young children are raised.

Chapter II

M R. FOSTER was left in the Decanting Room. The D.H.C. and his students stepped into the nearest lift and were carried up to the fifth floor. INFANT NURSERIES. NEO-PAVLOVIAN [1] CONDITIONING ROOMS, announced the notice board.

The Director opened a door. They were in a large bare room, very bright and sunny; for the whole of the southern wall was a single window. Half a dozen nurses, trousered and jacketed [2] in the regulation white viscose-linen uniform, their hair aseptically hidden under white caps, were engaged in setting out bowls of roses in a long row across the floor. Big bowls, packed tight with blossom. Thousands of petals, ripe-blown [3] and silkily smooth, like the cheeks of innumerable little cherubs, but of cherubs, in that bright light, not exclusively pink and Aryan, but also

---

1. *Neo-Pavlovian* [ˌniːəʊˌpævˈləʊvɪən]: this conditioning employs and adapts the findings of Ivan Petrovich Pavlov (1849-1936), a Russian physiologist famous above all for an experiment in which he produced a conditioned reflex in a dog.
2. *trousered and jacketed* : with trousers and jackets on (not a normal use of language).
3. *ripe-blown* [ˈraɪpəˈbləʊn]: fully-matured.

luminously Chinese, also Mexican, also apoplectic [1] with too much blowing of celestial trumpets, also pale as death, pale with the posthumous whiteness of marble.

The nurses stiffened to attention as the D.H.C. came in.

'Set out the books,' he said curtly.

In silence the nurses obeyed his command. Between the rose bowls the books were duly set out – a row of nursery quartos opened invitingly each at some gaily coloured image of beast or fish or bird.

'Now bring in the children.'

They hurried out of the room and returned in a minute or two, each pushing a kind of tall dumb-waiter [2] laden, on all its four wire-netted shelves, with eight-month-old babies, all exactly alike (a Bokanovsky Group, it was evident) and all (since their caste was Delta) dressed in khaki.[3]

'Put them down on the floor.'

The infants were unloaded.

'Now turn them so that they can see the flowers and books.'

Turned, the babies at once fell silent, then began to crawl towards those clusters of sleek colours, those shapes so gay and brilliant on the white pages. As they approached, the sun came out of a momentary eclipse behind a cloud. The roses flamed up as though with a sudden passion from within; a new and profound significance seemed to suffuse the shining pages of the books. From the ranks of the crawling babies came little squeals of excitement, gurgles and twitterings of pleasure.

The Director rubbed his hands. 'Excellent!' he said. 'It might almost have been done on purpose.'

1. *apoplectic* [æpə'plektɪk]: red in the face. Huxley uses a personifying simile: he imagines the roses as cherubs ['tʃerəbz], their different colours explained by analogy with differences of race or physical state among the cherubim (the usual plural when referring to the trumpet-blowing childlike angels).

2. *dumb-waiter* [ˌdʌm'weɪtəʳ]: a stand with shelves on it (usually used for food and plates at a dining-table, to replace a real waiter).

3. *khaki* ['kɑːki]: i.e. in khaki-coloured cloth – of a dull yellowish-brown colour (used for the uniforms of many armies).

The swiftest crawlers were already at their goal. Small hands reached out uncertainly, touched, grasped, unpetaling the transfigured roses, crumpling the illuminated pages of the books. The Director waited until all were happily busy. Then, 'Watch carefully,' he said. And, lifting his hand, he gave the signal.

The Head Nurse, who was standing by a switchboard at the other end of the room, pressed down a little lever.

There was a violent explosion. Shriller and ever shriller, a siren shrieked. Alarm bells maddeningly sounded.

The children started, screamed; their faces were distorted with terror.

'And now,' the Director shouted (for the noise was deafening), 'now we proceed to rub in the lesson with a mild electric shock.'

He waved his hand again, and the Head Nurse pressed a second lever. The screaming of the babies suddenly changed its tone. There was something desperate, almost insane, about the sharp spasmodic yelps [1] to which they now gave utterance. Their little bodies twitched and stiffened; their limbs moved jerkily as if to the tug of unseen wires.

'We can electrify that whole strip of floor,' bawled [2] the Director in explanation. 'But that's enough,' he signalled to the nurse.

The explosions ceased, the bells stopped ringing, the shriek of the siren died down from tone to tone into silence. The stiffly twitching bodies relaxed, and what had become the sob and yelp of infant maniacs broadened out once more into a normal howl of ordinary terror.

'Offer them the flowers and the books again.'

---

1. *yelps* : short cries (of pain in this case). The sound made by a dog which feels a sudden pain (or excitement). (The earlier "twitterings" are typical of little birds and suggest happiness.)
2. *bawled* [bɔld]: shouted or yelled (above the noise). The Director is not suffering, he merely wants to be heard.

The nurses obeyed; but at the approach of the roses, at the mere sight of those gaily-coloured images of pussy and cock-a-doodle-doo and baa-baa black sheep,[1] the infants shrank away in horror; the volume of their howling suddenly increased.

'Observe,' said the Director triumphantly, 'observe.'

Books and loud noises, flowers and electric shocks – already in the infant mind these couples were compromisingly linked; and after two hundred repetitions of the same or a similar lesson would be wedded indissolubly. What man has joined, nature is powerless to put asunder.[2]

'They'll grow up with what the psychologists used to call an "instinctive" hatred of books and flowers. Reflexes unalterably conditioned. They'll be safe from books and botany all their lives.' The Director turned to his nurses. 'Take them away again.'

Still yelling, the khaki babies were loaded on to their dumb-waiters and wheeled out, leaving behind them the smell of sour milk and a most welcome silence.

One of the students held up his hand; and though he could see quite well why you couldn't have lower-caste people wasting the Community's time over books, and that there was always the risk of their reading something which might undesirably decondition one of their reflexes, yet . . . well, he couldn't understand about the flowers. Why go to the trouble of making it psychologically impossible for Deltas to like flowers?

Patiently the D.H.C. explained. If the children were made to scream at the sight of a rose, that was on grounds of high economic policy. Not so very long ago (a century or

---

1. *pussy and cock-a-doodle-doo and baa-baa black sheep* : names of animals used with young children. "Pussy" [ˌp si] (or pussy-cat) means "cat"; "cock-a-doodle-doo" imitates the sound of the crowing of a cock and "baa-baa" the bleating of a sheep.

2. *What man has joined, nature is powerless to put asunder* : alludes to a phrase of the present-day marriage ceremony – "Those whom God hath joined together let no man put asunder" (separate). The meaning is that nothing can undo the effects of conditioning: no experience can pull apart the associated impressions.

thereabouts), Gammas, Deltas, even Epsilons, had been conditioned to like flowers – flowers in particular and wild nature in general. The idea was to make them want to be going out into the country at every available opportunity, and so compel them to consume transport.

'And didn't they consume transport?' asked the student.

'Quite a lot,' the D.H.C. replied. 'But nothing else.'

Primroses and landscapes, he pointed out, have one grave defect: they are gratuitous. A love of nature keeps no factories busy. It was decided to abolish the love of nature, at any rate among the lower classes; to abolish the love of nature, but *not* the tendency to consume transport. For of course it was essential that they should keep on going to the country, even though they hated it. The problem was to find an economically sounder reason for consuming transport than a mere affection for primroses and landscapes. It was duly found.

'We condition the masses to hate the country,' concluded the Director. 'But simultaneously we condition them to love all country sports. At the same time, we see to it that all country sports shall entail the use of elaborate apparatus. So that they consume manufactured articles as well as transport. Hence those electric shocks.'

'I see,' said the student, and was silent, lost in admiration.

There was a silence; then, clearing his throat, 'Once upon a time,' the Director began, 'while Our Ford 1 was still on earth,

---

1. *Our Ford* : compare the present-day Christian expression, "Our Lord" (i.e. God). The sentence starts with the formulaic opening for tales of the marvellous ("Once upon a time"), which is surprising, because the story is given a specific historical time and setting; assuming this is not a slip on Huxley's part, the implication is that, in this future society in which talking about the past is severely discouraged (so that one might have expected the story-telling formula to have fallen out of use), certain events from the past can nevertheless be narrated, but only because they are not treated as historical events (belonging to an earlier period in the same historical continuum), but to some partly-historical, partly-mythical time when ageless heroes (like Henry Ford) were "still on earth".

there was a little boy called Reuben Rabinovitch.[1] Reuben was the child of Polish-speaking parents.' The Director interrupted himself. 'You know what Polish is, I suppose?'

'A dead language.'

'Like French and German,' added another student, officiously showing off his learning.

'And "parent"?' questioned the D.H.C.

There was an uneasy silence. Several of the boys blushed.[2] They had not yet learned to draw the significant but often very fine distinction between smut [3] and pure science. One, at last, had the courage to raise a hand.

'Human beings used to be . . .' he hesitated; the blood rushed to his cheeks. ' Well, they used to be viviparous.'

'Quite right.' The Director nodded approvingly.

'And when the babies were decanted . . .'

'"Born,"' came the correction.

'Well, then they were the parents – I mean, not the babies, of course; the other ones.' The poor boy was overwhelmed with confusion.

'In brief,' the Director summed up, 'the parents were the father and the mother.' The smut that was really science fell with a crash [4] into the boys' eye-avoiding silence. 'Mother,' he

---

1. *Reuben Rabinovitch* : this name conforms perfectly to the model "Polish-sounding Jewish name"; probably Huxley wanted it to sound false, like an invented story-telling name.

2. *blushed* [blʌʃd]: turned red in the face (from embarassment, because the D.H.C. has used a bad word and mentioned a taboo subject).

3. *smut* [smʌt]: a bit of soot or dirt; often used figuratively, as here, to mean indecent or obscene matter. ("Parent" is a smutty word.)

4. *fell with a crash* : specks of smut normally fall (from chimneys) in complete silence, so it is especially effective to use the metaphor of a loud, violent noise to describe the impact of the taboo words "mother" and "father" on the boys' feelings. A few lines later Huxley substitutes "crash and crash" and then "wink and snigger" for the words themselves.

repeated loudly, rubbing in the science; and, leaning back in his chair, 'These,' he said gravely, 'are unpleasant facts; I know it. But, then, most historical facts *are* unpleasant.'

He returned to Little Reuben – to Little Reuben, in whose room, one evening, by an oversight, his father and mother (crash, crash!) happened to leave the radio turned on.

('For you must remember that in those days of gross viviparous reproduction, children were always brought up by their parents and not in State Conditioning Centres.')

While the child was asleep, a broadcast programme from London suddenly started to come through; and the next morning, to the astonishment of his crash and crash (the more daring of the boys ventured to grin at one another), Little Reuben woke up repeating word for word a long lecture by that curious old writer ('one of the very few whose works have been permitted to come down to us'), George Bernard Shaw,[1] who was speaking, according to a well-authenticated tradition, about his own genius. To Little Reuben's wink and snigger, this lecture was, of course, perfectly incomprehensible and, imagining that their child had suddenly gone mad, they sent for a doctor. He, fortunately, understood English, recognized the discourse as that which Shaw had broadcasted the previous evening, realized the significance of what had happened, and sent a letter to the medical press about it.

'The principle of sleep-teaching, or hypnopædia, had been discovered.' The D.H.C. made an impressive pause.

The principle had been discovered; but many, many years were to elapse before that principle was usefully applied.

'The case of Little Reuben occurred only twenty-three years after Our Ford's first T-Model was put on the market.'[2] (Here

---

1. *George Bernard Shaw* [ʃɔː]: Irish dramatist and critic (1856-1950); his work is witty and full of his own opinions about social reform.

2. *twenty-three years ... on the Market* : the Model T Ford automobile was put on the market in 1908, so Shaw's broadcast must have been made in 1931 (i.e. the year Huxley wrote BNW).

the Director made a sign of the T [1] on his stomach and all the students reverently followed suit.) 'And yet . . .'

Furiously the students scribbled. '*Hypnopædia, first used officially in A.F. 214. Why not before? Two reasons. (a) . . .*'

'These early experimenters,' the D.H.C. was saying, 'were on the wrong track.[2] They thought that hypnopædia could be made an instrument of intellectual education . . .'

(A small boy asleep on his right side, the right arm stuck out, the right hand hanging limply over the edge of the bed. Through a round grating in the side of a box a voice speaks softly.

'The Nile is the longest river in Africa and the second in length of all the rivers of the globe. Although falling short of the length of the Mississippi-Missouri, the Nile is at the head of all rivers as regards the length of its basin, which extends through 35 degrees of latitude . . .'

At breakfast the next morning, 'Tommy,' some one says, 'do you know which is the longest river in Africa?' A shaking of the head. 'But don't you remember something that begins: The Nile is the . . .'

'The-Nile-is-the-longest-river-in-Africa-and-the- second-in-length-of-all-the-rivers-of-the-globe . . .' The words come rushing out. 'Although-falling-short-of . . .'

'Well now, which is the longest river in Africa?'

The eyes are blank. 'I don't know.'

'But the Nile, Tommy.'

'The-Nile-is-the-longest-river-in-Africa-and-second . . .'

'Then which river is the longest, Tommy?'

Tommy bursts into tears. 'I don't know,' he howls.)[3]

---

1. *a sign of the T* : the equivalent, in the World State, of the sign of the cross. It shows piety, or respect, in relation to the founding moment of society based on automated mass production.

2. *on the wrong track* : not following the path that would lead them to their objective. (A standard idiom; cf. "on the right track".)

3. *he howls* [haʊlz]: he shouts (while crying, so it sounds something like the crying of a wolf). This whole passage in parenthesis is a fable told by the Director to illustrate what happens when sleep teaching is used as "an instrument of intellectual education", as it had been at first.

That howl, the Director made it plain, discouraged the earliest investigators. The experiments were abandoned. No further attempt was made to teach children the length of the Nile in their sleep. Quite rightly. You can't learn a science unless you know what it's all about.

'Whereas, if they'd only started on *moral* education,' said the Director, leading the way towards the door. The students followed him, desperately scribbling as they walked and all the way up in the lift. 'Moral education, which ought never, in any circumstances, to be rational.'[1]

'Silence, silence,' whispered a loud-speaker as they stepped out at the fourteenth floor, and 'Silence, silence,' the trumpet mouths indefatigably repeated [2] at intervals down every corridor. The students and even the Director himself rose automatically to the tips of their toes. They were Alphas, of course; but even Alphas have been well conditioned. 'Silence, silence.' All the air of the fourteenth floor was sibilant with the categorical imperative.

Fifty yards of tiptoeing brought them to a door which the Director cautiously opened. They stepped over the threshold into the twilight of a shuttered dormitory. Eighty cots stood in a row against the wall. There was a sound of light regular breathing and a continuous murmur, as of very faint voices remotely whispering.

A nurse rose as they entered and came to attention before the Director.

1. *Moral education ... ought never ... to be rational* : this justification inverts the theories of the great German philosopher Immanuel Kant (1724-1804); what Kant argued in his *Critique of Practical Reason* (1788) was that moral actions are guided by respect for duty, awareness of which is determined by reason, not by wishes or emotions. Kant's "categorical imperative" (mentioned a few lines further on in the text) summarises this moral obligation. Here, social engineering does the work of reason.

2. *the trumpet mouths indefatigably repeated* : the trumpet-shaped loudspeakers never stopped repeating. ("indefatigably" [ˌndɪˈfætɪgəbli] means "untiringly".)

'What's the lesson this afternoon?' he asked.

'We had Elementary Sex for the first forty minutes,' she answered. 'But now it's switched over to Elementary Class Consciousness.'

The Director walked slowly down the long line of cots. Rosy and relaxed with sleep, eighty little boys and girls lay softly breathing. There was a whisper under every pillow. The D.H.C. halted and, bending over one of the little beds, listened attentively.

'Elementary Class Consciousness, did you say? Let's have it repeated a little louder by the trumpet.'

At the end of the room a loud-speaker projected from the wall. The Director walked up to it and pressed a switch.

'. . . all wear green,' said a soft but very distinct voice, beginning in the middle of a sentence, 'and Delta children wear khaki. Oh no, I don't want to play with Delta children. And Epsilons are still worse. They're too stupid to be able to read or write. Besides, they wear black, which is such a beastly [1] colour. I'm so glad I'm a Beta.'

There was a pause; then the voice began again.

'Alpha children wear grey. They work much harder than we do, because they're so frightfully clever. I'm really awfully glad I'm a Beta, because I don't work so hard. And then we are much better than the Gammas and Deltas. Gammas are stupid. They all wear green, and Delta children wear khaki. Oh no, I *don't* want to play with Delta children. And Epsilons are still worse. They're too stupid to be able . . .'

The Director pushed back the switch. The voice was silent. Only its thin ghost continued to mutter from beneath the eighty pillows.

'They'll have that repeated forty or fifty times more before they wake; then again on Thursday, and again on Saturday. A hundred and twenty times three times a week for thirty months. After which they go on to a more advanced lesson.'

---

1. *beastly* [bi:stli]: nasty, horrible (colloquial). The voice is intended to sound like that of a middle or upper-class child of Huxley's own period expressing his or her class prejudices.

Roses and electric shocks, the khaki of Deltas and a whiff of asafœtida [1] – wedded indissolubly before the child can speak. But wordless conditioning is crude and wholesale; cannot bring home the finer distinctions, cannot inculcate the more complex courses of behaviour. For that there must be words, but words without reason. In brief, hypnopædia.

'The greatest moralizing and socializing force of all time.'

The students took it down in their little books. Straight from the horse's mouth.

Once more the Director touched the switch.

'. . . so frightfully clever,' the soft, insinuating, indefatigable voice was saying. ' I'm really awfully glad I'm a Beta, because . . .'

Not so much like drops of water, though water, it is true, can wear holes in the hardest granite; rather, drops of liquid sealing-wax, drops that adhere, incrust, incorporate themselves with what they fall on, till finally the rock is all one scarlet blob.[2]

'Till at last the child's mind is these suggestions, and the sum of the suggestions is the child's mind. And not the child's mind only. The adult's mind too – all his life long. The mind that judges and desires and decides – made up of these suggestions. But all these suggestions are our suggestions!' The Director almost shouted in his triumph. 'Suggestions from the State.' He banged the nearest table. 'It therefore follows . . .'

A noise made him turn round.

'Oh, Ford!' he said in another tone, 'I've gone and woken the children.'

---

1. *a whiff of asafoetida* [ˌæsəˈfetɪdə]: a short exposure to the smell of asafoetida, a kind of plant resin with a particularly bad smell. (The Beta child cannot then separate this stink from the Deltas' colour.)

2. *scarlet blob* : a more-or-less round mass of some substance, in this case formed of bright red sealing-wax (representing the suggestions arriving bit by bit during sleep) that covers and re-shapes the rock (the mental apparatus of the child). Huxley may have intended us to recognise this as an ironic inversion of the metaphor of knowledge acquisition proposed by the Greek Stoic philosophers Zeno and Chrysippus, who argued that our sense-perceptions imprint images on our minds as a seal does on wax.

Chapter III

O UTSIDE, in the garden, it was playtime. Naked in the warm June sunshine, six or seven hundred little boys and girls were running with shrill yells over the lawns, or playing ball games, or squatting silently in twos and threes among the flowering shrubs. The roses were in bloom, two nightingales soliloquized in the boskage, a cuckoo was just going out of tune among the lime trees. The air was drowsy [1] with the murmur of bees and helicopters.

The Director and his students stood for a short time watching a game of Centrifugal Bumble-puppy.[2] Twenty

1. *drowsy* ['drauzi]: made one feel sleepy. The adjective may recall the "drowsy numbness" experienced by the narrator in John Keats' "Ode to a Nightingale" (1819), as he listens to the nightingale; the references to boskage (an old-fashioned, poetic word for undergrowth in a wood), the cuckoo (which is proverbial for never "going out of tune"), lime trees and the humming of bees are also reminiscent of the nature poetry of the English Romantics.

2. *Centrifugal Bumble-puppy* [sen'trɪfjʊgl 'bʌmbəl,pʌpi]: an imaginary version of bumble-puppy, a game that involves hitting a ball spinning around a post. The BNW version needs elaborate equipment.

children were grouped in a circle round a chrome-steel tower. A ball thrown up so as to land on the platform at the top of the tower rolled down into the interior, fell on a rapidly revolving disk, was hurled through one or other of the numerous apertures pierced in the cylindrical casing, and had to be caught.

'Strange,' mused the Director, as they turned away, 'strange to think that even in Our Ford's day most games were played without more apparatus than a ball or two and a few sticks and perhaps a bit of netting. Imagine the folly of allowing people to play elaborate games which do nothing whatever to increase consumption. It's madness. Nowadays the Controllers won't approve of any new game unless it can be shown that it requires at least as much apparatus as the most complicated of existing games.' He interrupted himself.

'That's a charming little group,' he said, pointing.

In a little grassy bay between tall clumps of Mediterranean heather, two children, a little boy of about seven and a little girl who might have been a year older, were playing, very gravely and with all the focussed attention of scientists intent on a labour of discovery, a rudimentary sexual game.

'Charming, charming!' the D.H.C. repeated sentimentally.

'Charming,' the boys politely agreed. But their smile was rather patronizing. They had put aside similar childish amusements too recently to be able to watch them now without a touch of contempt. Charming? but it was just a pair of kids fooling about; that was all. Just kids.

'I always think,' the Director was continuing in the same rather maudlin tone,[1] when he was interrupted by a loud boo-hooing.[2]

From a neighbouring shrubbery emerged a nurse, leading by the hand a small boy, who howled as he went. An anxious-looking little girl trotted at her heels.

'What's the matter?' asked the Director.

---

1. *maudlin tone* : foolishly sentimental way of speaking (like someone who is drunk and tearful).
2. *boo-hooing* : wailing, the sound of a child crying (onomatopoeic).

The nurse shrugged her shoulders. 'Nothing much,' she answered. 'It's just that this little boy seems rather reluctant to join in the ordinary erotic play. I'd noticed it once or twice before. And now again to-day. He started yelling just now . . .'

'Honestly,' put in the anxious-looking little girl, 'I didn't mean to hurt him or anything. Honestly.'

'Of course you didn't, dear,' said the nurse reassuringly. 'And so,' she went on, turning back to the Director, 'I'm taking him in to see the Assistant Superintendent of Psychology. Just to see if anything's at all abnormal.'

'Quite right,' said the Director. 'Take him in. You stay here, little girl,' he added, as the nurse moved away with her still howling charge. 'What's your name?'

'Polly Trotsky.'[1]

'And a very good name too,'[2] said the Director. 'Run away now and see if you can find some other little boy to play with.'

The child scampered off into the bushes and was lost to sight.

'Exquisite little creature!' said the Director, looking after her. Then, turning to his students, 'What I'm going to tell you now,' he said, 'may sound incredible. But then, when you're not accustomed to history, most facts about the past do sound incredible.'

He let out the amazing truth. For a very long period before the time of Our Ford, and even for some generations afterwards, erotic play between children had been regarded as abnormal (there was a roar of laughter); and not only abnormal, actually immoral (no!): and had therefore been rigorously suppressed.

---

1. *Polly Trotsky* : Leon [Lev Davidovitch] Trotsky (1879 - 1940) was one of the leaders of the Russian Revolution. Attacked by Stalin in the 1920s and expelled from the Communist Party in 1927, he had been banished from Russia in 1929, just before BNW was written. "Polly" may allude to the nursery rhyme "Polly put the kettle on".

2. *'And a very good name too'* : another allusion to *Hard Times*. During his visit to the school, Mr Gradgrind wants to know the name of one little girl (Sissy Jupe); but in Dickens's novel the name is not approved of: "Sissy is not a name . . . Don't call yourself Sissy" replies Gradgrind.

A look of astonished incredulity appeared on the faces of his listeners. Poor little kids not allowed to amuse themselves? They could not believe it.

'Even adolescents,' the D.H.C. was saying, 'even adolescents like yourselves . . .'

'Not possible!'

'Barring [1] a little surreptitious auto-erotism and homosexuality – absolutely nothing.'

'*Nothing?*'

'In most cases, till they were over twenty years old.'

'Twenty years old?' echoed the students in a chorus of loud disbelief.

'Twenty,' the Director repeated. 'I told you that you'd find it incredible'.

'But what happened?' they asked. 'What were the results?'

'The results were terrible.' A deep resonant voice broke startlingly into the dialogue.

They looked round. On the fringe of the little group stood a stranger – a man of middle height, black-haired, with a hooked nose, full red lips, eyes very piercing and dark. 'Terrible,' he repeated.

The D.H.C. had at that moment sat down on one of the steel and rubber benches conveniently scattered through the gardens; but at the sight of the stranger, he sprang to his feet and darted forward, his hands outstretched, smiling with all his teeth, effusive.

'Controller! What an unexpected pleasure! Boys, what are you thinking of? This is the Controller; this is his fordship, Mustapha Mond.'[2]

1. *Barring* ['bɑːrɪŋ]: excluding, except for (a colloquial preposition).

2. *his fordship, Mustapha Mond* : "his fordship", like today's "his lordship", is a formal term of address that shows respect. The Controller's surname recalls that of Baron Alfred Mond (1868-1930), a British politician, Chairman of the Mond Nickel Company and organizer, in 1928, of the Mond Conference (in which the need for industrial reorganization was discussed by employers and union representatives). Mustapha Mond's first name alludes to that of Mustapha Kemal Ataturk (1880 - 1938), first president of the Turkish Republic. Huxley may have intended a pun on "must have a world" ("monde" is the French word for world).

In the four thousand rooms of the Centre the four thousand electric clocks simultaneously struck four. Discarnate [1] voices called from the trumpet mouths.

'Main Day-shift off duty. Second Day-shift take over. Main Day-shift off . . .'

In the lift, on their way up to the changing-rooms, Henry Foster and the Assistant Director of Predestination rather pointedly [2] turned their backs on Bernard Marx [3] from the Psychology Bureau: averted themselves from that unsavoury reputation.[4]

The faint hum and rattle of machinery still stirred the crimson air in the Embryo Store.[5] Shifts might come and go, one lupus-coloured face give place to another; majestically and for ever the conveyors crept forward with their load of future men and women.

Lenina Crowne [6] walked briskly towards the door.

1. *Discarnate* : dissociated from any body. (An unusual word).

2. *rather pointedly* : in a way that made clear to the person concerned that he was the motive.

3. *Bernard Marx* : the surname of course refers to Karl Marx (1818-1883). The first name may point to George Bernard Shaw or to Claude Bernard (1813-78), the French physiologist whose work gave rise to experimental medicine; or perhaps to Bernard Mannes Baruch (1870-1965), a U.S. economist who had a long career as a presidential advisor.

4. *unsavoury reputation* : notoriety as a socially disapproved of or morally questionable person.

5. *The faint hum . . . Embryo Store* : with this sentence we are returned to Lenina's experience. The rest of the chapter consists of four largely separate narrative sequences: (1) Mustapha Mond talking to the D.H.C.'s new students; (2a) Henry Foster and the Assistant Predestinator getting changed and chatting together; (2b) Bernard Marx's thoughts as he listens to them; (3) Lenina's conversation with Fanny Crowne in the female changing-room; (4) the sleep-teaching messages in the nurseries (from the top of page 67). We return to the Embryo Store (0) in the last paragraph of the chapter.

6. *Lenina Crowne* : the reference could be to John Crowne, an English dramatist who wrote fashionable satirical comedies such as *Sir Courtly Nice* (1685).

His fordship Mustapha Mond! The eyes of the saluting students almost popped out of their heads. Mustapha Mond! The Resident Controller for Western Europe! One of the Ten World Controllers. One of the Ten . . . and he sat down on the bench with the D.H.C., he was going to stay, to stay, yes, and actually talk to them . . . straight from the horse's mouth. Straight from the mouth of Ford himself.

Two shrimp-brown [1] children emerged from a neighbouring shrubbery, stared at them for a moment with large, astonished eyes, then returned to their amusements among the leaves.

'You all remember,' said the Controller, in his strong deep voice, 'you all remember, I suppose, that beautiful and inspired saying of Our Ford's: History is bunk. History,' he repeated slowly, 'is bunk.'[2]

He waved his hand; and it was as though, with an invisible feather whisk,[3] he had brushed away a little dust, and the dust was Harappa, was Ur of the Chaldees; some spider-webs, and they were Thebes and Babylon and Cnossos and Mycenae.[4] Whisk, whisk – and where was Odysseus, where was Job,[5] where were Jupiter and Gotama [6] and Jesus? Whisk – and those

---

1. *shrimp-brown* : of the same brown colour as shrimps.

2. *History is bunk* [bʌŋk]: i.e. history has no value, is a waste of time. Henry Ford made the statement that "History is more or less bunk" (quoted in the *Chicago Tribune*, 25 May 1916).

3. *feather whisk* : a brush with a bunch of feathers at the end, which can be moved rapidly and lightly (that is, whisked) so as to remove dust and spider's webs. (Mond's gesture implies that even the major material and cultural achievements of past civilizations can be swept away as easily and with as little thought as ordinary dirt.)

4. *Harappa . . . Mycenae* [maɪˈsiːnaɪ]: important archeological sites from India to Greece, at which the remains of ancient civilizations had been discovered.

5. *Job* : Old Testament prophet whose life and sufferings are described in the 18th book of the Bible, the Book of Job.

6. *Gotama* : (usually written "Gautama") one of the names of Buddha, whose teachings gave rise to the Buddhist religion, in the 6th Century.

specks of antique dirt called Athens and Rome, Jerusalem and
the Middle Kingdom [1] – all were gone. Whisk – the place where
Italy had been was empty. Whisk, the cathedrals; whisk, whisk,
King Lear and the Thoughts of Pascal.[2] Whisk, Passion; whisk,
Requiem; whisk, Symphony; whisk . . .

'Going to the Feelies [3] this evening, Henry?' enquired the
Assistant Predestinator. 'I hear the new one at the Alhambra is
first-rate. There's a love scene on a bearskin rug; they say it's
marvellous. Every hair of the bear reproduced. The most
amazing tactual effects.'

'That's why you're taught no history,' the Controller was
saying. 'But now the time has come . . .'
The D.H.C. looked at him nervously. There were those
strange rumours of old forbidden books hidden in a safe in the
Controller's study. Bibles, poetry – Ford knew what.[4]
Mustapha Mond intercepted his anxious glance and the
corners of his red lips twitched ironically.
'It's all right, Director,' he said in a tone of faint derision, 'I
won't corrupt them.'
The D.H.C. was overwhelmed with confusion.

Those who feel themselves despised do well to look
despising. The smile on Bernard Marx's face was contemptuous.
Every hair on the bear indeed!

1. *Middle Kingdom* : that is, the period in which Egyptian civilization
    was at its height (the Twelfth Dynasty, 1991-1876 B.C.).
2. *Thoughts of Pascal* : Blaise Pascal (1623-62), a French philosopher.
    The *Pensées* ("Thoughts") are his religious writing.
3. *the feelies* ['fiːliːz]: a form of entertainment developed from
    cinema as we know it; instead of just seeing the moving pictures
    (the movies), the audience feels the experience and is supplied
    with appropriate smells. A description of experiencing a Feeling
    Picture is given in Chapter 11.
4. *Ford knew what* : a variation of the exclamatory expression "God
    knows", in the past tense because it is the D.H.C.'s reported
    thought.

'I shall make a point of going,' said Henry Foster.

Mustapha Mond leaned forward, shook a finger at them. 'Just try to realize it,' he said, and his voice sent a strange thrill quivering along their diaphragms. 'Try to realize what it was like to have a viviparous mother.'

That smutty word again. But none of them dreamed, this time, of smiling.

'Try to imagine what "living with one's family" meant.'

They tried; but obviously without the smallest success.

'And do you know what a "home" was?'

They shook their heads.

From her dim crimson cellar Lenina Crowne shot up seventeen stories, turned to the right as she stepped out of the lift, walked down a long corridor and, opening the door marked GIRLS' DRESSING-ROOM, plunged into a deafening chaos of arms and bosoms [1] and underclothing. Torrents of hot water were splashing into or gurgling out of a hundred baths. Rumbling and hissing, eighty vibro-vacuum massage machines [2] were simultaneously kneading and sucking the firm and sunburnt flesh of eighty superb female specimens. Every one was talking at the top of her voice. A Synthetic Music machine was warbling out a super-cornet solo.

'Hullo, Fanny,' said Lenina to the young woman who had the pegs and locker next to hers.

Fanny worked in the Bottling Room, and her surname was also Crowne. But as the two thousand million inhabitants of the planet had only ten thousand names between them, the coincidence was not particularly surprising.

---

1. *bosoms* ['bʊzəmz]: female breasts.
2. *vibro-vacuum massage machines* ['vaɪbrəʊ'vækjʊəm 'mæsɑːʒ] (later, "vibro-vacs"): these invented machines help keep the women young-looking by pressing and stretching (kneading [n ːd ɴ]) the flesh.

Lenina pulled at her zippers – downwards on the jacket, downwards with a double-handed gesture at the two that held trousers, downwards again to loosen her undergarment. Still wearing her shoes and stockings, she walked off towards the bathrooms.

Home, home – a few small rooms, stiflingly over-inhabited by a man, by a periodically teeming [1] woman, by a rabble of boys and girls of all ages. No air, no space; an understerilized prison; darkness, disease, and smells.

(The Controller's evocation was so vivid that one of the boys, more sensitive than the rest, turned pale at the mere description and was on the point of being sick.)

Lenina got out of the bath, towelled herself dry, took hold of a long flexible tube plugged into the wall, presented the nozzle to her breast, as though she meant to commit suicide, pressed down the trigger. A blast of warmed air dusted her with the finest talcum powder. Eight different scents and eau-de-Cologne were laid on [2] in little taps over the wash-basin. She turned on the third from the left, dabbled herself with chypre [3] and, carrying her shoes and stockings in her hand, went out to see if one of the vibro-vacuum machines were free.

And home was as squalid psychically as physically. Psychically, it was a rabbit hole, a midden,[4] hot with the frictions of tightly packed life, reeking with emotion. What suffocating intimacies, what dangerous, insane, obscene relationships between the members of the family group! Maniacally, the mother brooded over her children (*her*

1. *periodically teeming* : regularly teeming with (i.e. bearing large numbers of) babies.
2. *laid on* : supplied (as an integral feature of the system).
3. *chypre* [ʃɪprə]: perfume made from sandalwood (French).
4. *midden* : a bad-smelling ("reeking") mass of animal droppings and other decomposing organic matter, as found on a farm; the micro-organisms in it produce heat.

children) . . . brooded over them like a cat over its kittens; but a
cat that could talk, a cat that could say, 'My baby, my baby,' over
and over again. 'My baby, and oh, oh, at my breast, the little
hands, the hunger, and that unspeakable agonizing pleasure! Till
at last my baby sleeps, my baby sleeps with a bubble of white
milk at the corner of his mouth. My little baby sleeps . . .'

'Yes,' said Mustapha Mond, nodding his head, 'you may
well shudder.'[1]

'Who are you going out with to-night? ' Lenina asked,
returning from the vibro-vac like a pearl illuminated from
within, pinkly glowing.

'Nobody.'

Lenina raised her eyebrows in astonishment.

'I've been feeling rather out of sorts lately,' Fanny explained.
'Dr. Wells advised me to have a Pregnancy Substitute.'

'But, my dear, you're only nineteen. The first Pregnancy
Substitute isn't compulsory till twenty-one.'

'I know, dear. But some people are better if they begin
earlier. Dr. Wells [2] told me that brunettes with wide pelvises,
like me, ought to have their first Pregnancy Substitute at
seventeen. So I'm really two years late, not two years early.' She
opened the door of her locker and pointed to the row of boxes
and labelled phials [3] on the upper shelf.

'SYRUP OF CORPUS LUTEUM.' Lenina read the names aloud.
'OVARIN, GUARANTEED FRESH: NOT TO BE USED AFTER AUGUST 1ST,
A.F. 632. MAMMARY GLAND EXTRACT: TO BE TAKEN THREE TIMES
DAILY, BEFORE MEALS, WITH A LITTLE WATER. PLACENTIN: 5CC TO BE

---

1. *you may well shudder* ['ʃʌdə]: your feeling of revulsion, as shown
   by the spasms of shaking passing through your body, are
   completely understandable.
2. *Dr Wells* : H.G. Wells (1886-1946), the English author, was the
   best-known and most important writer of literary utopias.
3. *phials* ['faɪəlz]: little bottles. They contain the hormones (ovarin
   and placentin) and other components of the treatment that
   simulates the bodily changes associated with pregnancy.

INJECTED INTRAVENALLY EVERY THIRD DAY . . . Ugh!' Lenina shuddered. 'How I loathe intravenals, don't you?'
    'Yes. But when they do one good . . .' Fanny was a particularly sensible girl.

Our Ford – or Our Freud,[1] as, for some inscrutable reason, he chose to call himself whenever he spoke of psychological matters – Our Freud had been the first to reveal the appalling dangers of family life. The world was full of fathers – was therefore full of misery; full of mothers – therefore of every kind of perversion from sadism to chastity; full of brothers, sisters, uncles, aunts – full of madness and suicide.
    'And yet, among the savages of Samoa,[2] in certain islands off the coast of New Guinea. . .'[3]
    The tropical sunshine lay like warm honey on the naked bodies of children tumbling promiscuously among the hibiscus blossoms. Home was in any one of twenty palm-thatched houses. In the Trobriands conception was the work of ancestral ghosts; nobody had ever heard of a father.
    'Extremes,' said the Controller, 'meet. For the good reason that they were made to meet.'

'Dr. Wells says that a three months' Pregnancy Substitute now will make all the difference to my health for the next three or four years.'
    'Well, I hope he's right,' said Lenina. 'But, Fanny, do you really mean to say that for the next three months you're not supposed to . . .'

1. *Our Freud* : the World State seems to treat Ford and Freud as two aspects of the same founding luminary figure. Sigmund Freud (1856-1939) is usually considered the founder of psychoanalysis.
2. *Samoa* : island in the south Pacific.
3. *certain islands off the coast of New Guinea* : this phrase introduces a sudden vivid evocation of life on the Trobriand Islands.

'Oh no, dear. Only for a week or two, that's all. I shall spend the evening at the Club playing Musical Bridge.[1] I suppose you're going out?'

Lenina nodded.

'Who with?'

'Henry Foster.'

'Again?' Fanny's kind, rather moon-like face took on an incongruous expression of pained and disapproving astonishment. 'Do you mean to tell me you're *still* going out with Henry Foster?'

Mothers and fathers, brothers and sisters. But there were also husbands, wives, lovers. There were also monogamy and romance.

'Though you probably don't know what those are,' said Mustapha Mond.

They shook their heads.

Family, monogamy, romance. Everywhere exclusiveness, everywhere a focussing of interest, a narrow channelling of impulse and energy.

'But every one belongs to every one else,' he concluded, citing the hypnopædic proverb.

The students nodded, emphatically agreeing with a statement which upwards of sixty-two thousand repetitions in the dark had made them accept, not merely as true, but as axiomatic, self-evident, utterly indisputable.

'But after all,' Lenina was protesting, 'it's only about four months now since I've been having Henry.'[2]

---

1. *Musical Bridge* : this must be a variation on the card game (bridge) as we know it.

2. *I've been having Henry* : present-day equivalents are "going out with Henry" or "that Henry and I have been together". Here the verb refers directly to the sexual act that governs the relationship (which is why "have" is used as a dynamic verb, in the "-ing" form).

'*Only* four months! I like that. And what's more,' Fanny went on, pointing an accusing finger, 'there's been nobody else except Henry all that time. Has there?'

Lenina blushed scarlet; but her eyes, the tone of her voice remained defiant. 'No, there hasn't been any one else,' she answered almost truculently.[1] 'And I jolly well don't see why there should have been.'

'Oh, she jolly well [2] doesn't see why there should have been,' Fanny repeated, as though to an invisible listener behind Lenina's left shoulder. Then, with a sudden change of tone, 'But seriously,' she said, 'I really do think you ought to be careful. It's such horribly bad form [3] to go on and on like this with one man. At forty, or thirty-five, it wouldn't be so bad. But at *your* age, Lenina! No, it really won't do. And you know how strongly the D.H.C. objects to anything intense or long-drawn. Four months of Henry Foster, without having another man – why, he'd be furious if he knew . . .'

'Think of water under pressure in a pipe.' They thought of it. 'I pierce it once,' said the Controller. 'What a jet!'[4]

He pierced it twenty times. There were twenty piddling little fountains.

'My baby. My baby . . . !'

'Mother!' The madness is infectious.

'My love, my one and only, precious, precious . . .'

Mother, monogamy, romance. High spurts the fountain; fierce and foamy the wild jet. The urge has but a single outlet. My love, my baby. No wonder those poor pre-moderns were mad and wicked and miserable. Their world didn't allow them

---

1. *truculently* ['trʌkjʊləntli]: aggressively, as if wanting to argue.
2. *jolly well* : really – a colloquial way of intensifying the verb.
3. *bad form* : socially disapproved of; this is why her steady relationship is unacceptable (it "won't do").
4. *What a jet!* : a powerful stream (of water in this case, coming out from a single hole). With many holes the water pours out ("spurts") less forcefully.

to take things easily, didn't allow them to be sane, virtuous, happy. What with [1] mothers and lovers, what with the prohibitions they were not conditioned to obey, what with the temptations and the lonely remorses, what with all the diseases and the endless isolating pain, what with the uncertainties and the poverty – they were forced to feel strongly. And feeling strongly (and strongly, what was more, in solitude, in hopelessly individual isolation), how could they be stable?

'Of course there's no need to give him up. Have somebody else from time to time, that's all. He has other girls, doesn't he?'

Lenina admitted it.

'Of course he does. Trust Henry Foster to be the perfect gentleman – always correct. And then there's the Director to think of. You know what a stickler. . .'[2]

Nodding, 'He patted me on the behind this afternoon,' said Lenina.

'There, you see!' Fanny was triumphant. 'That shows what he stands for. The strictest conventionality.'

'Stability,' said the Controller, 'stability. No civilization without social stability. No social stability without individual stability.' His voice was a trumpet. Listening, they felt larger, warmer.

The machine turns, turns and must keep on turning – for ever. It is death if it stands still. A thousand millions scrabbled the crust of the earth. The wheels began to turn. In a hundred and fifty years there were two thousand millions. Stop all the wheels. In a hundred and fifty weeks there are once more only a thousand millions; a thousand thousand thousand men and women have starved to death.

Wheels must turn steadily, but cannot turn untended. There must be men to tend them, men as steady as the wheels upon their axles, sane men, obedient men, stable in contentment.

1. *What with* . . . : taking into account not only . . . but also . . .
2. *stickler* : punctilious person who insists on every detail being correct. She was perhaps going to say "what a stickler (for the right behaviour) he is".

Crying: My baby, my mother, my only, only love; groaning: My sin, my terrible God; screaming with pain, muttering with fever, bemoaning old age and poverty – how can they tend the wheels? And if they cannot tend the wheels . . . The corpses of a thousand thousand thousand men and women would be hard to bury or burn.

'And after all,' Fanny's tone was coaxing, 'it's not as though there were anything painful or disagreeable about having one or two men besides Henry. And seeing that, you *ought* to be a little more promiscuous. . .'

'Stability,' insisted the Controller, 'stability. The primal and the ultimate need. Stability. Hence all this.'
With a wave of his hand he indicated the gardens, the huge building of the Conditioning Centre, the naked children furtive in the undergrowth or running across the lawns.

Lenina shook her head. 'Somehow,' she mused, 'I hadn't been feeling very keen on promiscuity lately. There are times when one doesn't. Haven't you found that too, Fanny?'
Fanny nodded her sympathy and understanding. 'But one's got to make the effort,' she said sententiously, 'one's got to play the game. After all, every one belongs to every one else.'
'Yes, every one belongs to every one else,' Lenina repeated slowly and, sighing, was silent for a moment; then, taking Fanny's hand, gave it a little squeeze. 'You're quite right, Fanny. As usual. I'll make the effort.'

Impulse arrested spills over, and the flood is feeling, the flood is passion, the flood is even madness: it depends on the force of the current, the height and strength of the barrier. The unchecked stream flows smoothly down its appointed channels into a calm well-being. (The embryo is hungry; day in, day out, the blood-surrogate pump unceasingly turns its eight hundred revolutions a minute. The decanted infant howls; at once a nurse appears with a bottle of external secretion. Feeling lurks in that

interval of time between desire and its consummation. Shorten
that interval, break down all those old unnecessary barriers.
'Fortunate boys!' said the Controller. 'No pains have been
spared to make your lives emotionally easy – to preserve you, so
far as that is possible, from having emotions at all.'
'Ford's in his flivver,'[1] murmured the D.H.C. 'All's well with
the world.'

'Lenina Crowne?' said Henry Foster, echoing the Assistant
Predestinator's question as he zipped up his trousers. 'Oh, she's
a splendid girl. Wonderfully pneumatic.[2] I'm surprised you
haven't had her.'
'I can't think how it is I haven't,' said the Assistant
Predestinator. 'I certainly will. At the first opportunity.'
From his place on the opposite side of the changing-room
aisle, Bernard Marx overheard what they were saying and
turned pale.

'And to tell the truth,' said Lenina, 'I'm beginning to get just
a tiny bit bored with nothing but Henry every day.' She pulled
on her left stocking. ' Do you know Bernard Marx?' she asked in
a tone whose excessive casualness was evidently forced.
Fanny looked startled. 'You don't mean to say . . .?'

1. *Ford's in his flivver* : "flivver" is an outmoded slang word, which
   here means a small cheap car. The D.H.C. is alluding
   (consciously?) to the well-known lines by the poet Robert
   Browning (1812 - 1889) in his play *Pippa Passes*, expressing
   satisfaction with the state of the world: "God's in his heaven - /
   All's right with the world!". Huxley's modifications bring out
   the ironic aspect of the allusion.

2. *pneumatic* [njuː'mætɪk]: this word, which normally indicates that
   something uses compressed air (like a pneumatic drill), is used
   in a non-standard way in *BNW*. Instead of saying a woman is
   "pretty" she is referred to as "pneumatic", a term based on her
   sexual attributes – her "sex appeal". In T.S. Eliot's 1918 poem
   "Whispers of Immortality", a woman's breasts are described as
   giving "promise of pneumatic bliss"; Huxley had alluded to this
   passage when describing the girls of Los Ángeles, the "City of
   Dreadful Night", in *Jesting Pilate* (London, 1926; 1957 ed.: p. 265).

'Why not? Bernard's an Alpha-Plus. Besides, he asked me to go to one of the Savage Reservations [1] with him. I've always wanted to see a Savage Reservation.'

'But his reputation?'

'What do I care about his reputation?'

'They say he doesn't like Obstacle Golf.'

'They say, they say,' mocked Lenina.

'And then he spends most of his time by himself *alone*.' There was horror in Fanny's voice.

'Well, he won't be alone when he's with me. And anyhow, why are people so beastly to him? I think he's rather sweet.' She smiled to herself; how absurdly shy he had been! Frightened almost – as though she were a World Controller and he a Gamma-Minus machine minder.

'Consider your own lives,' said Mustapha Mond. 'Has any of you ever encountered an insurmountable obstacle?'

The question was answered by a negative silence.

'Has any of you been compelled to live through a long time-interval between the consciousness of a desire and its fulfilment?'

'Well,' began one of the boys, and hesitated.

'Speak up,' said the D.H.C. 'Don't keep his fordship waiting.'

'I once had to wait nearly four weeks before a girl I wanted would let me have her.'

'And you felt a strong emotion in consequence?'

'Horrible!'

'Horrible; precisely,' said the Controller. 'Our ancestors were so stupid and short-sighted that when the first reformers came along and offered to deliver them from those horrible emotions, they wouldn't have anything to do with them.'

---

1. *Savage Reservations* : enclosed areas in which tribal cultures are allowed to continue their traditional way of life, like today's North American Indian Reservations. (We learn more about them in Chapter 6)

'Talking about her as though she were a bit of meat.' Bernard ground [1] his teeth. 'Have her here, have her there. Like mutton. Degrading her to so much mutton. She said she'd think it over, she said she'd give me an answer this week. Oh, Ford, Ford, Ford.' He would have liked to go up to them and hit them in the face – hard, again and again.

'Yes, I really do advise you to try her,' Henry Foster was saying.

'Take Ectogenesis.[2] Pfitzner and Kawaguchi had got the whole technique worked out. But would the Governments look at it? No. There was something called Christianity. Women were forced to go on being viviparous.'

'He's so ugly!' said Fanny.

'But I rather like his looks.'

'And then so *small*.' Fanny made a grimace; smallness was so horribly and typically low-caste.

'I think that's rather sweet,' said Lenina. 'One feels one would like to pet him. You know. Like a cat.'

Fanny was shocked. 'They say somebody made a mistake when he was still in the bottle – thought he was a Gamma and put alcohol into his blood-surrogate. That's why he's so stunted.'

'What nonsense!' Lenina was indignant.

'Sleep teaching was actually prohibited in England. There was something called liberalism. Parliament, if you know what that was, passed a law against it. The records survive. Speeches

1. *ground* : past tense of "grind", meaning to rub together with force.
2. *Ectogenesis* : the generation and development of babies outside the mother's body (so-called "test-tube babies"). (Now usually without a capital letter.)

about liberty of the subject. Liberty to be inefficient and miserable. Freedom to be a round peg in a square hole.'[1]

'But, my dear chap, you're welcome, I assure you. You're welcome.' Henry Foster patted the Assistant Predestinator on the shoulder. 'Every one belongs to every one else, after all.'

One hundred repetitions three nights a week for four years, thought Bernard Marx, who was a specialist on hypnopædia. Sixty-two thousand four hundred repetitions make one truth. Idiots!

'Or the Caste System. Constantly proposed, constantly rejected. There was something called democracy. As though men were more than physico-chemically equal.'

'Well, all I can say is that I'm going to accept his invitation.'

Bernard hated them, hated them. But they were two, they were large, they were strong.

'The Nine Years' War began in A.F. 141.'

'Not even if it *were* true about the alcohol in his blood-surrogate.'

'Phosgene,[2] chloropicrin, ethyl iodoacetate, diphenylcyanarsine, trichlormethyl chloroformate, dichlorethyl sulphide. Not to mention hydrocyanic acid.'

---

1. *a round peg in a square hole* : idiomatic expression to refer to someone who doesn't "fit in", who has problems coping with those he or she lives or works with.

2. *Phosgene* ['fɒzdʒɪːn]: a colourless gas ($COCl_2$) used as a poison gas in the First World War. This, and the other poisonous chemicals listed (dichlorethyl sulphide, for example, is mustard-gas) must have been used as chemical weapons nearly 500 years before, in the Nine Years' War (2049-2058 A.D.).

'Which I simply don't believe,' Lenina concluded.

'The noise of fourteen thousand aeroplanes advancing in open order. But in the Kurfurstendamm [1] and the Eighth Arrondissement,[2] the explosion of the anthrax bombs[3] is hardly louder than the popping of a paper bag.'[4]

'Because I do want to see a Savage Reservation.'

$CH_3C_6H_2(NO_2)_3+Hg(CNO)_2=$[5] well, what? An enormous hole in the ground, a pile of masonry, some bits of flesh and mucus, a foot, with the boot still on it, flying through the air and landing, flop, in the middle of the geraniums – the scarlet ones; such a splendid show that summer!

'You're hopeless, Lenina, I give you up.'

'The Russian technique for infecting water supplies was particularly ingenious.'

Back turned to back, Fanny and Lenina continued their changing in silence.

'The Nine Years' War, the great Economic Collapse. There was a choice between World Control and destruction. Between stability and . . .'

1. *Kurfustendamm* : a large, wide street in Berlin, with shops and cafés.
2. *Eighth Arrondissement* : fashionable, classy area in central Paris, from L'Arc de Triomphe to the Champs-Elysées.
3. *anthrax bombs* : bombs containing the bacillus that causes anthrax, an infectious disease that usually affects sheep and cattle but can also kill humans. (Huxley was anticipating something not yet in existence in 1931.)
4. *popping of a paper bag* : noise made by bursting a paper bag full of air.
5. $CH_3C_6H_2(NO_2)_3 + Hg(CNO)_2 = $: formula for producing an explosion using T.N.T. (Trinitrotoluene), a high explosive. Instead of using the word "explosion", Mond lists its effects.

'Fanny Crowne's a nice girl too,' said the Assistant Predestinator.

In the nurseries, the Elementary Class Consciousness lesson was over, the voices were adapting future demand to future industrial supply. 'I do love flying,' they whispered, 'I do love flying, I do love having new clothes, I do love . . .'

'Liberalism, of course, was dead of anthrax, but all the same you couldn't do things by force.'

'Not nearly so pneumatic as Lenina. Oh, not nearly.'

'But old clothes are beastly,' continued the untiring whisper. 'We always throw away old clothes. Ending is better than mending, ending is better than mending, ending is better . . .'

'Government's an affair of sitting, not hitting. You rule with the brains and the buttocks,[1] never with the fists. For example, there was the conscription of consumption.'

'There, I'm ready,' said Lenina; but Fanny remained speechless and averted. 'Let's make peace, Fanny darling.'

'Every man, woman and child compelled to consume so much a year. In the interests of industry. The sole result . . .'

'Ending is better than mending. The more stitches, the less riches; the more stitches . . .'

'One of these days,' said Fanny, with dismal emphasis, 'you'll get into trouble.'

---

1. *buttocks* ['bʌtəks]: the part of the body you sit on. This is contrasted with the fists, the tightly closed hands used for punching.

'Conscientious objection [1] on an enormous scale. Anything not to consume. Back to nature.'

'I do love flying, I do love flying.'

'Back to culture. Yes, actually to culture. You can't consume much if you sit still and read books.'

'Do I look all right?' Lenina asked. Her jacket was made of bottle-green acetate cloth with green viscose fur at the cuffs and collar.

'Eight hundred Simple Lifers were mowed down by machine guns at Golders Green.'[2]

'Ending is better than mending, ending is better than mending.'

Green corduroy shorts and white viscose-woollen stockings turned down below the knee.

'Then came the famous British Museum Massacre. Two thousand culture fans gassed with dichlorethyl sulphide.'

A green-and-white jockey cap shaded Lenina's eyes; her shoes were bright green and highly polished.

'In the end,' said Mustapha Mond, 'the Controllers realized that force was no good. The slower but infinitely surer methods of ectogenesis, neo-Pavlovian conditioning and hypnopædia . . .'

1. *Conscientious objection* : refusal to perform a social duty for religious or ethical reasons. In our world the duty is usually that of military service, but here the duty is to consume goods. The objectors are called "simple lifers".

2. *mowed* [məʊd] *down . . . Golders Green* : decimated by the sweeping action of the guns. (The main, or core meaning of the verb "mow", which frequently has "mown" as past participle, is "to cut".) Golders Green is in north London.

And round her waist she wore a silver-mounted green morocco-surrogate cartridge belt, bulging (for Lenina was not a freemartin) with the regulation supply of contraceptives.

'The discoveries of Pfitzner and Kawaguchi were at last made use of. An intensive propaganda against viviparous reproduction . . .'

'Perfect!' cried Fanny enthusiastically. She could never resist Lenina's charm for long. 'And what a perfectly *sweet* Malthusian belt!'[1]

'Accompanied by a campaign against the Past; by the closing of museums, the blowing up of historical monuments (luckily most of them had already been destroyed during the Nine Years' War); by the suppression of all books published before A.F. 150.'

'I simply must get one like it,' said Fanny.

'There were some things called the pyramids, for example.'

'My old black-patent bandolier. . .'[2]

'And a man called Shakespeare. You've never heard of them, of course.'

'It's an absolute disgrace – that bandolier of mine.'

---

1. *Malthusian* [mæl'θjuːzɪən] *belt* : named after Thomas R. Malthus (1766-1834), an English economist famous for his argument that a world shortage of food was inevitable because population growth tends to be geometrical (e.g. 1, 3, 9, 27, 81 etc) while food production increases arithmetically (e.g. 1, 3, 5, 7, 9 etc). The belt is for carrying contraceptives.
2. *black-patent bandolier* ['blæk'peɪtnt ˌbændə'lɪəʳ]: a shoulder-belt with spaces for cartridges, made of shiny black leather.

'Such are the advantages of a really scientific education.'

'The more stitches the less riches; the more stitches the less . . .'

'The introduction of Our Ford's first T-Model . . .'

'I've had it nearly three months.'

'Chosen as the opening date of the new era.'

'Ending is better than mending; ending is better . . .'

'There was a thing, as I've said before, called Christianity.'

'Ending is better than mending.'

'The ethics and philosophy of under-consumption . . .'

'I love new clothes, I love new clothes, I love . . .'

'So essential when there was under-production; but in an age of machines and the fixation of nitrogen [1] – positively a crime against society.'

'Henry Foster gave it me.'

'All crosses had their tops cut and became T's.[2] There was also a thing called God.'

'It's real morocco-surrogate.'

'We have the World State now. And Ford's Day celebrations, and Community Sings, and Solidarity Services.'

1. *fixation of nitrogen* : conversion of nitrogen gas from the earth's atmosphere into stable combined forms.
2. *All crosses . . . T's* : everywhere, the Christian symbol of the cross was replaced by capital "T" (as in the Model-T Ford).

'Ford, how I hate them!' Bernard Marx was thinking.

'There was a thing called Heaven; but all the same they used to drink enormous quantities of alcohol.'

'Like meat, like so much meat.'

'There was a thing called the soul and a thing called immortality.'

'Do ask Henry where he got it.'

'But they used to take morphia and cocaine.'

'And what makes it worse, she thinks of herself as meat.'

'Two thousand pharmacologists and biochemists were subsidized in A.F. 178.'

'He does look glum,'[1] said the Assistant Predestinator, pointing at Bernard Marx.

'Six years later it was being produced commercially. The perfect drug.'

'Let's bait [2] him.'

'Euphoric, narcotic, pleasantly hallucinant.'

---

1. *glum* [glʌm]: sad, gloomy, without enthusiasm and positive thoughts.
2. *bait* : to torment someone (i.e. to provoke Marx into getting angry).

'Glum, Marx, glum.' The clap on the shoulder made him start, look up. It was that brute Henry Foster. 'What you need is a gramme of *soma*.'[1]

'All the advantages of Christianity and alcohol; none of their defects.'

'Ford, I should like to kill him!' But all he did was to say, 'No, thank you,' and fend off the proffered tube of tablets.

'Take a holiday from reality whenever you like, and come back without so much as a headache or a mythology.'

'Take it,' insisted Henry Foster, 'take it.'

'Stability was practically assured.'

'One cubic centimetre cures ten gloomy sentiments,' said the Assistant Predestinator, citing a piece of homely hypnopædic wisdom.

'It only remained to conquer old age.'

'Damn you, damn you!' shouted Bernard Marx.

'Hoity-toity.'[2]

1. *soma* : this is the name of the "perfect drug" being described by Mond in the other sequence in counterpoint. It makes the user feel happy with life, dulls the senses and brings on fantasies and hallucinations. (It is the name for the intoxicating juice of a plant, used in ancient Indian religious ceremonies.)
2. *Hoity-toity* ['hɔɪti'tɔɪti]: a colloquial interjection expressing disapproval of someone (Marx in this case) for being snobbish or supercilious, for holding themselves apart from and above the others. (Now a little old-fashioned.)

'Gonadal hormones, transfusion of young blood, magnesium salts . . .'

'And do remember that a gramme is better than a damn.' They went out, laughing.

'All the physiological stigmata [1] of old age have been abolished. And along with them, of course . . .'

'Don't forget to ask him about that Malthusian belt,' said Fanny.

'Along with them all the old man's mental peculiarities. Characters remain constant throughout a whole lifetime.'

'. . . two rounds of Obstacle Golf to get through before dark. I must fly.'

'Work, play – at sixty our powers and tastes are what they were at seventeen. Old men in the bad old days used to renounce, retire, take to religion, spend their time reading, thinking – *thinking!*'

'Idiots, swine!'[2] Bernard Marx was saying to himself, as he walked down the corridor to the lift.

'Now – such is progress – the old men work, the old men copulate, the old men have no time, no leisure from pleasure, not a moment to sit down and think – or if ever by some unlucky chance such a crevice of time should yawn in the solid

1. *stigmata* ['stɪgmətə]: marks associated with something shameful. In this society no one wants to admit to being old, so the bodily signs of old age – wrinkles in the skin and so on – would be felt as a disgrace. The hormones, transfusion, etc, prevent them.
2. *swine* [swaɪn]: pigs (literally); here used as a strong term of abuse. (The plural is the same as the singular.)

substance of their distractions, there is always *soma*, delicious *soma*, half a gramme for a half-holiday, a gramme for a weekend, two grammes for a trip to the gorgeous East, three for a dark eternity on the moon; returning whence [1] they find themselves on the other side of the crevice, safe on the solid ground of daily labour and distraction, scampering from feely to feely, from girl to pneumatic girl, from Electro-magnetic Golf Course to . . .'

'Go away, little girl,' shouted the D.H.C. angrily. 'Go away, little boy! Can't you see that his fordship's busy? Go and do your erotic play somewhere else.'

'Poor little children!' said the Controller.

Slowly, majestically, with a faint humming of machinery, the Conveyors moved forward, thirty-three centimetres an hour. In the red darkness glinted innumerable rubies.

---

1. *whence* : from which (i.e. from the setting of their soma-induced fantasies).

Chapter IV

§ 1

THE lift was crowded with men from the Alpha Changing Rooms, and Lenina's entry was greeted by many friendly nods and smiles. She was a popular girl and, at one time or another, had spent a night with almost all of them.

They were dear boys, she thought, as she returned their salutations. Charming boys! Still, she did wish that George Edzel's [1] ears weren't quite so big (perhaps he'd been given just a spot too much parathyroid at metre 328?). And looking at Benito Hoover,[2] she couldn't help remembering that he was really too hairy when he took his clothes off.

Turning, with eyes a little saddened by the recollection of Benito's curly blackness, she saw in a corner the small thin body, the melancholy face of Bernard Marx.

1. *George Edzel* : the surname recalls the name of Henry Ford's son, Edsel, who took over as President of the Ford Motor Company in 1919.
2. *Benito Hoover* : Benito Mussolini (1883-1945), had become head of the first Fascist government in 1922. Herbert Clark Hoover (1874 - 1964), a Republican, was elected U.S. President in 1928, promising prosperity based on "rugged individualism".

Bernard!' she stepped up to him. 'I was looking for you.' Her voice rang clear above the hum of the mounting lift. The others looked round curiously. 'I wanted to talk to you about our New Mexico plan.' Out of the tail of her eye she could see Benito Hoover gaping with astonishment. The gape annoyed her. 'Surprised I shouldn't be begging to go with *him* again!' she said to herself. Then aloud, and more warmly than ever, 'I'd simply *love* to come with you for a week in July,' she went on. (Anyhow, she was publicly proving her unfaithfulness to Henry. Fanny ought to be pleased, even though it was Bernard.) 'That is,' Lenina gave him her most deliciously significant smile, 'if you still want to have me.'

Bernard's pale face flushed. 'What on earth for?' she wondered, astonished, but at the same time touched by this strange tribute to her power.

'Hadn't we better talk about it somewhere else?' he stammered, looking horribly uncomfortable.

'As though I'd been saying something shocking,' thought Lenina. 'He couldn't look more upset if I'd made a dirty joke – asked him who his mother was, or something like that.'

'I mean, with all these people about . . .' He was choked with confusion.

Lenina's laugh was frank and wholly unmalicious. 'How funny you are!' she said; and she quite genuinely did think him funny. 'You'll give me at least a week's warning, won't you,' she went on in another tone. 'I suppose we take the Blue Pacific Rocket? Does it start from the Charing-T Tower?[1] Or is it from Hampstead?'[2]

Before Bernard could answer, the lift came to a standstill.

'Roof!' called a creaking voice.

---

1. *Charing T-Tower* : this rocket station is presumably situated in central London, where Charing Cross railway station is now.
2. *Hampstead* : a district in north London.

The liftman was a small simian creature, dressed in the black tunic of an Epsilon-Minus Semi-Moron.[1]

'Roof!'

He flung open the gates. The warm glory of afternoon sunlight made him start and blink his eyes. 'Oh, roof!' he repeated in a voice of rapture. He was as though suddenly and joyfully awakened from a dark annihilating stupor. 'Roof'

He smiled up with a kind of doggily expectant adoration into the faces of his passengers. Talking and laughing together, they stepped out into the light. The liftman looked after them.

'Roof?' he said once more, questioningly.

Then a bell rang, and from the ceiling of the lift a loudspeaker began, very softly and yet very imperiously, to issue its commands.

'Go down,' it said, 'go down. Floor Eighteen. Go down, go down. Floor Eighteen. Go down, go . . .'

The liftman slammed the gates, touched a button and instantly dropped back into the droning twilight of the well, the twilight of his own habitual stupor.

It was warm and bright on the roof. The summer afternoon was drowsy with the hum of passing helicopters; and the deeper drone of the rocket-planes hastening, invisible, through the bright sky five or six miles overhead was like a caress on the soft air. Bernard Marx drew a deep breath. He looked up into the sky and round the blue horizon and finally down into Lenina's face.

'Isn't it beautiful!' His voice trembled a little.

She smiled at him with an expression of the most sympathetic understanding. 'Simply perfect for Obstacle Golf,' she answered rapturously. 'And now I must fly, Bernard. Henry gets cross if I keep him waiting. Let me know in good time

1. *Epsilon-Minus Semi-Moron* : the lowest category of people. Their appearance and behaviour is ape-like (simian), and their intelligence is little better than that of a moron [ˌmɔːrɒn], as we call people with a very low mental level (but who can, nevertheless, carry out simple tasks, unlike those classified as imbeciles or idiots).

about the date.' And waving her hand, she ran away across the wide flat roof towards the hangars. Bernard stood watching the retreating twinkle of the white stockings, the sunburnt knees vivaciously bending and unbending, again, again, and the softer rolling of those well-fitted corduroy shorts beneath the bottle-green jacket. His face wore an expression of pain.

'I should say she was pretty,' said a loud and cheery voice just behind him.

Bernard started, and looked round. The chubby red face of Benito Hoover was beaming down at him – beaming with manifest cordiality. Benito was notoriously good-natured. People said of him that he could have got through life without ever touching *soma*. The malice and bad tempers from which other people had to take holidays never afflicted him. Reality for Benito was always sunny.

'Pneumatic too. And how!' Then, in another tone, 'But, I say,' he went on, 'you do look glum! What you need is a gramme of *soma*.' Diving into his right-hand trouser-pocket, Benito produced a phial. 'One cubic centimetre cures ten gloomy . . . But, I say!'

Bernard had suddenly turned and rushed away.

Benito stared after him. 'What can be the matter with the fellow?' he wondered, and, shaking his head, decided that the story about the alcohol having been put into the poor chap's blood-surrogate must be true. 'Touched his brain, I suppose.'

He put away the *soma* bottle, and taking out a packet of sex-hormone chewing-gum, stuffed a plug into his cheek and walked slowly away towards the hangars, ruminating.

Henry Foster had had his machine wheeled out of its lock-up and, when Lenina arrived, was already seated in the cockpit, waiting.

'Four minutes late,' was all his comment, as she climbed in beside him. He started the engines and threw the helicopter screws into gear. The machine shot vertically into the air. Henry accelerated; the humming of the propeller shrilled from hornet to wasp, from wasp to mosquito;[1] the speedometer showed that they were rising at the best part of two kilometres a minute. London diminished beneath them. The huge table-topped buildings were no more, in a few seconds, than a bed of geometrical mushrooms sprouting from the green of park and garden. In the midst of them, thin-stalked, a taller, slenderer fungus, the Charing-T Tower lifted towards the sky a disk of shining concrete.

Like the vague torsos of fabulous athletes, huge fleshy clouds lolled on the blue air above their heads. Out of one of them suddenly dropped a small scarlet insect, buzzing as it fell.

'There's the Red Rocket,' said Henry, 'just come in from New York.' Looking at his watch, 'Seven minutes behind time,' he added, and shook his head. 'These Atlantic services – they're really scandalously unpunctual.'

He took his foot off the accelerator. The humming of the screws overhead dropped an octave and a half, back through wasp and hornet to bumble-bee, to cockchafer, to stag-beetle. The upward rush of the machine slackened off; a moment later they were hanging motionless in the air. Henry pushed at a lever; there was a click. Slowly at first, then faster and faster, till it was a circular mist before their eyes, the propeller in front of them began to revolve. The wind of a horizontal speed whistled ever more shrilly in the stays.[2] Henry kept his eye on the revolution-counter; when the needle touched the twelve hundred mark, he threw the helicopter screws out of gear. The machine had enough forward momentum to be able to fly on its planes.

1. *the humming . . . mosquito* : Huxley uses an extended analogy to describe how the noise of the helicopter changes as it speeds up. A hornet is a species of large wasp and makes a low-pitched noise, while the humming of a mosquito is, in D.H. Lawrence's words, like a "small, high, hateful bugle". Three paragraphs later Henry decelerates, and Huxley returns to the analogy, adding the low-frequency buzzing of the bumble-bee (Bombus terrestris), the cockchafer beetle and the stag-beetle.

2. *whistled . . . in the stays* : made an increasingly high sound as it was forced between the supports of the overhead rotor (the "screws") and the wings ("planes").

Lenina looked down through the window in the floor between her feet. They were flying over the six kilometre zone of park-land that separated Central London from its first ring of satellite suburbs. The green was maggoty with fore-shortened life.[1] Forests of Centrifugal Bumble-puppy towers gleamed between the trees. Near Shepherd's Bush two thousand Beta-Minus mixed doubles were playing Riemann-surface tennis.[2] A double row of Escalator Fives Courts [3] lined the main road from Notting Hill to Willesden. In the Ealing stadium a Delta gymnastic display and community sing was in progress.

What a hideous colour khaki is,' remarked Lenina, voicing the hypnopædic prejudices of her caste.

The buildings of the Hounslow Feely Studio covered seven and a half hectares. Near them a black and khaki army of labourers was busy revitrifying [4] the surface of the Great West Road. One of the huge travelling crucibles was being tapped as they flew over. The molten stone poured out in a stream of dazzling incandescence across the road; the asbestos [5] rollers came and went; at the tail of an insulated watering-cart the steam rose in white clouds.

1. *maggoty with foreshortened life* : a maggot ['mægət] is a legless larva of a fly, so if something is maggoty it is infested with these grubs. In painting, forms that are supposed to recede into the distance are represented with the more distant parts proportionately smaller (foreshortened) to create the illusion of depth. In this case, looking down on the park from an angle, the effect of foreshortening is to make the people look like maggots – small, shapeless and numerous.

2. *Riemann-surface tennis* : this must be a more sophisticated version of tennis, played on a non-flat surface. Georg F.B. Riemann (1826-1866) was a German mathematician who developed non-Euclidean geometry.

3. *Escalator-Fives Courts* : fives is a game played with a gloved hand in a walled court (like squash); this is presumably a variant that adds up-and-down movement.

4. *revitrifying* : renewing the glass, or glass-like, surface.

5. *asbestos* : a fire-resistant insulating material.

At Brentford the Television Corporation's factory was like a small town.

'They must be changing the shift,' said Lenina.

Like aphides [1] and ants, the leaf-green Gamma girls, the black Semi-Morons swarmed round the entrances, or stood in queues to take their places in the monorail tram-cars. Mulberry-coloured Beta-Minuses came and went among the crowd. The roof of the main building was alive with the alighting and departure of helicopters.

My word,' said Lenina, 'I'm glad I'm not a Gamma.'

Ten minutes later they were at Stoke Poges [2] and had started their first round of Obstacle Golf.

§ 2

With eyes for the most part downcast and, if ever they lighted on a fellow creature, at once and furtively averted, Bernard hastened across the roof. He was like a man pursued, but pursued by enemies he does not wish to see, lest they should seem more hostile even than he had supposed, and he himself be made to feel guiltier and even more helplessly alone.

'That horrible Benito Hoover!' And yet the man had meant well enough. Which only made it, in a way, much worse. Those who meant well behaved in the same way as those who meant badly. Even Lenina was making him suffer. He remembered those weeks of timid indecision, during which he had looked and longed and despaired of ever having the courage to ask her. Dared he face the risk of being humiliated by a contemptuous refusal? But if she were to say yes, what rapture! Well, now she had said it and he was still wretched [3] – wretched that she should have thought it such a perfect afternoon for Obstacle Golf, that she should have trotted away to join Henry Foster,

1. *aphides* ['eɪfɪdɪːz]: little insects that suck plant juices (sing. aphid or aphis).
2. *Stoke Poges* ['stəʊk 'pəʊdʒɪz]: village in Buckinghamshire, west of London.
3. *wretched* ['retʃɪd]: feeling miserable.

that she should have found him funny for not wanting to talk of
their most private affairs in public. Wretched, in a word,
because she had behaved as any healthy and virtuous English
girl ought to behave and not in some other, abnormal,
extraordinary way.

He opened the door of his lock-up and called to a lounging
couple of Delta-Minus attendants to come and push his machine
out on to the roof. The hangars were staffed by a single
Bokanovsky Group, and the men were twins, identically small,
black and hideous. Bernard gave his orders in the sharp, rather
arrogant and even offensive tone of one who does not feel
himself too secure in his superiority. To have dealings with
members of the lower castes was always, for Bernard, a most
distressing experience. For whatever the cause (and the current
gossip about the alcohol in his blood-surrogate may very likely –
for accidents will happen – have been true) Bernard's physique
was hardly better than the average Gamma. He stood eight
centimetres short of the standard Alpha height and was slender
in proportion. Contact with members of the lower castes always
reminded him painfully of this physical inadequacy. 'I am I, and
wish I wasn't'; his self-consciousness was acute and distressing.
Each time he found himself looking on the level, instead of
downward, into a Delta's face, he felt humiliated. Would the
creature treat him with the respect due to his caste? The
question haunted him. Not without reason. For Gammas, Deltas
and Epsilons had been to some extent conditioned to associate
corporeal mass with social superiority. Indeed, a faint
hypnopædic prejudice in favour of size was universal. Hence
the laughter of the women to whom he made proposals, the
practical joking of his equals among the men. The mockery
made him feel an outsider; and feeling an outsider he behaved
like one, which increased the prejudice against him and
intensified the contempt and hostility aroused by his physical
defects. Which in turn increased his sense of being alien and
alone. A chronic fear of being slighted [1] made him avoid his

---

1. *slighted* : treated as inferior, not shown proper respect.

equals, made him stand, where his inferiors were concerned, self-consciously on his dignity. How bitterly he envied men like Henry Foster and Benito Hoover! Men who never had to shout at an Epsilon to get an order obeyed; men who took their position for granted; men who moved through the caste system as a fish through the water – so utterly at home as to be unaware either of themselves or of the beneficent and comfortable element in which they had their being.

Slackly,[1] it seemed to him, and with reluctance, the twin attendants wheeled his plane out on the roof.

'Hurry up!' said Bernard irritably. One of them glanced at him. Was that a kind of bestial derision that he detected in those blank grey eyes? 'Hurry up!' he shouted more loudly, and there was an ugly rasp in his voice.

He climbed into the plane and, a minute later, was flying southwards, towards the river.

The various Bureaux of Propaganda and the College of Emotional Engineering were housed in a single sixty-story building in Fleet Street.[2] In the basement and on the lower floors were the presses and offices of the three great London newspapers – *The Hourly Radio,* an upper caste sheet, the pale-green *Gamma Gazette,* and, on khaki paper and in words exclusively of one syllable, *The Delta Mirror.* Then came the Bureaux of Propaganda by Television, by Feeling Picture, and by Synthetic Voice and Music respectively – twenty-two floors of them. Above were the research laboratories and the padded rooms in which the Sound-Track writers and Synthetic Composers did their delicate work. The top eighteen floors were occupied by the College of Emotional Engineering.

Bernard landed on the roof of Propaganda House and stepped out.

---

1. *slackly* : without sufficient care and effort.
2. *Fleet Street* : in Central London, it is where most leading English newspapers have their offices (though no longer their presses).

'Ring down to Mr Helmholtz Watson,'[1] he ordered the Gamma-Plus porter, 'and tell him that Mr Bernard Marx is waiting for him on the roof.'

He sat down and lit a cigarette.

Helmholtz Watson was writing when the message came down.

'Tell him I'm coming at once,' he said and hung up the receiver. Then, turning to his secretary, 'I'll leave you to put my things away,' he went on in the same official and impersonal tone; and, ignoring her lustrous smile, got up and walked briskly to the door.

He was a powerfully built man, deep-chested, broad-shouldered, massive, and yet quick in his movements, springy and agile. The round strong pillar of his neck supported a beautifully shaped head. His hair was dark and curly, his features strongly marked. In a forcible emphatic way, he was handsome and looked, as his secretary was never tired of repeating, every centimetre an Alpha-Plus. By profession he was a lecturer at the College of Emotional Engineering (Department of Writing) and in the intervals of his educational activities, a working Emotional Engineer. He wrote regularly for *The Hourly Radio*, composed feely scenarios, and had the happiest knack [2] for slogans and hypnopædic rhymes.

'Able,' was the verdict of his superiors. 'Perhaps' (and they would shake their heads, would significantly lower their voices) 'a little *too* able.'

---

1. *Helmholtz Watson* : Hermann L.F. Von Helmholtz (1821-94) was a German scientist who studied perception, nervous impulses in animals and whose studies in electricity and dynamics led the way to the wave theory of light. The surname probably refers to Sir William Watson (1858-1935), a now forgotten English poet who wrote grand-sounding but predictable 'public', or ceremonial, poetry; Huxley may also intend us to think of John B. Watson (1878-1958), the American psychologist who promoted behaviourism, the theory that psychology, as a science, must be based on observable behaviour, objectively measured.

2. *the happiest knack* : a special talent.

Yes, a little too able; they were right. A mental excess had produced in Helmholtz Watson effects very similar to those which, in Bernard Marx, were the result of a physical defect. Too little bone and brawn [1] had isolated Bernard from his fellow men, and the sense of this apartness, being, by all the current standards, a mental excess, became in its turn a cause of wider separation. That which had made Helmholtz so uncomfortably aware of being himself and all alone was too much ability. What the two men shared was the knowledge that they were individuals. But whereas the physically defective Bernard had suffered all his life from the consciousness of being separate, it was only quite recently that, grown aware of his mental excess, Helmholtz Watson had also become aware of his difference from the people who surrounded him. This Escalator-Squash champion, this indefatigable lover (it was said that he had had six hundred and forty different girls in under four years), this admirable committee man and best mixer had realized quite suddenly that sport, women, communal activities were only, so far as he was concerned, second bests.[2] Really, and at the bottom, he was interested in something else. But in what? In what? That was the problem which Bernard had come to discuss with him – or rather, since it was always Helmholtz who did all the talking, to listen to his friend discussing, yet once more.

Three charming girls from the Bureau of Propaganda by Synthetic Voice waylaid him as he stepped out of the lift.

'Oh, Helmholtz darling, *do* come and have a picnic supper with us on Exmoor.'[3] They clung round him imploringly.

He shook his head, he pushed his way through them. 'No, no.'

'We're not inviting any other man.'

But Helmholtz remained unshaken even by this delightful promise. 'No,' he repeated, 'I'm busy.' And he held resolutely

---

1. *brawn* [brɔːn]: muscular strength.
2. *second bests* : not the best things, substitutes of less value.
3. *Exmoor* : a green area of great beauty in south-west England.

on his course. The girls trailed after him. It was not till he had
actually climbed into Bernard's plane and slammed the door
that they gave up pursuit. Not without reproaches.

'These women!' he said, as the machine rose into the air.
'These women!' And he shook his head, he frowned. 'Too
awful.' Bernard hypocritically agreed, wishing, as he spoke the
words, that he could have as many girls as Helmholtz did, and
with as little trouble. He was seized with a sudden urgent need
to boast. 'I'm taking Lenina Crowne to New Mexico with me,' he
said in a tone as casual as he could make it.

'Are you?' said Helmholtz, with a total absence of interest.
Then after a little pause, 'This last week or two,' he went on,
'I've been cutting all my committees and all my girls. You can't
imagine what a hullabaloo [1] they've been making about it at the
College. Still, it's been worth it, I think. The effects . . .' He
hesitated. 'Well, they're odd, they're very odd.'

A physical shortcoming could produce a kind of mental
excess. The process, it seemed, was reversible. Mental excess
could produce, for its own purposes, the voluntary blindness
and deafness of deliberate solitude, the artificial impotence of
asceticism.

The rest of the short flight was accomplished in silence.
When they had arrived and were comfortably stretched out on
the pneumatic sofas in Bernard's room, Helmholtz began again.

Speaking very slowly, 'Did you ever feel,' he asked, 'as
though you had something inside you that was only waiting for
you to give it a chance to come out? Some sort of extra power
that you aren't using – you know, like all the water that goes
down the falls instead of through the turbines?' He looked at
Bernard questioningly.

'You mean all the emotions one might be feeling if things
were different?'

Helmholtz shook his head. 'Not quite. I'm thinking of a
queer feeling I sometimes get, a feeling that I've got something

---

1. *hullabaloo* [ˌhʌləbə'luː] (dated): loud; angry protests.

important to say and the power to say it – only I don't know what it is, and I can't make any use of the power. If there was some different way of writing . . . Or else something else to write about . . .' He was silent; then, 'You see,' he went on at last, 'I'm pretty good at inventing phrases – you know, the sort of words that suddenly make you jump, almost as though you'd sat on a pin, they seem so new and exciting even though they're about something hypnopædically obvious. But that doesn't seem enough. It's not enough for the phrases to be good; what you make with them ought to be good too.'

'But your things are good, Helmholtz.'

'Oh, as far as they go.' Helmholtz shrugged his shoulders. 'But they go such a little way. They aren't important enough, somehow. I feel I could do something much more important. Yes, and more intense, more violent. But what? What is there more important to say? And how can one be violent about the sort of things one's expected to write about ? Words can be like X-rays, if you use them properly – they'll go through anything. You read and you're pierced. That's one of the things I try to teach my students – how to write piercingly. But what on earth's the good of being pierced by an article about a Community Sing, or the latest improvement in scent organs ? Besides, can you make words really piercing – you know, like the very hardest X-rays – when you're writing about that sort of thing? Can you say something about nothing? That's what it finally boils down to.[1] I try and I try . . .'

'Hush!' said Bernard suddenly, and lifted a warning finger; they listened. 'I believe there's somebody at the door,' he whispered.

Helmholtz got up, tiptoed across the room, and with a sharp quick movement flung the door wide open. There was, of course, nobody there.

'I'm sorry,' said Bernard, feeling and looking uncomfortably foolish. 'I suppose I've got things on my nerves a bit. When people are suspicious with you, you start being suspicious with them.'

---

1. *boils down to* : can be reduced to (i.e. the real question, finally).

He passed his hand across his eyes, he sighed, his voice became plaintive. He was justifying himself. 'If you knew what I'd had to put up with recently,' he said almost tearfully – and the uprush [1] of his self-pity was like a fountain suddenly released. 'If you only knew!'

Helmholtz Watson listened with a certain sense of discomfort. 'Poor little Bernard!' he said to himself. But at the same time he felt rather ashamed for his friend. He wished Bernard would show a little more pride.

---

1. *uprush* : sudden presence (as it came to the surface).

Chapter V

By eight o'clock the light was failing. The loud-speakers in the tower of the Stoke Poges Club House began, in a more than human tenor, to announce the closing of the courses. Lenina and Henry abandoned their game and walked back towards the Club. From the grounds of the Internal and External Secretion Trust came the lowing of those thousands of cattle which provided, with their hormones and their milk, the raw materials for the great factory at Farnham Royal.

An incessant buzzing of helicopters filled the twilight. Every two and a half minutes a bell and the screech of whistles announced the departure of one of the light monorail trains which carried the lower-caste golfers back from their separate course to the metropolis.

Lenina and Henry climbed into their machine and started off. At eight hundred feet Henry slowed down the helicopter screws, and they hung for a minute or two poised above the fading landscape. The forest of Burnham Beeches stretched like a great pool of darkness towards the bright shore of the western sky. Crimson at the horizon, the last of the sunset faded, through orange, upwards into yellow and a pale watery green. Northwards, beyond and above the trees, the Internal and External Secretions factory glared with a fierce electric brilliance from every window of its twenty stories. Beneath them lay the buildings of the Golf Club – the huge lower-caste barracks and, on the other side of a dividing wall, the smaller houses reserved for Alpha and Beta members. The approaches to the monorail station were black with the ant-like pullulation [1] of lower-caste activity. From under the glass vault a lighted train shot out into the open. Following its south-easterly course across the dark plain their eyes were drawn to the majestic buildings of the Slough [2] Crematorium. For the safety of night-flying planes, its four tall chimneys were flood-lighted and tipped with crimson danger signals. It was a landmark.

'Why do the smoke-stacks have those things like balconies round them?' enquired Lenina.

'Phosphorus recovery,' exclaimed Henry telegraphically. 'On their way up the chimney the gases go through four separate treatments. P_2O_5 used to go right out of circulation every time they cremated some one. Now they recover over ninety-eight per cent of it. More than a kilo and a half per adult corpse. Which makes the best part of four hundred tons of phosphorus every year from England alone.' Henry spoke with a happy pride, rejoicing whole-heartedly in the achievement, as though it had been his own. 'Fine to think we can go on being socially useful even after we're dead. Making plants grow.'

Lenina, meanwhile, had turned her eyes away and was looking perpendicularly downwards at the monorail station. 'Fine,' she agreed. 'But queer that Alphas and Betas won't make any more plants grow than those nasty little Gammas and Deltas and Epsilons down there.'

---

1. *pullulation* ['pʌljʊleɪʃn]: swarming, very rapid multiplication.
2. *Slough* [slaʊ]: town to the west of London, near Heathrow Airport (about 30 km from Charing Cross).

'All men are physico-chemically equal,' said Henry sententiously. 'Besides, even Epsilons perform indispensable services.'

'Even an Epsilon . . .' Lenina suddenly remembered an occasion when, as a little girl at school, she had woken up in the middle of the night and become aware, for the first time, of the whispering that had haunted all her sleeps. She saw again the beam of moonlight, the row of small white beds; heard once more the soft, soft voice that said (the words were there, unforgotten, unforgettable after so many night-long repetitions): 'Every one works for every one else. We can't do without any one. Even Epsilons are useful. We couldn't do without Epsilons. Every one works for every one else. We can't do without any one . . .' Lenina remembered her first shock of fear and surprise; her speculations through half a wakeful hour; and then, under the influence of those endless repetitions, the gradual soothing of her mind, the soothing, the smoothing, the stealthy creeping of sleep . . .

'I suppose Epsilons don't really mind being Epsilons,' she said aloud.

'Of course they don't. How can they? They don't know what it's like being anything else. We'd mind, of course. But then we've been differently conditioned. Besides, we start with a different heredity.'

'I'm glad I'm not an Epsilon,' said Lenina, with conviction.

'And if you were an Epsilon,' said Henry, 'your conditioning would have made you no less thankful that you weren't a Beta or an Alpha.' He put his forward propeller into gear and headed the machine towards London. Behind them, in the west, the crimson and orange were almost faded; a dark bank of cloud had crept into the zenith. As they flew over the Crematorium, the plane shot upwards on the column of hot air rising from the chimneys, only to fall as suddenly when it passed into the descending chill beyond.

'What a marvellous switchback !'¹ Lenina laughed delightedly. But Henry's tone was almost, for a moment, melancholy. 'Do you know what that switchback was?' he said. 'It was some human being finally and definitely disappearing. Going up in a squirt of hot gas. It would be curious to know who it was – a man or a woman, an Alpha or an Epsilon . . .' He sighed. Then, in a resolutely cheerful voice, 'Anyhow,' he concluded, 'there's one thing we can be certain of; whoever he may have been, he was happy when he was alive. Everybody's happy now.'

'Yes, everybody's happy now,' echoed Lenina. They had heard the words repeated a hundred and fifty times every night for twelve years.

Landing on the roof of Henry's forty-story apartment house in Westminster, they went straight down to the dining-hall. There, in a loud and cheerful company, they ate an excellent meal. *Soma* was served with the coffee. Lenina took two half-gramme tablets and Henry three. At twenty past nine they walked across the street to the newly opened Westminster Abbey Cabaret.² It was a night almost without clouds, moonless and starry; but of this on the whole depressing fact Lenina and Henry were fortunately unaware. The electric sky-signs effectively shut off the outer darkness. 'CALVIN STOPES ³ AND HIS SIXTEEN SEXOPHONISTS.'⁴ From the façade of the new Abbey the

1. *switchback* : usually, an up-and-down track, as on a Big Dipper at the funfair; here, a similar upwards movement and rapid descent while flying.

2. *Westminster Abbey Cabaret* : this "new Abbey", which houses a nightclub dedicated to the religion of the senses, has presumably replaced today's medieval building, situated near the Houses of Parliament.

3. *CALVIN STOPES* : The name of the Genevan religious reformer, John Calvin (1509-64), is generally associated with a severe Protestant doctrine that requires strict adherence to the scriptures and faith in God's grace, and asserts election and predestination. Mary Stopes (1880-1958), a paleobotanist, became well-known in the Twenties as an advocate of birth control and her book Married Love was widely read.

4. *SEXOPHONISTS* [ˌseks'sɒfənɪsts]: as this is a pun (combining "saxophonist" and "sex"), it could be pronounced [ˌseksə'fəʊnɪsts].

giant letters invitingly glared. 'LONDON'S FINEST SCENT AND COLOUR ORGAN. ALL THE LATEST SYNTHETIC MUSIC.' They entered. The air seemed hot and somehow breathless with the scent of ambergris [1] and sandalwood. On the domed ceiling of the hall, the colour organ had momentarily painted a tropical sunset. The Sixteen Sexophonists were playing an old favourite: 'There ain't no Bottle [2] in all the world like that dear little Bottle of mine.' Four hundred couples were five-stepping round the polished floor. Lenina and Henry were soon the four hundred and first. The sexophones wailed like melodious cats under the moon, moaned in the alto and tenor registers as though the little death [3] were upon them. Rich with a wealth of harmonics, their tremulous chorus mounted towards a climax, louder and ever louder – until at last, with a wave of his hand, the conductor let loose the final shattering note of ether [4] music and blew the sixteen merely human blowers clean out of existence.[5] Thunder in A flat major. And then, in all but silence, in all but darkness, there followed a gradual deturgescence, a *diminuendo* sliding gradually, through quarter tones, down, down to a faintly whispered dominant chord that lingered on (while the five-four rhythms still pulsed below) charging the darkened seconds with an intense expectancy. And at last expectancy was fulfilled. There was a sudden explosive sunrise, and simultaneously, the Sixteen burst into song:

1. *ambergris* ['æmbəgriːs]: substance from whales' intestines used in perfumes.
2. *ain't no Bottle* : is no bottle (pop-song English, based on slang).
3. *the little death* : momentary loss of consciousness, especially during orgasm (an association taken up in the words "climax" and "deturgescence").
4. *ether* ['iːθə]: a liquid derived from alcohol, used as an anaesthetic; ether music must be potent synthesized music.
5. *blew ... existence* : reduced to nothing the much feebler man-made music; this is the language of 1920s gangsters ("blow out" = kill; "clean" was common as an adverb meaning completely).

> Bottle of mine, it's you I've always wanted!
> Bottle of mine, why was I ever decanted?
>   Skies are blue inside of you,
>   The weather's always fine;
> For
> There ain't no Bottle in all the world
> Like that dear little Bottle of mine.

Five-stepping with the other four hundred round and round Westminster Abbey, Lenina and Henry were yet dancing in another world – the warm, the richly coloured, the infinitely friendly world of *soma*-holiday. How kind, how good-looking, how delightfully amusing every one was! 'Bottle of mine, it's you I've always wanted . . .' But Lenina and Henry had what they wanted . . . They were inside, here and now – safely inside with the fine weather, the perennially blue sky. And when, exhausted, the Sixteen had laid by their sexophones and the Synthetic Music apparatus was producing the very latest in slow Malthusian Blues, they might have been twin embryos gently rocking together on the waves of a bottled ocean of blood-surrogate.

'Good-night, dear friends. Good-night, dear friends.' The loud-speakers veiled their commands [1] in a genial [2] and musical politeness. 'Good-night, dear friends . . .'

Obediently, with all the others, Lenina and Henry left the building. The depressing stars had travelled quite some way across the heavens. But though the separating screen of the sky-signs had now to a great extent dissolved, the two young people still retained their happy ignorance of the night.

Swallowed half an hour before closing time, that second dose of *soma* had raised a quite impenetrable wall between the actual universe and their minds. Bottled, they crossed the street;

---

1. *veiled their commands* : the command which is hidden beneath the courteous valedictions is "Please leave!".
2. *genial* ['dʒiːnɪəl]: pleasantly friendly, well-meaning.

bottled, they took the lift up to Henry's room on the twenty-eighth floor. And yet, bottled as she was, and in spite of that second gramme of soma, Lenina did not forget to take all the contraceptive precautions prescribed by the regulations. Years of intensive hypnopædia and, from twelve to seventeen, Malthusian drill three times a week had made the taking of these precautions almost as automatic and inevitable as blinking.

'Oh, and that reminds me,' she said, as she came back from the bathroom, 'Fanny Crowne wants to know where you found that lovely green morocco-surrogate cartridge belt you gave me.'

§ 2

Alternate Thursdays were Bernard's Solidarity Service days. After an early dinner at the Aphroditæum [1] (to which Helmholtz had recently been elected under Rule Two) he took leave of his friend and, hailing a taxi on the roof, told the man to fly to the Fordson Community Singery.[2] The machine rose a couple of hundred metres, then headed eastwards, and as it turned, there before Bernard's eyes, gigantically beautiful, was the Singery. Flood-lighted, its three hundred and twenty metres of white Carrara-surrogate [3] gleamed with a snowy incandescence over Ludgate Hill;[4] at each of the four corners of its helicopter platform an immense T shone crimson against the night, and from the mouths of twenty-four vast golden trumpets rumbled a solemn synthetic music.

---

1. *Aphroditaeum* [ˌæfrə'daɪtɪːəm]: Aphrodite was the Goddess of Love and Beauty in Greek mythology. (Huxley himself had been an editor of a distinguished literary review in London, *The Athenaeum*.)
2. *Fordson Community Singery* ['sɪŋəri]: the building where groups of people come together to sing.
3. *Carrara-surrogate* : material that substitutes the famous white marble from Carrara.
4. *Ludgate Hill* : looking along this street in east-central London you would today see St Paul's cathedral.

'Damn, I'm late,' Bernard said to himself as he first caught sight of Big Henry, the Singery clock. And sure enough, as he was paying off his cab, Big Henry sounded the hour. 'Ford,' sang out an immense bass voice from all the golden trumpets. 'Ford, Ford, Ford . . .' Nine times. Bernard ran for the lift.

The great auditorium for Ford's Day celebrations and other massed Community Sings was at the bottom of the building. Above it, a hundred to each floor, were the seven thousand rooms used by Solidarity Groups for their fortnightly services. Bernard dropped down to floor thirty-three, hurried along the corridor, stood hesitating for a moment outside Room 3210, then, having wound himself up,[1] opened the door and walked in.

Thank Ford! he was not the last. Three chairs of the twelve arranged round the circular table were still unoccupied. He slipped into the nearest of them as inconspicuously as he could and prepared to frown at the yet later comers whenever they should arrive.

Turning towards him, 'What were you playing this afternoon?' the girl on his left enquired. 'Obstacle, or Electromagnetic?'

Bernard looked at her (Ford! it was Morgana Rothschild)[2] and blushingly had to admit that he had been playing neither. Morgana stared at him with astonishment. There was an awkward silence.

Then pointedly she turned away and addressed herself to the more sporting man on her left.

1. *wound himself up* : he prepared himself to face a demanding situation ("wound" [waυnd] is here the past participle of "wind").

2. *Morgana Rothschild* : her first name recalls that of John Pierpoint Morgan, a New York financier and industrial organizer, and his son. The name could also be connected with Thomas Hunt Morgan, a U.S. biologist who won the Nobel prize in 1933 and formulated the theory of the gene as carrier of inheritable characteristics. Also relevant is Morgan le Fay; in the legends, she used her magic powers against King Arthur, who was unable to rid himself of her unwelcome interference just as Bernard cannot. The Rothschilds are a prominent and enormously wealthy banking family.

'A good beginning for a Solidarity Service,' thought Bernard miserably, and foresaw for himself yet another failure to achieve atonement.[1] If only he had given himself time to look round instead of scuttling for the nearest chair! He could have sat between Fifi Bradlaugh and Joanna Diesel.[2] Instead of which he had gone and blindly planted himself next to Morgana. *Morgana!* Ford! Those black eyebrows of hers – that eyebrow, rather – for they met above the nose. Ford! And on his right was Clara Deterding.[3] True, Clara's eyebrows didn't meet. But she was really too pneumatic. Whereas Fifi and Joanna were absolutely right. Plump, blonde, not too large . . . And it was that great lout,[4] Tom Kawaguchi, who now took the seat between them.

The last arrival was Sarojini Engels.[5]

'You're late,' said the President of the Group severely. 'Don't let it happen again.'

Sarojini apologized and slid into her place between Jim Bokanovsky and Herbert Bakunin.[6] The group was now

1. *atonement* : reparations, expiation.

2. *Fifi Bradlaugh* ['brædlɔː] *and Joanna Diesel* : Charles Bradlaugh (1833-91), an English freethinker, was famous for his radical championship of individual liberty. Rudolf Diesel (1858-1913) was the German engineer who designed the first commercially successful diesel engine (1897).

3. *Clara Deterding* : the first name recalls that of Clara Bryant, Henry Ford's wife. Sir Henry Wilhelm August Deterding (1866-1939), a Dutchman, was managing director of the Royal Dutch-Shell group of companies.

4. *lout* [laʊt]: impolite, brutish sort of person.

5. *Sarojini Engels* : Frederick Engels (1820-95) was, together with Karl Marx, co-author of *The Manifesto of the Communist Party* (1848); Huxley probably also had in mind Mrs Sarojini Naidu, an Indian political leader he had once met.

6. *Herbert Bakunin* : Mikhail Bakunin (1814-76), a Russian revolutionist and anarchist. The first name may be another reference to President Hoover (see p. 75, n. 2) or perhaps to Herbert Spencer (1820-1903), an English philosopher who saw the evolutionist principle of the survival of the fittest at work in the areas of life studied by biology, psychology, sociology and ethics.

complete, the solidarity circle perfect and without flaw. Man, woman, man, in a ring of endless alternation round the table. Twelve of them ready to be made one, waiting to come together, to be fused, to lose their twelve separate identities in a larger being.

The President stood up, made the sign of the T and, switching on the synthetic music, let loose the soft indefatigable beating of drums and a choir of instruments – near-wind and super-string – that plangently repeated and repeated the brief and unescapably haunting melody of the First Solidarity Hymn. Again, again – and it was not the ear that heard the pulsing rhythm, it was the midriff;[1] the wail and clang of those recurring harmonies haunted, not the mind, but the yearning bowels of compassion.[2]

The President made another sign of the T and sat down. The service had begun. The dedicated *soma* tablets were placed in the centre of the dinner table. The loving cup [3] of strawberry ice-cream soma was passed from hand to hand and, with the formula, 'I drink to my annihilation,' twelve times quaffed.[4] Then to the accompaniment of the synthetic orchestra the First Solidarity Hymn was sung.

> Ford, we are twelve; oh, make us one,
> Like drops within the Social River;
> Oh, make us now together run
> As swiftly as thy shining Flivver.[5]

1. *midriff*: abdomen, belly.
2. *bowels of compassion* : this phrase comes from the Bible, from the First Epistle General of John, Ch. 3, verse 17 - an exhortation to demonstrate brotherly love in acts, not just words. Huxley ironically makes the literal meaning of the word "bowels" ([ˌba ɜlz] i.e. intestines) as pertinent as the figurative sense it had in the Bible (the deepest, innermost part of something).
3. *loving cup* : cup passed round at the end of a feast, usually with a drink which everyone shares (often written "loving-cup").
4. *quaffed* [kwɒfd]: profusely drunk down.
5. *Flivver* : see note 1, p. 62; here, an epithet for the Model-T car.

Twelve yearning stanzas. And then the loving cup was passed a second time. 'I drink to the Greater Being' was now the formula. All drank. Tirelessly the music played. The drums beat. The crying and clashing of the harmonies were an obsession in the melted bowels. The Second Solidarity Hymn was sung.

> Come, Greater Being, Social Friend,
> Annihilating Twelve-in-One!
> We long to die, for when we end,
> Our larger life has but begun.

Again twelve stanzas. By this time the *soma* had begun to work. Eyes shone, cheeks were flushed, the inner light of universal benevolence broke out on every face in happy, friendly smiles. Even Bernard felt himself a little melted. When Morgana Rothschild turned and beamed at him, he did his best to beam back. But the eyebrow, that black two-in-one – alas, it was still there; he couldn't ignore it, couldn't, however hard he tried. The melting hadn't gone far enough. Perhaps if he had been sitting between Fifi and Joanna . . . For the third time the loving cup went round. 'I drink to the imminence of His Coming,' said Morgana Rothschild, whose turn it happened to be to initiate the circular rite. Her tone was loud, exultant. She drank and passed the cup to Bernard. 'I drink to the imminence of His Coming,' he repeated, with a sincere attempt to feel that the Coming was imminent; but the eyebrow continued to haunt him, and the Coming, so far as he was concerned, was horribly remote. He drank and handed the cup to Clara Deterding. 'It'll be a failure again,' he said to himself. 'I know it will.' But he went on doing his best to beam.

The loving cup had made its circuit. Lifting his hand, the President gave a signal; the chorus broke out into the Third Solidarity Hymn.

> Feel how the Greater Being comes!
> Rejoice and, in rejoicings, die!
> Melt in the music of the drums!
> For I am you and you are I.

As verse succeeded verse the voices thrilled [1] with an ever intenser excitement. The sense of the Coming's imminence was like an electric tension in the air. The President switched off the music and, with the final note of the final stanza, there was absolute silence – the silence of stretched expectancy, quivering and creeping with a galvanic life.[2] The President reached out his hand; and suddenly a Voice, a deep strong Voice, more musical than any merely human voice, richer, warmer, more vibrant with love and yearning and compassion, a wonderful, mysterious, supernatural Voice spoke from above their heads. Very slowly, 'Oh, Ford, Ford, Ford,' it said diminishingly and on a descending scale. A sensation of warmth radiated thrillingly out from the solar plexus to every extremity of the bodies of those who listened; tears came into their eyes; their hearts, their bowels seemed to move within them, as though with an independent life. 'Ford!' they were melting, 'Ford!' dissolved, dissolved. Then, in another tone, suddenly, startlingly. 'Listen!' trumpeted the Voice. 'Listen!' They listened. After a pause, sunk to a whisper, but a whisper, somehow, more penetrating than the loudest cry. 'The feet of the Greater Being,' it went on, and repeated the words: 'The feet of the Greater Being.' The whisper almost expired. 'The feet of the Greater Being are on the stairs.' And once more there was silence; and the expectancy, momentarily relaxed, was stretched again, tauter, tauter, almost to the tearing point. The feet of the Greater Being – oh, they heard them, they heard them, coming softly down the stairs, coming nearer and nearer down the invisible stairs. The feet of the Greater Being. And suddenly the tearing point was reached. Her eyes staring, her lips parted, Morgana Rothschild sprang to her feet.

'I hear him,' she cried. 'I hear him.'

'He's coming,' shouted Sarojini Engels.

'Yes, he's coming, I hear him.' Fifi Bradlaugh and Tom Kawaguchi rose simultaneously to their feet.

---

1. *thrilled* : vibrated, radiated strongly pleasurable feelings.
2. *with a galvanic life* : as if their movements were caused by electrical currents (refers back to the "electric tension in the air").

'Oh, oh, oh!' Joanna inarticulately testified.

'He's coming!' yelled Jim Bokanovsky.

The President leaned forward and, with a touch, released a delirium of cymbals and blown brass, a fever of tom-tomming.

'Oh, he's coming!' screamed Clara Deterding. 'Aie!' and it was as though she were having her throat cut.

Feeling that it was time for him to do something, Bernard also jumped up and shouted: 'I hear him; he's coming.' But it wasn't true. He heard nothing and, for him, nobody was coming. Nobody – in spite of the music, in spite of the mounting excitement. But he waved his arms, he shouted with the best of them; and when the others began to jig and stamp and shuffle,[1] he also jigged and shuffled.

Round they went, a circular procession of dancers, each with hands on the hips of the dancer preceding, round and round, shouting in unison, stamping to the rhythm of the music with their feet, beating it, beating it out with hands on the buttocks in front; twelve pairs of hands beating as one; as one, twelve buttocks slabbily [2] resounding. Twelve as one, twelve as one. 'I hear him, I hear him coming.' The music quickened; faster beat the feet, faster, faster fell the rhythmic hands. And all at once a great synthetic bass boomed out the words which announced the approaching atonement and final consummation of solidarity, the coming of the Twelve-in-One, the incarnation of the Greater Being. 'Orgy-porgy,'[3] it sang, while the tom-toms continued to beat their feverish tattoo:

Orgy-porgy, Ford and fun,
Kiss the girls and make them One.

---

1. *jig and stamp and shuffle* : different kinds of dance movements.
2. *slabbily* : "slabby" is an unusual adjective meaning "muddy"; here, with a noise like mud being slapped.
3. *'Orgy-porgy'* [ˈɔːdʒi ˈpɔːdʒi]: pun on the name of the boy, Georgie, in the traditional nursery rhyme - "Georgie Porgie, pudding and pie / Kissed the girls and made them cry; / When the boys came out to play / Georgie Porgie ran away".

Boys at one with girls at peace;
Orgy-porgy gives release.

'Orgy-porgy,' the dancers caught up the liturgical refrain,
'Orgy-porgy, Ford and fun, kiss the girls . . .' And as they sang,
the lights began slowly to fade – to fade and at the same time to
grow warmer, richer, redder, until at last they were dancing in
the crimson twilight of an Embryo Store. 'Orgy-porgy . . .' In
their blood-coloured and fœtal darkness the dancers continued
for a while to circulate, to beat and beat out the indefatigable
rhythm. 'Orgy-porgy . . .' Then the circle wavered, broke, fell in
partial disintegration on the ring of couches which surrounded –
circle enclosing circle – the table and its planetary chairs. 'Orgy-
porgy . . .' Tenderly the deep Voice crooned and cooed; in the
red twilight it was as though some enormous negro dove [1] were
hovering benevolently over the now prone or supine dancers.

They were standing on the roof; Big Henry had just sung
eleven. The night was calm and warm.
'Wasn't it wonderful?' said Fifi Bradlaugh. 'Wasn't it simply
wonderful?' She looked at Bernard with an expression of
rapture, but of rapture in which there was no trace of agitation
or excitement – for to be excited is still to be unsatisfied. Hers
was the calm ecstasy of achieved consummation, the peace, not
of mere vacant satiety and nothingness, but of balanced life, of
energies at rest and in equilibrium. A rich and living peace. For
the Solidarity Service had given as well as taken, drawn off only
to replenish. She was full, she was made perfect, she was still
more than merely herself. 'Didn't you think it was wonderful?'
she insisted, looking into Bernard's face with those
supernaturally shining eyes.

---

1. *negro dove* [dʌv]: doves are birds of the *Columbidae* family. It is
   white doves in particular that are commonly recognised as a
   symbol of peace; in this case the dove is said to be "negro"
   presumably because the dancing is reminiscent of African tribal
   dances and the deep voice is like that of some black singers.

'Yes, I thought it was wonderful,' he lied and looked away; the sight of her transfigured face was at once an accusation and an ironical reminder of his own separateness. He was as miserably isolated now as he had been when the service began – more isolated by reason of his unreplenished emptiness, his dead satiety. Separate and unatoned, while the others were being fused into the Greater Being; alone even in Morgana's embrace – much more alone, indeed, more hopelessly himself than he had ever been in his life before. He had emerged from that crimson twilight into the common electric glare with a self-consciousness intensified to the pitch of agony. He was utterly miserable, and perhaps (her shining eyes accused him), perhaps it was his own fault. 'Quite wonderful,' he repeated; but the only thing he could think of was Morgana's eyebrow.

Chapter VI

§ 1

ODD, odd, *odd*, was Lenina's verdict on Bernard Marx. So odd, indeed, that in the course of the succeeding weeks she had wondered more than once whether she shouldn't change her mind about the New Mexico holiday, and go instead to the North Pole with Benito Hoover. The trouble was that she knew the North Pole, had been there with George Edzel only last summer, and what was more, found it pretty grim. Nothing to do, and the hotel too hopelessly old-fashioned – no television laid on in the bedrooms, no scent organ, only the most putrid synthetic music, and not more than twenty-five Escalator-Squash Courts for over two hundred guests. No, decidedly she couldn't face the North Pole again. Added to which, she had only been to America once before. And even then, how inadequately! A cheap week-end in New York – had it been with Jean-Jacques Habibullah [1] or

---

1. *Jean-Jacques Habibullah* : the first name recalls that of Jean-Jacques Rousseau (1712-78), the French political philosopher and man of letters who advocated a return to nature, to the life of the "noble savage". Habibullah Khan (1872-1919) had been Amir of Afghanistan before the Nationalist uprising; under his enlightened leadership, from 1901 until his assassination, roads were laid and steps taken to introduce modern machinery.

Bokanovsky Jones? She couldn't remember. Anyhow, it was of absolutely no importance. The prospect of flying West again, and for a whole week, was very inviting. Moreover, for at least three days of that week they would be in the Savage Reservation. Not more than half a dozen people in the whole Centre had ever been inside a Savage Reservation. As an Alpha-Plus psychologist, Bernard was one of the few men she knew entitled to a permit. For Lenina, the opportunity was unique. And yet, so unique also was Bernard's oddness, that she had hesitated to take it, had actually thought of risking the Pole again with funny old Benito. At least Benito was normal. Whereas Bernard . . .

'Alcohol in his blood-surrogate,' was Fanny's explanation of every eccentricity. But Henry, with whom, one evening when they were in bed together, Lenina had rather anxiously discussed her new lover, Henry had compared poor Bernard to a rhinoceros.

'You can't teach a rhinoceros tricks,' he had explained in his brief and vigorous style. 'Some men are almost rhinoceroses; they don't respond properly to conditioning. Poor devils! Bernard's one of them. Luckily for him, he's pretty good at his job. Otherwise the Director would never have kept him. However,' he added consolingly, 'I think he's pretty harmless.'

Pretty harmless, perhaps; but also pretty disquieting. That mania, to start with, for doing things in private. Which meant, in practice, not doing anything at all. For what was there that one *could* do in private. (Apart, of course, from going to bed: but one couldn't do that all the time.) Yes, what was there? Precious little.[1] The first afternoon they went out together was particularly fine. Lenina had suggested a swim at the Torquay Country Club followed by dinner at the Oxford Union. But Bernard thought there would be too much of a crowd. Then what about a round of Electro-magnetic Golf at St. Andrews?[2]

1. *precious little* : almost nothing. (An idiom.)
2. *St. Andrews* : this well-known golf course is in Scotland; since Torquay is a sea resort in Devon, in South-West England, while the Oxford Union is a debating society/social club at the University of Oxford, these places have obviously been chosen to demonstrate how easy travel has become.

But again, no: Bernard considered that Electro-magnetic Golf was a waste of time.

'Then what's time for?' asked Lenina in some astonishment.

Apparently, for going walks in the Lake District;[1] for that was what he now proposed. Land on the top of Skiddaw and walk for a couple of hours in the heather [2] 'Alone with you, Lenina.'

'But, Bernard, we shall be alone all night.'

Bernard blushed and looked away. 'I meant, alone for talking,' he mumbled.

'Talking? But what about?' Walking and talking – that seemed a very odd way of spending an afternoon.

In the end she persuaded him, much against his will, to fly over to Amsterdam to see the Semi-Demi-Finals of the Women's Heavyweight Wrestling Championship.

'In a crowd,' he grumbled. 'As usual.' He remained obstinately gloomy the whole afternoon; wouldn't talk to Lenina's friends (of whom they met dozens in the ice-cream *soma* bar between the wrestling bouts);[3] and in spite of his misery absolutely refused to take the half-gramme raspberry sundae which she pressed upon him. 'I'd rather be myself,' he said. 'Myself and nasty. Not somebody else, however jolly.'

'A gramme in time saves nine,'[4] said Lenina, producing a bright treasure of sleep-taught wisdom.

Bernard pushed away the proffered glass impatiently.

'Now don't lose your temper,' she said. 'Remember, one cubic centimetre cures ten gloomy sentiments.'

---

1. *Lake District* : area of green hills (such as Skiddaw) and several lakes in North-West England. (We normally say either "going for/on walks" or "going walking".)
2. *heather* ['heðə]: a low evergreen shrub, usually with light- purple flowers, found in upland areas.
3. *bouts* [bauts]: sessions, encounters.
4. *'A gramme in time saves nine'* : cf. the common proverb, "A stitch in time saves nine" - i.e. a quick repair at the right time can prevent the damage from getting worse.

'Oh, for Ford's sake, be quiet!' he shouted. Lenina shrugged her shoulders. 'A gramme is always better than a damn,' she concluded with dignity, and drank the sundae herself.

On their way back across the Channel, Bernard insisted on stopping his propeller and hovering on his helicopter screws within a hundred feet of the waves. The weather had taken a change for the worse; a south-westerly wind had sprung up, the sky was cloudy.

'Look,' he commanded.

'But it's horrible,' said Lenina, shrinking back from the window. She was appalled by the rushing emptiness of the night, by the black foam-flecked water heaving beneath them, by the pale face of the moon, so haggard [1] and distracted among the hastening clouds. 'Let's turn on the radio. Quick!' She reached for the dialling knob on the dashboard [2] and turned it at random.

'. . . skies are blue inside of you,' sang sixteen tremoloing falsettos, 'the weather's always . . .'

Then a hiccough [3] and silence. Bernard had switched off the current.

'I want to look at the sea in peace,' he said. 'One can't even look with that beastly noise going on.'

'But it's lovely. And I don't want to look.'

'But I do,' he insisted. 'It makes me feel as though . . .' he hesitated, searching for words with which to express himself, 'as though I were more *me*, if you see what I mean. More on my own, not so completely a part of something else. Not just a cell in the social body. Doesn't it make you feel like that, Lenina?'

But Lenina was crying. 'It's horrible, it's horrible,' she kept repeating. 'And how can you talk like that about not wanting to be a part of the social body? After all, every one works for every one else. We can't do without any one. Even Epsilons . . .'

---

1. *haggard* ['hægəd]: tired-looking, marked, as if by worry and overwork.
2. *dashboard* : the instrument panel in a car.
3. *hiccough* ['hɪkʌp] (same as "hiccup"): short, sharp sound.

'Yes, I know,' said Bernard derisively. " Even Epsilons are useful"! So am I. And I damned well wish I weren't!'

Lenina was shocked by his blasphemy. 'Bernard !' she protested in a voice of amazed distress. 'How can you ?'

In a different key, 'How can I?' he repeated meditatively. 'No, the real problem is: How is it that I can't, or rather – because, after all, I know quite well why I can't – what would it be like if I could, if I were free – not enslaved by my conditioning.

'But, Bernard, you're saying the most awful things.'

'Don't you wish you were free, Lenina?'

'I don't know what you mean. I am free. Free to have the most wonderful time. Everybody's happy nowadays.'

He laughed, 'Yes, "Everybody's happy nowadays." We begin giving the children that at five. But wouldn't you like to be free to be happy in some other way, Lenina? In your own way, for example; not in everybody else's way.'

'I don't know what you mean,' she repeated. Then, turning to him, 'Oh, do let's go back, Bernard,' she besought; 'I do so hate it here.'

'Don't you like being with me ?'

'But of course, Bernard! It's this horrible place.'

'I thought we'd be more . . . more *together* here – with nothing but the sea and moon. More together than in that crowd, or even in my rooms. Don't you understand that?'

'I don't understand anything,' she said with decision, determined to preserve her incomprehension intact. 'Nothing. Least of all,' she continued in another tone, 'why you don't take *soma* when you have these dreadful ideas of yours. You'd forget all about them. And instead of feeling miserable, you'd be jolly. So jolly,' she repeated and smiled, for all the puzzled anxiety in her eyes, with what was meant to be an inviting and voluptuous cajolery.[1]

---

1. *cajolery* [kə'dʒəʊləri]: use of pleasing encouragements to gently persuade someone to do what you want them to do.

He looked at her in silence, his face unresponsive and very grave – looked at her intently. After a few seconds Lenina's eyes flinched away; she uttered a nervous little laugh, tried to think of something to say and couldn't. The silence prolonged itself. When Bernard spoke at last, it was in a small tired voice. 'All right, then,' he said, 'we'll go back.' And stepping hard on the accelerator, he sent the machine rocketing up into the sky. At four thousand he started his propeller. They flew in silence for a minute or two. Then, suddenly, Bernard began to laugh. Rather oddly, Lenina thought; but still, it was laughter.

'Feeling better?' she ventured to ask.

For answer, he lifted one hand from the controls and, slipping his arm round her, began to fondle her breasts.

'Thank Ford,' she said to herself, 'he's all right again.'

Half an hour later they were back in his rooms. Bernard swallowed four tablets of *soma* at a gulp, turned on the radio and television and began to undress.

'Well,' Lenina inquired, with significant archness [1] when they met next afternoon on the roof, 'did you think it was fun yesterday?'

Bernard nodded. They climbed into the plane. A little jolt, and they were off.

'Every one says I'm awfully pneumatic,' said Lenina reflectively, patting her own legs.

'Awfully.' But there was an expression of pain in Bernard's eyes. 'Like meat,' he was thinking.

She looked up with a certain anxiety. 'But you don't think I'm *too* plump, do you?'

He shook his head. Like so much meat.

'You think I'm all right.' Another nod. 'In every way?'

'Perfect,' he said aloud. And inwardly, 'She thinks of herself that way. She doesn't mind being meat.'

---

1. *with significant archness* ['ɑːtʃnəs]: in a deliberately mischievous way (so that the real point of her question would be recognised as "So now you see that I was right" - a playful attack on Bernard).

Lenina smiled triumphantly. But her satisfaction was premature.

'All the same,' he went on, after a little pause, 'I still rather wish it had all ended differently.'

'Differently?' Were there other endings?

'I didn't want it to end with our going to bed,' he specified.

Lenina was astonished.

'Not at once, not the first day.'

'But then what . . .?'

He began to talk a lot of incomprehensible and dangerous nonsense. Lenina did her best to stop the ears of her mind; but every now and then a phrase would insist on becoming audible. '. . . to try the effect of arresting my impulses,' she heard him say. The words seemed to touch a spring in her mind.

'Never put off till to-morrow the fun you can have to-day' [1] she said gravely.

'Two hundred repetitions, twice a week from fourteen to sixteen and a half,' was all his comment. The mad bad talk rambled on. 'I want to know what passion is,' she heard him saying. 'I want to feel something strongly.'

'When the individual feels, the community reels,'[2] Lenina pronounced.

'Well, why shouldn't it reel a bit?'

'Bernard!'

But Bernard remained unabashed.[3]

'Adults intellectually and during working hours,'[4] he went on. 'Infants where feeling and desire are concerned'

'Our Ford loved infants.'

---

1. *'Never put off ...* : cf. the proverb, "Never put off till tomorrow what may be done today" (from the Fourteenth Century).

2. *reels* : rocks and shakes, as if about to fall after being hit.

3. *unabashed* [ˌʌnə'bæʃt]: not disturbed or made embarassed by Lenina's shocked tone.

4. *'Adults ... working hours'* : i.e. "We are all adults as regards our intellectual abilities and performance at work."

Ignoring the interruption, 'It suddenly struck me the other day,' continued Bernard, 'that it might be possible to be an adult all the time.'

'I don't understand.' Lenina's tone was firm.

'I know you don't. And that's why we went to bed together yesterday – like infants – instead of being adults and waiting.'

'But it was fun,' Lenina insisted. 'Wasn't it?'

'Oh, the greatest fun,' he answered, but in a voice so mournful, with an expression so profoundly miserable, that Lenina felt all her triumph suddenly evaporate. Perhaps he had found her too plump, after all.

'I told you so,' was all that Fanny said, when Lenina came and made her confidences. 'It's the alcohol they put in his surrogate.'

'All the same,' Lenina insisted, 'I do like him. He has such awfully nice hands. And the way he moves his shoulders – that's very attractive.' She sighed. 'But I wish he weren't so odd.'

§ 2

Halting for a moment outside the door of the Director's room, Bernard drew a deep breath and squared his shoulders, bracing himself to meet the dislike and disapproval which he was certain of finding within. He knocked and entered.

'A permit for you to initial, Director,' he said as airily as possible,[1] and laid the paper on the writing-table.

The Director glanced at him sourly. But the stamp of the World Controller's Office was at the head of the paper and the signature of Mustapha Mond, bold and black, across the bottom. Everything was perfectly in order. The Director had no choice. He pencilled his initials – two small pale letters abject at the feet of Mustapha Mond – and was about to return the paper without a word of comment or genial Ford-speed,[2] when his eye was caught by something written in the body of the permit.

1. *as airily as possible* : trying to seem as carefree and high-spirited as he could.
2. *Ford-speed* : like our (now rarely used) "godspeed", meaning "May God help you as you go on your way".

'For the New Mexican Reservation?' he said, and his tone, the face he lifted to Bernard, expressed a kind of agitated astonishment.

Surprised by his surprise, Bernard nodded. There was a silence.

The Director leaned back in his chair, frowning. 'How long ago was it?' he said, speaking more to himself than to Bernard. 'Twenty years, I suppose. Nearer twenty-five. I must have been your age . . .' He sighed and shook his head.

Bernard felt extremely uncomfortable. A man so conventional, so scrupulously correct as the Director – and to commit so gross a solecism![1] It made him want to hide his face, to run out of the room. Not that he himself saw anything intrinsically objectionable in people talking about the remote past; that was one of those hypnopædic prejudices he had (so he imagined) completely got rid of. What made him feel shy was the knowledge that the Director disapproved – disapproved and yet had been betrayed into doing the forbidden thing. Under what inward compulsion? Through his discomfort Bernard eagerly listened.

'I had the same idea as you,' the Director was saying. 'Wanted to have a look at the savages. Got a permit for New Mexico and went there for my summer holiday. With the girl I was having at the moment. She was a Beta-Minus, and I think' (he shut his eyes), 'I think she had yellow hair. Anyhow, she was pneumatic, particularly pneumatic; I remember that. Well, we went there, and we looked at the savages, and we rode about on horses and all that. And then – it was almost the last day of my leave – then . . . well, she got lost. We'd gone riding up one of those revolting mountains, and it was horribly hot and oppressive, and after lunch we went to sleep. Or at least I did. She must have gone for a walk, alone. At any rate, when I woke up, she wasn't there. And the most frightful thunderstorm I've

---

1. *solecism* ['sɒlɪsɪzəm]: an impropriety, an offence against accepted rules of behaviour (because he is talking about the distant past).

ever seen was just bursting on us. And it poured and roared and flashed; and the horses broke loose and ran away; and I fell down, trying to catch them, and hurt my knee, so that I could hardly walk. Still, I searched and I shouted and I searched. But there was no sign of her. Then I thought she must have gone back to the rest-house by herself. So I crawled down into the valley by the way we had come. My knee was agonizingly painful, and I'd lost my *soma*. It took me hours. I didn't get back to the rest-house till after midnight. And she wasn't there; she wasn't there,' the Director repeated. There was a silence. 'Well,' he resumed at last, 'the next day there was a search. But we couldn't find her. She must have fallen into a gully [1] somewhere; or been eaten by a mountain lion. Ford knows. Anyhow it was horrible. It upset me very much at the time. More than it ought to have done, I dare say. Because, after all, it's the sort of accident that might have happened to any one; and, of course, the social body persists although the component cells may change.' But this sleep-taught consolation did not seem to be very effective. Shaking his head, 'I actually dream about it sometimes,' the Director went on in a low voice. 'Dream of being woken up by that peal of thunder and finding her gone; dream of searching and searching for her under the trees.' He lapsed into the silence of reminiscence.

'You must have had a terrible shock,' said Bernard, almost enviously.

At the sound of his voice the Director started into a guilty realization of where he was; shot a glance at Bernard, and averting his eyes, blushed darkly; looked at him again with sudden suspicion and, angrily on his dignity,[2] 'Don't imagine,' he said, 'that I'd had any indecorous relation with the girl.

---

1. *gully* [gʌli]: deep, narrow channel formed by water-erosion.
2. *on his dignity* : Huxley leaves the verb out; the Director suddenly stands on his dignity again when he realizes that he has exposed himself to a social inferior. He thought Bernard's reply was a condescending attempt to sympathize with someone who had become over-attached to one person.

Nothing emotional, nothing long-drawn. It was all perfectly healthy and normal.' He handed Bernard the permit. 'I really don't know why I bored you with this trivial anecdote.' Furious with himself for having given away a discreditable secret, he vented his rage on Bernard. The look in his eyes was now frankly malignant. 'And I should like to take this opportunity, Mr Marx,' he went on, 'of saying that I'm not at all pleased with the reports I receive of your behaviour outside working hours. You may say that this is not my business. But it is. I have the good name of the Centre to think of. My workers must be above suspicion, particularly those of the highest castes. Alphas are so conditioned that they do not *have* to be infantile in their emotional behaviour. But that is all the more reason for their making a special effort to conform. It is their duty to be infantile, even against their inclination. And so, Mr Marx, I give you fair warning.' The Director's voice vibrated with an indignation that had now become wholly righteous and impersonal – was the expression of the disapproval of Society itself. 'If ever I hear again of any lapse from a proper standard of infantile decorum, I shall ask for your transference to a Sub-Centre – preferably to Iceland. Good morning.' And swivelling round in his chair, he picked up his pen and began to write.

'That'll teach him,' he said to himself. But he was mistaken. For Bernard left the room with a swagger,[1] exulting, as he banged the door behind him, in the thought that he stood alone, embattled against the order of things; elated by the intoxicating consciousness of his individual significance and importance. Even the thought of persecution left him undismayed, was rather tonic than depressing.[2] He felt strong enough to meet and overcome affliction, strong enough to face even Iceland. And this confidence was the greater for his not for a moment really believing that he would be called upon to face anything at all.

---

1. *swagger* ['swægə]: a way of moving that showed he was very pleased with himself.
2. *rather . . . depressing* : made him feel more, not less, full of life and enthusiasm.

People simply weren't transferred for things like that. Iceland was just a threat. A most stimulating and life-giving threat. Walking along the corridor, he actually whistled.

Heroic was the account he gave that evening of his interview with the D.H.C. 'Whereupon,' it concluded, 'I simply told him to go to the Bottomless Past [1] and marched out of the room. And that was that.' He looked at Helmholtz Watson expectantly, awaiting his due reward of sympathy, encouragement, admiration. But no word came. Helmholtz sat silent, staring at the floor.

He liked Bernard; he was grateful to him for being the only man of his acquaintance with whom he could talk about the subjects he felt to be important. Nevertheless, there were things in Bernard which he hated. This boasting, for example. And the outbursts of an abject self-pity with which it alternated. And his deplorable habit of being bold after the event, and full, in absence, of the most extraordinary presence of mind. He hated these things – just because he liked Bernard. The seconds passed. Helmholtz continued to stare at the floor. And suddenly Bernard blushed and turned away.

§ 3

The journey was quite uneventful. The Blue Pacific Rocket was two and a half minutes early at New Orleans, lost four minutes in a tornado over Texas, but flew into a favourable air current at Longitude 95 West, and was able to land at Santa Fé less than forty seconds behind schedule time.

'Forty seconds on a six and a half hour flight. Not so bad,' Lenina conceded.

They slept that night at Santa Fé. The hotel was excellent – incomparably better, for example, than that horrible Aurora Bora Palace in which Lenina had suffered so much the previous

---

1. *Bottomless Past* : Bernard claims that he used a standard World State abusive expression to show the D.H.C. what a low opinion he had of him. "Go to the Bottomless Past" is like our "Go to Hell". (Hell is often referred to as "the bottomless pit".)

summer. Liquid air, television, vibro-vacuum massage, radio, boiling caffeine solution, hot contraceptives, and eight different kinds of scent were laid on in every bedroom. The synthetic music plant was working as they entered the hall and left nothing to be desired. A notice in the lift announced that there were sixty Escalator-Squash-Racquet Courts in the hotel, and that Obstacle and Electro-magnetic Golf could both be played in the park.

'But it sounds simply too lovely,' cried Lenina. 'I almost wish we could stay here. Sixty Escalator-Squash Courts . . .'

'There won't be any in the Reservation,' Bernard warned her. 'And no scent, no television, no hot water, even. If you feel you can't stand it, stay here till I come back.'

Lenina was quite offended. 'Of course I can stand it. I only said it was lovely here because . . . well, because progress is lovely, isn't it ?'

'Five hundred repetitions once a week from thirteen to seventeen,' said Bernard wearily, as though to himself.

'What did you say?'

'I said that progress was lovely. That's why you mustn't come to the Reservation unless you really want to.'

'But I do want to.'

'Very well, then,' said Bernard; and it was almost a threat.

Their permit required the signature of the Warden of the Reservation, at whose office next morning they duly presented themselves. An Epsilon-Plus negro porter took in Bernard's card, and they were admitted almost immediately.

The Warden was a blond and brachycephalic [1] Alpha-Minus, short, red, moon-faced, and broad-shouldered, with a loud booming [2] voice, very well adapted to the utterance of hypnopædic wisdom. He was a mine of irrelevant information and unasked-for good advice. Once started, he went on and on – boomingly.

---

1. *brachycephalic* ['brækɪsɪˌfælɪk]: short headed (with the skull almost as wide as it is long).
2. *booming* : resounding, deep and hollow.

'. . . five hundred and sixty thousand square kilometres, divided into four distinct Sub-Reservations, each surrounded by a high-tension wire fence.'

At this moment, and for no apparent reason, Bernard suddenly remembered that he had left the eau-de-Cologne tap in his bathroom wide open and running.

'. . . supplied with current from the Grand Canyon hydroelectric station.'

'Cost me a fortune by the time I get back.' With his mind's eye, Bernard saw the needle on the scent meter creeping round and round, ant-like, indefatigably. 'Quickly telephone to Helmholtz Watson.'

'. . . upwards of five thousand kilometres of fencing at sixty thousand volts.'

'You don't say so,' said Lenina politely, not knowing in the least what the Warden had said, but taking her cue from his dramatic pause. When the Warden started booming, she had inconspicuously swallowed half a gramme of *soma*, with the result that she could now sit, serenely not listening, thinking of nothing at all, but with her large blue eyes fixed on the Warden's face in an expression of rapt attention.

'To touch the fence is instant death,' pronounced the Warden solemnly. 'There is no escape from a Savage Reservation.'

The word 'escape' was suggestive. 'Perhaps,' said Bernard, half rising, 'we ought to think of going.' The little black needle was scurrying, an insect, nibbling through time, eating into his money.

'No escape,' repeated the Warden, waving him back into his chair; and as the permit was not yet countersigned, Bernard had no choice but to obey. 'Those who are born in the Reservation – and remember, my dear young lady,' he added, leering obscenely at Lenina, and speaking in an improper whisper, 'remember that, in the Reservation, children still *are* born, yes, actually born, revolting as that may seem . . .' (He hoped that this reference to a shameful subject would make Lenina blush; but she only smiled with simulated intelligence and said, 'You don't say so !' Disappointed, the Warden began again.) 'Those, I repeat, who are born in the Reservation are destined to die there.'

'Destined to die . . . A decilitre of eau-de-Cologne every minute. Six litres an hour. Perhaps,' Bernard tried again, 'we ought . . .'

Leaning forward, the Director tapped the table with his forefinger. 'You ask me how many people live in the Reservation. And I reply' – triumphantly – 'I reply that we do not know. We can only guess.'

'You don't say so.'

'My dear young lady, I do say so.'

Six times twenty-four – no, it would be nearer six times thirty-six. Bernard was pale and trembling with impatience. But inexorably the booming continued.

'. . . about sixty thousand Indians and half-breeds . . . absolute savages . . . our inspectors occasionally visit . . . otherwise, no communication whatever with the civilized world . . . still preserve their repulsive habits and customs . . . marriage, if you know what that is, my dear young lady; families . . . no conditioning . . . monstrous superstitions . . . Christianity and totemism and ancestor worship . . . extinct languages, such as Zuñi [1] and Spanish and Athapascan . . .[2] pumas, porcupines and other ferocious animals . . . infectious diseases . . . priests . . . venomous lizards . . .'

'You don't say so?'

They got away at last. Bernard dashed to the telephone. Quick, quick; but it took him nearly three minutes to get on to Helmholtz Watson. 'We might be among the savages already,' he complained. 'Damned incompetence!'

'Have a gramme,' suggested Lenina.

---

1. *Zuñi* : an Indian tribe from a pueblo village near Gallup in western New Mexico, and their language.

2. *Athapascan* : a large, extensively spoken family of North American Indian languages. The Southern Athapascan, or Apachean, group consisted of seven languages, spoken by the Navaho and six Apache tribes in Arizona, New Mexico, Texas and northern Mexico; Navaho still had 80,000 speakers in the mid-twentieth century.

He refused, preferring his anger. And at last, thank Ford, he was through and, yes, it was Helmholtz; Helmholtz, to whom he explained what had happened, and who promised to go round at once, at once, and turn off the tap, yes, at once, but took this opportunity to tell him what the D.H.C. had said, in public, yesterday evening . . .

'What? He's looking out for some one to take my place?' Bernard's voice was agonized. 'So it's actually decided? Did he mention Iceland? You say he did? Ford! Iceland . . .' He hung up the receiver and turned back to Lenina. His face was pale, his expression utterly dejected.

'What's the matter?' she asked.

'The matter?' He dropped heavily into a chair. 'I'm going to be sent to Iceland.'

Often in the past he had wondered what it would be like to be subjected (*soma*-less and with nothing but his own inward resources to rely on) to some great trial, some pain, some persecution; he had even longed for affliction. As recently as a week ago, in the Director's office, he had imagined himself courageously resisting, stoically accepting suffering without a word. The Director's threats had actually elated him, made him feel larger than life. But that, as he now realized, was because he had not taken the threats quite seriously; he had not believed that, when it came to the point, the D.H.C. would ever do anything. Now that it looked as though the threats were really to be fulfilled, Bernard was appalled. Of that imagined stoicism, that theoretical courage, not a trace was left.

He raged against himself – what a fool! – against the Director – how unfair not to give him that other chance, that other chance which, he now had no doubt at all, he had always intended to take. And Iceland, Iceland . . .

Lenina shook her head. 'Was and will make me ill,' she quoted, 'I take a gramme and only am.'

In the end she persuaded him to swallow four tablets ofsoma. Five minutes later roots and fruits were abolished; the flower of the present rosily blossomed. A message from the porter announced that, at the Warden's orders, a Reservation

Guard had come round with a plane and was waiting on the roof of the hotel. They went up at once. An octoroon [1] in Gamma-green uniform saluted and proceeded to recite the morning's programme.

A bird's-eye view of ten or a dozen of the principal pueblos,[2] then a landing for lunch in the valley of Malpais.[3] The rest-house was comfortable there, and up at the pueblo the savages would probably be celebrating their summer festival. It would be the best place to spend the night.

They took their seats in the plane and set off. Ten minutes later they were crossing the frontier that separated civilization from savagery. Uphill and down, across the deserts of salt or sand, through forests, into the violet depth of canyons, over crag and peak and table-topped mesa,[4] the fence marched on and on, irresistibly the straight line, the geometrical symbol of triumphant human purpose. And at its foot, here and there, a mosaic of white bones, a still unrotted carcase dark on the tawny ground marked the place where deer or steer,[5] puma or porcupine or coyote, or the greedy turkey buzzards drawn down by the whiff of carrion [6] and fulminated as though by a poetic justice, had come too close to the destroying wires.

'They never learn,' said the green-uniformed pilot, pointing down at the skeletons on the ground below them. 'And they never will learn,' he added and laughed, as though he had somehow scored a personal triumph over the electrocuted animals.

Bernard also laughed; after two grammes of soma the joke seemed, for some reason, good. Laughed and then, almost immediately, dropped off to sleep and, sleeping, was carried

1. *octoroon* [ɒktə'ruːn]: person who has one-eighth black parentage.
2. *pueblos* : communal habitations of the Indians in South-West U.S.A.
3. *Malpais* : in New Mexico, not far from El Paso (near the Mexican border).
4. *mesa* ['meɪsæ]: a flat-topped hill.
5. *steer* : young castrated bull, usually in a herd kept for meat.
6. *turkey . . . carrion* : large birds (vultures) attracted by the smell of a dead animal's flesh.

over Taos and Tesuque; over Nambe and Picuris and Pojoaque, over Sia and Cochiti, over Laguna and Acoma and the Enchanted Mesa, over Zuñi and Cibola and Ojo Caliente, and woke at last to find the machine standing on the ground, Lenina carrying the suit-cases into a small square house, and the Gamma-green octoroon talking incomprehensibly with a young Indian.

'Malpais,' explained the pilot, as Bernard stepped out. 'This is the rest-house. And there's a dance this afternoon at the pueblo. He'll take you there.' He pointed to the sullen young savage. 'Funny, I expect.' He grinned. 'Everything they do is funny.' And with that he climbed into the plane and started up the engines. 'Back to-morrow. And remember,' he added reassuringly to Lenina, 'they're perfectly tame; savages won't do you any harm. They've got enough experience of gas bombs to know that they mustn't play any tricks.' Still laughing, he threw the helicopter screws into gear, accelerated, and was gone.

Chapter VII

THE mesa was like a ship becalmed in a strait of lion-coloured dust. [1] The channel wound between precipitous banks, and slanting from one wall to the other across the valley ran a streak of green – the river and its fields. On the prow of that stone ship in the centre of the strait, and seemingly a part of it, a shaped and geometrical outcrop of the naked rock, stood the pueblo of Malpais. Block above block, each story smaller than the one below, the tall houses rose like stepped and amputated pyramids into the blue sky. At their feet lay a straggle of low buildings, a criss-cross of walls; and on three sides the precipices fell sheer into the plain. A few columns of smoke mounted perpendicularly into the windless air and were lost.

'Queer,' said Lenina. 'Very queer.' It was her ordinary word of condemnation. 'I don't like it. And I don't like that man.' She pointed to the Indian guide who had been appointed to take them up to the pueblo. Her feeling was evidently reciprocated; the very back of the man as he walked along before them, was hostile, sullenly contemptuous.

1. *The mesa ... dust* : this rock formation, a plateau with steep sides, resembles a motionless ship in a narrow waterway (strait).

'Besides,' she lowered her voice, 'he smells.'

Bernard did not attempt to deny it. They walked on.

Suddenly it was as though the whole air had come alive and were pulsing, pulsing with the indefatigable movement of blood. Up there, in Malpais, the drums were being beaten. Their feet fell in with the rhythm of that mysterious heart; they quickened their pace. Their path led them to the foot of the precipice. The sides of the great mesa ship towered over them, three hundred feet to the gunwale.[1]

'I wish we could have brought the plane,' said Lenina, looking up resentfully at the blank impending rock-face. 'I hate walking. And you feel so small when you're on the ground at the bottom of a hill.'

They walked along for some way in the shadow of the mesa, rounded a projection, and there, in a water-worn ravine, was the way up the companion ladder. They climbed. It was a very steep path that zigzagged from side to side of the gully. Sometimes the pulsing of the drums was all but inaudible, at others they seemed to be beating only just round the corner.

When they were half-way up, an eagle flew past so close to them that the wind of his wings blew chill on their faces. In a crevice of the rock lay a pile of bones. It was all oppressively queer, and the Indian smelt stronger and stronger. They emerged at last from the ravine into the full sunlight. The top of the mesa was a flat deck of stone.

'Like the Charing-T Tower,' was Lenina's comment. But she was not allowed to enjoy her discovery of this reassuring resemblance for long. A padding [2] of soft feet made them turn round. Naked from throat to navel, their dark-brown bodies painted with white lines ('like asphalt tennis courts,' Lenina was

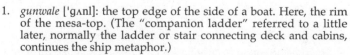

1. *gunwale* ['gʌnl]: the top edge of the side of a boat. Here, the rim of the mesa-top. (The "companion ladder" referred to a little later, normally the ladder or stair connecting deck and cabins, continues the ship metaphor.)

2. *padding* : they hear the noise made by bare feet being placed gently on the sandy ground.

later to explain), their faces inhuman with daubings [1] of scarlet, black and ochre, two Indians came running along the path. Their black hair was braided [2] with fox fur and red flannel. Cloaks of turkey feathers fluttered from their shoulders; huge feather diadems exploded gaudily [3] round their heads. With every step they took came the clink and rattle of their silver bracelets, their heavy necklaces of bone and turquoise beads. They came on without a word, running quietly in their deerskin moccasins. One of them was holding a feather brush; the other carried, in either hand, what looked at a distance like three or four pieces of thick rope. One of the ropes writhed [4] uneasily, and suddenly Lenina saw that they were snakes.

The men came nearer and nearer; their dark eyes looked at her, but without giving any sign of recognition, any smallest sign that they had seen her or were aware of her existence. The writhing snake hung limp again with the rest. The men passed.

'I don't like it,' said Lenina. 'I don't like it.'

She liked even less what awaited her at the entrance to the pueblo, where their guide had left them while he went inside for instructions. The dirt, to start with, the piles of rubbish, the dust, the dogs, the flies. Her face wrinkled up into a grimace of disgust. She held her handkerchief to her nose.

'But how can they live like this ?' she broke out in a voice of indignant incredulity. (It wasn't possible.)

Bernard shrugged his shoulders philosophically. 'Anyhow,' he said, 'they've been doing it for the last five or six thousand years. So I suppose they must be used to it by now.'

'But cleanliness is next to fordliness,'[5] she insisted.

1. *daubings* ['dɔːbɪŋz]: crudely painted marks or blobs (usually called "daubs").
2. *braided* ['breɪdɪd]: with strands interwoven.
3. *exploded gaudily* ['gɔːdɪli]: burst upwards in an excessively bright display. (The verb is used metaphorically.)
4. *writhed* [raɪðd]: twisted and turned (as snakes do).
5. *cleanliness is next to fordliness* : we say "Cleanliness ['klenlɪnɪs] is next to Godliness"; i.e. being cleanly (keeping oneself clean by habit) is linked to spiritual purity.

'Yes, and civilization is sterilization,' Bernard went on, concluding on a tone of irony the second hypnopædic lesson in elementary hygiene. 'But these people have never heard of Our Ford, and they aren't civilized. So there's no point in . . .'

'Oh!' She gripped his arm. 'Look.'

An almost naked Indian was very slowly climbing down the ladder from the first-floor terrace of a neighbouring house – rung after rung,[1] with the tremulous caution of extreme old age. His face was profoundly wrinkled and black, like a mask of obsidian.[2] The toothless mouth had fallen in. At the corners of the lips and on each side of the chin a few long bristles gleamed almost white against the dark skin. The long unbraided hair hung down in grey wisps round his face. His body was bent and emaciated to the bone, almost fleshless. Very slowly he came down, pausing at each rung before he ventured another step.

'What's the matter with him?' whispered Lenina. Her eyes were wide with horror and amazement.

'He's old, that's all,' Bernard answered as carelessly as he could. He too was startled; but he made an effort to seem unmoved.

'Old ?' she repeated. 'But the Director's old; lots of people are old, they're not like that.'

'That's because we don't allow them to be like that. We preserve them from diseases. We keep their internal secretions artificially balanced at a youthful equilibrium. We don't permit their magnesium-calcium ratio [3] to fall below what it was at thirty. We give them transfusions of young blood. We keep their metabolism permanently stimulated. So, of course, they don't look like that. Partly,' he added, 'because most of them die long before they reach this old creature's age. Youth almost unimpaired till sixty, and then, crack! the end.'

---

1. *rung* : horizontal bar of a ladder.
2. *obsidian* : vitreous volcanic rock, like dark bottle glass.
3. *magnesium-calcium ratio* ['reɪʃɪəʊ]: the relative quantity of these elements (which has effects on the body's nervous system).

But Lenina was not listening. She was watching the old man. Slowly, slowly he came down. His feet touched the ground. He turned. In their deep-sunken orbits his eyes were still extraordinarily bright. They looked at her for a long moment expressionlessly, without surprise, as though she had not been there at all. Then slowly, with bent back, the old man hobbled past them and was gone.

'But it's terrible,' Lenina whispered. 'It's awful. We ought not to have come here.' She felt in her pocket for her *soma* – only to discover that, by some unprecedented oversight, she had left the bottle down at the rest-house. Bernard's pockets were also empty.

Lenina was left to face the horrors of Malpais unaided. They came crowding in on her thick and fast. The spectacle of two young women giving the breast to their babies made her blush and turn away her face. She had never seen anything so indecent in her life. And what made it worse was that, instead of tactfully ignoring it, Bernard proceeded to make open comments on this revoltingly viviparous scene. Ashamed, now that the effects of the *soma* had worn off, of the weakness he had displayed that morning in the hotel, he went out of his way to show himself strong and unorthodox.

'What a wonderfully intimate relationship,' he said, deliberately outrageous. 'And what an intensity of feeling it must generate! I often think one may have missed something in not having had a mother. And perhaps you've missed something in not *being* a mother, Lenina. Imagine yourself sitting there with a little baby of your own . . .'

'Bernard! How can you?' The passage of an old woman with ophthalmia and a disease of the skin distracted her from her indignation.

'Let's go away,' she begged. 'I don't like it.'

But at this moment their guide came back and, beckoning to them to follow, led the way down the narrow street between the houses. They rounded a corner. A dead dog was lying on a rubbish heap; a woman with a goitre [1] was looking for lice [2] in the hair of a small girl. Their guide halted at the foot of a ladder, raised his hand perpendicularly, then darted it horizontally forward. They did what he mutely commanded – climbed the ladder and walked through the doorway, to which it gave access, into a long narrow room, rather dark and smelling of smoke and cooked grease and long-worn, long-unwashed clothes. At the further end of the room was another doorway, through which came a shaft of sunlight and the noise, very loud and close, of the drums.

They stepped across the threshold and found themselves on a wide terrace. Below them, shut in by the tall houses, was the village square, crowded with Indians. Bright blankets, and feathers in black hair, and the glint of turquoise, and dark skins shining with heat. Lenina put her handkerchief to her nose again. In the open space at the centre of the square were two circular platforms of masonry and trampled clay – the roofs, it was evident, of underground chambers; for in the centre of each platform was an open hatchway, with a ladder emerging from the lower darkness. A sound of subterranean flute-playing came up and was almost lost in the steady remorseless persistence of the drums.

Lenina liked the drums. Shutting her eyes she abandoned herself to their soft repeated thunder, allowed it to invade her consciousness more and more completely, till at last there was nothing left in the world but that one deep pulse of sound. It reminded her reassuringly of the synthetic noises made at Solidarity Services and Ford's Day celebrations. 'Orgy-porgy,' she whispered to herself. These drums beat out just the same rhythms.

There was a sudden startling burst of singing – hundreds of male voices crying out fiercely in harsh metallic unison. A few long notes and silence, the thunderous silence of the drums;

1. *goitre* ['gɔɪtə]: abnormal swelling of the thyroid gland (in the neck).
2. *lice* [laɪs]: small parasitic insects that live on animals and people living in dirty conditions. ("Louse" in the singular.)

then shrill, in a neighing [1] treble, the women's answer. Then again the drums; and once more the men's deep savage affirmation of their manhood.

Queer – yes. The place was queer, so was the music, so were the clothes and the goitres and the skin diseases and the old people. But the performance itself – there seemed to be nothing specially queer about that.

'It reminds me of a lower-caste Community Sing,' she told Bernard.

But a little later it was reminding her a good deal less of that innocuous function. For suddenly there had swarmed up from those round chambers underground a ghastly troop of monsters. Hideously masked or painted out of all semblance of humanity, they had tramped out a strange limping dance round the square; round and again round, singing as they went, round and round – each time a little faster; and the drums had changed and quickened their rhythm, so that it became like the pulsing of fever in the ears; and the crowd had begun to sing with the dancers, louder and louder; and first one woman had shrieked, and then another and another, as though they were being killed; and then suddenly the leader of the dancers broke out of the line, ran to a big wooden chest which was standing at one end of the square, raised the lid and pulled out a pair of black snakes. A great yell went up from the crowd, and all the other dancers ran towards him with outstretched hands. He tossed the snakes to the first-comers, then dipped back into the chest for more. More and more, black snakes and brown and mottled – he flung them out. And then the dance began again on a different rhythm. Round and round they went with their snakes, snakily, with a soft undulating movement at the knees and hips. Round and round. Then the leader gave a signal, and one after another, all the snakes were flung down in the middle of the square; an old man came up from underground and sprinkled them with corn meal, and from the other hatchway came a woman and

---

1. *neighing* [neɪjɪŋ]: sounding like the cry of a horse.

sprinkled them with water from a black jar. Then the old man lifted his hand and, startlingly, terrifyingly, there was absolute silence. The drums stopped beating, life seemed to have come to an end. The old man pointed towards the two hatchways that gave entrance to the lower world. And slowly, raised by invisible hands from below, there emerged from the one a painted image of an eagle, from the other that of a man, naked, and nailed to a cross.[1] They hung there, seemingly self-sustained, as though watching. The old man clapped his hands. Naked but for a white cotton breech-cloth,[2] a boy of about eighteen stepped out of the crowd and stood before him, his hands crossed over his chest, his head bowed. The old man made the sign of the cross over him and turned away. Slowly, the boy began to walk round the writhing heap of snakes. He had completed the first circuit and was half-way through the second when, from among the dancers, a tall man wearing the mask of a coyote and holding in his hand a whip of plaited leather, advanced towards him. The boy moved on as though unaware of the other's existence. The coyote-man raised his whip; there was a long moment of expectancy, then a swift movement, the whistle of the lash and its loud flat-sounding impact on the flesh. The boy's body quivered; but he made no sound, he walked on at the same slow, steady pace. The coyote struck again, again; and at every blow at first a gasp and then a deep groan went up from the crowd. The boy walked on. Twice, thrice, four times round he went. The blood was streaming. Five times round, six times round. Suddenly Lenina covered her face with her hands and began to sob. 'Oh, stop them, stop them!' she implored. But the whip fell and fell inexorably. Seven times round. Then all at once the boy staggered and, still without a

1. *painted image ... a cross* : the eagle represents Pookong - there is a mixture of tribal myth and Christian figures in the Malpais belief system. (Other gods, such as Awonawilona, are later mentioned alongside Jesus and Our Lady of Acoma.)
2. *breech-cloth* : cloth covering the top of the legs, backside and lower belly - something like a present-day miniskirt.

sound, pitched forward on to his face. Bending over him, the old man touched his back with a long white feather, held it up for a moment, crimson, for the people to see, then shook it thrice over the snakes. A few drops fell, and suddenly the drums broke out again into a panic of hurrying notes; there was a great shout. The dancers rushed forward, picked up the snakes and ran out of the square. Men, women, children, all the crowd ran after them. A minute later the square was empty, only the boy remained, prone [1] where he had fallen, quite still. Three old women came out of one of the houses, and with some difficulty lifted him and carried him in. The eagle and the man on the cross kept guard for a little while over the empty pueblo; then, as though they had seen enough, sank slowly down through their hatchways, out of sight, into the nether [2] world.

Lenina was still sobbing. 'Too awful,' she kept repeating, and all Bernard's consolations were in vain. 'Too awful! That blood!' She shuddered. 'Oh, I wish I had my *soma*.'

There was the sound of feet in the inner room.

Lenina did not move, but sat with her face in her hands, unseeing, apart. Only Bernard turned round.

The dress of the young man who now stepped out on to the terrace was Indian; but his plaited hair was straw-coloured, his eyes a pale blue, and his skin a white skin, bronzed.

'Hullo. Good-morrow,'[3] said the stranger, in faultless but peculiar English. 'You're civilized, aren't you? You come from the Other Place, outside the Reservation?'

'Who on earth . . . ?'[4] Bernard began in astonishment.

---

1. *prone* [praʊn]: lying flat and immobile.

2. *nether* : lower. ("Nether world" often means "Hell".)

3. *'Hullo. Good-morrow'* : this greeting ("Hello, good day to you") introduces us to the "faultless but peculiar" speech of John, the Savage, in which archaic forms (as here) and borrowings from Shakespeare's plays are mixed with up-to-date English.

4. *'Who on earth...?'* : Bernard asks, "Who are you?" - the words "on earth" are commonly added to emphasise surprise and incomprehension.

The young man sighed and shook his head. 'A most unhappy gentleman.'[1] And, pointing to the bloodstains in the centre of the square, 'Do you see that damned spot?'[2] he asked in a voice that trembled with emotion.

'A gramme is better than a damn,' said Lenina mechanically from behind her hands. 'I wish I had my *soma*!'

'*I* ought to have been there.' The young man went on. 'Why wouldn't they let me be the sacrifice? I'd have gone round ten times – twelve, fifteen. Palowhtiwa only got as far as seven. They could have had twice as much blood from me. The multitudinous seas incarnadine.'[3] He flung out his arms in a lavish gesture; then, despairingly, let them fall again. 'But they wouldn't let me. They disliked me for my complexion.[4] It's always been like that. Always.' Tears stood in the young man's eyes; he was ashamed and turned away.

Astonishment made Lenina forget the deprivation of *soma*. She uncovered her face and, for the first time, looked at the stranger. 'Do you mean to say that you *wanted* to be hit with that whip ?'

Still averted from her, the young man made a sign of affirmation. 'For the sake of the pueblo – to make the rain come and the corn grow. And to please Pookong and Jesus. And then to show that I can bear pain without crying out. Yes,' and his voice suddenly took on a new resonance, he turned with a proud squaring of the shoulders, a proud, defiant lifting of the chin, 'to show that I'm a man . . . Oh !' He gave a gasp and was

---

1. '*A most unhappy gentleman*' : this sounds Shakespearean (because "most unhappy" is common in his plays).

2. *damned spot* : Lady Macbeth, in Shakespeare's *Macbeth*, obsessed with a spot of blood she sees on her hand, cries "Out, damned spot". See *Macbeth*, Act V, Scene 1, line 39. (Future references to Shakespeare will follow this pattern.)

3. *The multitudinous* [ˌmʌltɪ'tjuːdɪnəs] *seas incarnadine* [ɪn'kɑːnədaɪn]: *Macbeth*, II, 2, 62. (Enough blood to make all the seas blood-red.)

4. *They disliked ... complexion* : Shakespeare, *The Merchant of Venice*, II, 1, 1 ("Mislike me not for my complexion").

silent, gaping.[1] He had seen, for the first time in his life, the face of a girl whose cheeks were not the colour of chocolate or dog-skin, whose hair was auburn and permanently waved, and whose expression (amazing novelty!) was one of benevolent interest. Lenina was smiling at him; such a nice-looking boy, she was thinking, and a really beautiful body. The blood rushed up into the young man's face; he dropped his eyes, raised them again for a moment only to find her still smiling at him, and was so much overcome that he had to turn away and pretend to be looking very hard at something on the other side of the square.

Bernard's questions made a diversion. Who? How? When? From where? Keeping his eyes fixed on Bernard's face (for so passionately did he long to see Lenina smiling that he simply dared not look at her), the young man tried to explain himself. Linda and he – Linda was his mother (the word made Lenina look uncomfortable) – were strangers in the Reservation. Linda had come from the Other Place long ago, before he was born, with a man who was his father. (Bernard pricked up his ears.)[2] She had gone walking alone in those mountains over there to the North, had fallen down a steep place and hurt her head. ('Go on, go on,' said Bernard excitedly.) Some hunters from Malpais had found her and brought her to the pueblo. As for the man who was his father, Linda had never seen him again. His name was Tomakin. (Yes, 'Thomas' was the D.H.C.'s first name.) He must have flown away, back to the Other Place, away without her – a bad, unkind, unnatural man.

'And so I was born in Malpais,' he concluded. 'In Malpais.' And he shook his head.

The squalor of that little house on the outskirts of the pueblo! A space of dust and rubbish separated it from the village. Two famine-stricken [3] dogs were nosing obscenely in the

---

1. *gaping* ['geɪpɪŋ]: with his mouth wide open in surprise.
2. *pricked up his ears* : listened with special attention.
3. *famine-stricken* : afflicted with severe hunger, starving.

garbage at its door. Inside, when they entered, the twilight stank and was loud with flies.

'Linda!' the young man called.

From the inner room a rather hoarse female voice said, 'Coming.'

They waited. In bowls on the floor were the remains of a meal, perhaps of several meals.

The door opened. A very stout blonde squaw [1] stepped across the threshold and stood looking at the strangers, staring incredulously, her mouth open. Lenina noticed with disgust that two of the front teeth were missing. And the colour of the ones that remained . . . She shuddered. It was worse than the old man. So fat. And all the lines in her face, the flabbiness, the wrinkles. And the sagging cheeks, with those purplish blotches. And the red veins on her nose, the bloodshot eyes. And that neck – that neck; and the blanket she wore over her head ragged [2] and filthy. And under the brown sack-shaped tunic those enormous breasts, the bulge of the stomach, the hips. Oh, much worse than the old man, much worse! And suddenly the creature burst out in a torrent of speech, rushed at her with outstretched arms and – Ford ! Ford ! it was too revolting, in another moment she'd be sick – pressed her against the bulge, the bosom, and began to kiss her. Ford! to *kiss*, slobberingly,[3] and smelt too horrible, obviously never had a bath, and simply reeked of that beastly stuff that was put into Delta and Epsilon bottles (no, it wasn't true about Bernard), positively stank of alcohol. She broke away as quickly as she could.

A blubbered [4] and distorted face confronted her; the creature was crying.

---

1. *squaw* [skwɔː]: North American Indian woman.
2. *ragged* ['rægɪd]: in bad condition, broken in places and with uneven edges (refers to the blanket).
3. *slobberingly* : in a way that was wet with saliva.
4. *blubbered* ['blʌbəd]: swollen (because she was weeping).

'Oh, my dear, my dear.' The torrent of words flowed
sobbingly. 'If you knew how glad after all these years! A
civilized face. Yes, and civilized clothes. Because I thought I
should never see a piece of real acetate silk again.' She fingered
the sleeve of Lenina's shirt. The nails were black. 'And those
adorable viscose velveteen shorts ! Do you know, dear, I've still
got my old clothes, the ones I came in, put away in a box. I'll
show them you afterwards. Though, of course, the acetate has
all gone into holes. But such a lovely white bandolier though I
must say your green morocco is even lovelier. Not that it did *me*
much good, that bandolier.' Her tears began to flow again. 'I
suppose John told you. What I had to suffer – and not a gramme
of *soma* to be had. Only a drink of *mescal* 1 every now and then,
when Popé used to bring it. Popé is a boy I used to know. But it
makes you feel so bad afterwards, the *mescal* does, and you're
sick with the *peyotl*;2 besides, it always made that awful feeling
of being ashamed much worse the next day. And I *was* so
ashamed. Just think of it: me, a Beta – having a baby: put
yourself in my place.' (The mere suggestion made Lenina
shudder.) 'Though it wasn't my fault, I swear; because I still
don't know how it happened, seeing that I did all the
Malthusian drill – you know, by numbers, One, two, three, four,
always, I swear it; but all the same it happened; and of course
there wasn't anything like an Abortion Centre here. Is it still
down in Chelsea,3 by the way?' she asked. Lenina nodded. 'And
still flood-lighted on Tuesdays and Fridays?' Lenina nodded
again. 'That lovely pink glass tower!' Poor Linda lifted her face
and with closed eyes ecstatically contemplated the bright
remembered image. 'And the river at night,' she whispered.

1. *mescal* ['meskll] or [‚mes'kæl]: intoxicating liquor distilled from
   the juices of the agave cactus.
2. *peyotl* : usually anglicized to "peyote" [peɪˈəʊti], this is the
   Nahuatl word for a cactus found in Mexico; the reference here is
   to the hallucinogenic intoxicant prepared from the buttons at its
   top.
3. *Chelsea* : district in south-west London.

Great tears oozed slowly out from between her tight-shut
eyelids. 'And flying back in the evening from Stoke Poges. And
then a hot bath and vibro-vacuum massage . . . But there.' She
drew a deep breath, shook her head, opened her eyes again,
sniffed once or twice, then blew her nose on her fingers and
wiped them on the skirt of her tunic. 'Oh, I'm so sorry,' she said
in response to Lenina's involuntary grimace of disgust. 'I
oughtn't to have done that. I'm sorry. But what *are* you to do
when there aren't any handkerchiefs? I remember how it used to
upset me, all that dirt, and nothing being aseptic. I had an awful
cut on my head when they first brought me here. You can't
imagine what they used to put on it. Filth, just filth.
"Civilization is Sterilization," I used to say to them. And
"Streptocock-Gee to Banbury-T, to see a fine bathroom and
W.C."[1] as though they were children. But of course they didn't
understand. How should they? And in the end I suppose I got
used to it. And anyhow, how can you keep things clean when
there isn't hot water laid on? And look at these clothes. This
beastly wool isn't like acetate. It lasts and lasts. And you're
supposed to mend it if it gets torn. But I'm a Beta; I worked in
the Fertilizing Room, nobody ever taught me to do anything like
that. It wasn't my business. Besides, it never used to be right to
mend clothes. Throw them away when they've got holes in
them and buy new. " The more stitches, the less riches." Isn't
that right? Mending's anti-social. But it's all different here. It's
like living with lunatics. Everything they do is mad.' She looked
round; saw John and Bernard had left them and were walking
up and down in the dust and garbage outside the house; but
none the less confidentially lowering her voice, and leaning,
while Lenina stiffened and shrank, so close that the blown reek
of embryo-poison [2] stirred the hair on her cheek. 'For instance,'

---

1. *"Streptocock-Gee ... W.C."* : the present-day nursery rhyme begins
   "Ride a cock-horse to Banbury Cross / To see a fine lady ride on a
   white horse"; horses in baby-language are often called "Gee-
   gees", while streptococci are bacteria. (Banbury is in Oxfordshire.)
2. *blown reek of embryo-poison* : the strong, bad smell of alcohol.

she hoarsely whispered, 'take the way they have one another here. Mad, I tell you, absolutely mad. Everybody belongs to every one else – don't they? don't they?' she insisted, tugging at Lenina's sleeve. Lenina nodded her averted head, let out the breath she had been holding and managed to draw another one, relatively untainted. 'Well, here,' the other went on, 'nobody's supposed to belong to more than one person. And if you have people in the ordinary way, the others think you're wicked and anti-social. They hate and despise you. Once a lot of women came and made a scene because their men came to see me. Well, why not? And then they rushed at me . . . No, it was too awful. I can't tell you about it.' Linda covered her face with her hands and shuddered. 'They're so hateful, the women here. Mad, mad and cruel. And of course they don't know anything about Malthusian drill, or bottles, or decanting, or anything of that sort. So they're having children all the time – like dogs. It's too revolting. And to think that I . . . Oh, Ford, Ford, Ford! And yet John *was* a great comfort to me. I don't know what I should have done without him. Even though he did get so upset whenever a man . . . Quite as a tiny boy, even. Once (but that was when he was bigger) he tried to kill poor Waihusiwa – or was it Popé? – just because I used to have them sometimes. Because I never *could* make him understand that that was what civilized people ought to do. Being mad's infectious, I believe. Anyhow, John seems to have caught it from the Indians. Because, of course, he was with them a lot. Even though they were so beastly to him and wouldn't let him do all the things the other boys did. Which was a good thing in a way, because it made it easier for me to condition him a little. Though you've no idea how difficult that is. There's so much one doesn't know; it wasn't my business to know. I mean, when a child asks you how a helicopter works or who made the world – well, what are you to answer if you're a Beta and have always worked in the Fertilizing Room? What are you to answer?'

Chapter VIII

OUTSIDE, in the dust and among the garbage (there were four dogs now), Bernard and John were walking slowly up and down. 'So hard for me to realize,' Bernard was saying, 'to reconstruct.'

As though we were living on different planets, in different centuries. A mother, and all this dirt, and gods, and old age, and disease . . .' He shook his head. 'It's almost inconceivable. I shall never understand unless you explain.'

'Explain what?'

'This.' He indicated the pueblo. 'That.' And it was the little house outside the village. 'Everything. All your life.'

'But what is there to say?'

'From the beginning. As far back as you can remember.'

'As far back as I can remember.' John frowned. There was a long silence.

It was very hot.[1] They had eaten a lot of tortillas [2] and sweet corn. Linda said, 'Come and lie down, Baby.' They lay down

---

1. *It was very hot* : this is the beginning of John's recollections, a series of flashbacks given in free indirect speech.
2. *tortillas* [tɔːˈtɪ(l)jəs]: flat round pancakes made from maize flour.

together in the big bed. 'Sing,' and Linda sang. Sang 'Streptocock-Gee to Banbury-T' and 'Bye, Baby Banting,[1] soon you'll need decanting.' Her voice got fainter and fainter . . .

There was a loud noise, and he woke with a start. A man was standing by the bed, enormous, frightening. He was saying something to Linda, and Linda was laughing. She had pulled the blanket up to her chin, but the man pulled it down again. His hair was like two black ropes, and round his arm was a lovely silver bracelet with blue stones in it. He liked the bracelet;[2] but all the same he was frightened; he hid his face against Linda's body. Linda put her hand on him and he felt safer. In those other words he did not understand so well, she said to the man, 'Not with John here.' The man looked at him, then again at Linda, and said a few words in a soft voice. Linda said, 'No.' But the man bent over the bed towards him and his face was huge, terrible; the black ropes of hair touched the blanket. 'No,' Linda said again, and he felt her hand squeezing him more tightly. 'No, no!' But the man took hold of one of his arms, and it hurt. He screamed. The man put out his other hand and lifted him up. Linda was still holding him, still saying 'No, no.' The man said something short and angry, and suddenly her hands were gone. 'Linda, Linda.' He kicked and wriggled; but the man carried him across to the door, opened it, put him down on the floor in the middle of the other room, and went away, shutting the door behind him. He got up, he ran to the door. Standing on tiptoe he could just reach the big wooden latch. He lifted it and pushed; but the door wouldn't open. 'Linda,' he shouted. She didn't answer.

He remembered a huge room, rather dark; and there were big wooden things with strings fastened to them,[3] and lots of

1. *'Bye, Baby Banting...* : a nursery rhyme based on today's "Bye, baby bunting / Daddy's gone a-hunting" (etc). ("Banting", a fat-reducing dieting procedure, suggests the baby is too big.)
2. *He liked the bracelet* : "He" here (and afterwards) refers to John.
3. *big wooden things ... them* : looms, the apparatus for weaving yarn ("strings") into textiles.

women standing round them – making blankets, Linda said. Linda told him to sit in the corner with the other children, while she went and helped the women. He played with the little boys for a long time. Suddenly people started talking very loud, and there were the women pushing Linda away, and Linda was crying. She went to the door and he ran after her. He asked her why they were angry. 'Because I broke something,' she said. And then she got angry too. 'How should I know how to do their beastly weaving?' she said. 'Beastly savages.' He asked her what savages were. When they got back to their house, Popé [1] was waiting at the door, and he came in with them. He had a big gourd [2] full of stuff that looked like water; only it wasn't water, but something with a bad smell that burnt your mouth and made you cough. Linda drank some and Popé drank some, and then Linda laughed a lot and talked very loud; and then she and Popé went into the other room. When Popé went away, he went into the room. Linda was in bed and so fast asleep that he couldn't wake her.

Popé used to come often. He said the stuff in the gourd was called *mescal*; but Linda said it ought to be called *soma*; only it made you feel ill afterwards. He hated Popé. He hated them all – all the men who came to see Linda. One afternoon, when he had been playing with the other children – it was cold, he remembered, and there was snow on the mountains – he came back to the house and heard angry voices in the bedroom. They were women's voices, and they said words he didn't understand; but he knew they were dreadful words. Then suddenly, crash! something was upset; he heard people moving about quickly, and there was another crash and then a noise like hitting a mule, only not so bony; then Linda screamed. 'Oh, don't, don't, don't!' she said. He ran in. There were three women

1. *Popé* : this name may allude to Popé of San Juan, "a leader in the great 1680 Pueblo Indian rebellion against the Spaniards" (Firchow, 1984: Ch. 3).
2. *gourd* [gʊəd]: spherical container made from the hard-cased fruit of the gourd plant.

in dark blankets. Linda was on the bed. One of the women was holding her wrists. Another was lying across her legs, so that she couldn't kick. The third was hitting her with a whip. Once, twice, three times; and each time Linda screamed. Crying, he tugged at the fringe of the woman's blanket. 'Please, please.' With her free hand she held him away. The whip came down again, and again Linda screamed. He caught hold of the woman's enormous brown hand between his own and bit it with all his might. She cried out, wrenched her hand free, and gave him such a push that he fell down. While he was lying on the ground she hit him three times with the whip. It hurt more than anything he had ever felt – like fire. The whip whistled again, fell. But this time it was Linda who screamed.

'But why did they want to hurt you, Linda?' he asked that night. He was crying, because the red marks of the whip on his back still hurt so terribly. But he was also crying because people were so beastly and unfair, and because he was only a little boy and couldn't do anything against them. Linda was crying too. She was grown up, but she wasn't big enough to fight against three of them. It wasn't fair for her either. ' Why did they want to hurt you, Linda?'

'I don't know. How should I know?' It was difficult to hear what she said, because she was lying on her stomach and her face was in the pillow. 'They say those men are *their* men,' she went on; and she did not seem to be talking to him at all; she seemed to be talking with some one inside herself. A long talk which he didn't understand; and in the end she started crying louder than ever.

'Oh, don't cry, Linda. Don't cry.'

He pressed himself against her. He put his arm round her neck. Linda cried out. 'Oh, be careful. My shoulder! Oh!' and she pushed him away, hard. His head banged against the wall. 'Little idiot!' she shouted; and then, suddenly, she began to slap him. Slap, slap . . .

'Linda,' he cried out. 'Oh, mother, don't!'

'I'm not your mother. I won't be your mother.'

'But, Linda . . . Oh!' She slapped him on the cheek.

'Turned into a savage,' she shouted. 'Having young ones like an animal . . . If it hadn't been for you, I might have gone to the Inspector, I might have got away. But not with a baby. That would have been too shameful.'

He saw that she was going to hit him again, and lifted his arm to guard his face. 'Oh don't, Linda, please don't.'

'Little beast!' She pulled down his arm; his face was uncovered.

'Don't, Linda.' He shut his eyes, expecting the blow.

But she didn't hit him. After a little time, he opened his eyes again and saw that she was looking at him. He tried to smile at her. Suddenly she put her arms round him and kissed him again and again.

Sometimes, for several days, Linda didn't get up at all. She lay in bed and was sad. Or else she drank the stuff that Popé brought and laughed a great deal and went to sleep. Sometimes she was sick. Often she forgot to wash him, and there was nothing to eat except cold tortillas. He remembered the first time she found those little animals in his hair, how she screamed and screamed.

The happiest times were when she told him about the Other Place. 'And you really can go flying, whenever you like?'

'Whenever you like.' And she would tell him about the lovely music that came out of a box, and all the nice games you could play, and the delicious things to eat and drink, and the light that came when you pressed a little thing in the wall, and the pictures that you could hear and feel and smell, as well as see, and another box for making nice smells, and the pink and green and blue and silver houses as high as mountains, and everybody happy and no one ever sad or angry, and every one belonging to every one else, and the boxes where you could see and hear what was happening at the other side of the world, and babies in lovely clean bottles – everything so clean, and no nasty smells, no dirt at all – and people never lonely, but living together and being so jolly and happy, like the summer dances here in Malpais, but much happier, and the happiness being

there every day, every day.... He listened by the hour. And
sometimes, when he and the other children were tired with too
much playing, one of the old men of the pueblo would talk to
them, in those other words, of the great Transformer of the
World, and of the long fight between Right Hand and Left
Hand, between Wet and Dry; of Awonawilona, who made a
great fog by thinking in the night, and then made the whole
world out of the fog; of Earth Mother and Sky Father; of
Ahaiyuta and Marsailema, the twins of War and Cha:. e; of
Jesus and Pookong; of Mary and Etsanatlehi, the woman who
makes herself young again; of the Black Stone at Laguna and the
great Eagle and Our Lady of Acoma.[1] Strange stories, all the
more wonderful to him for being told in the other words and so
not fully understood. Lying in bed, he would think of Heaven
and London and Our Lady of Acoma and the rows and rows of
babies in clean bottles and Jesus flying up and Linda flying up
and the great Director of World Hatcheries and Awonawilona.

Lots of men came to see Linda. The boys began to point their
fingers at him. In the strange other words they said that Linda
was bad; they called her names he did not understand, but that
he knew were bad names. One day they sang a song about her,
again and again. He threw stones at them. They threw back; a
sharp stone cut his cheek. The blood wouldn't stop; he was
covered with blood.

1. *Acoma* : see below, p. 173, note 1. Huxley took the Zuñi names
   (Awonawilona, Ahaiyuta, Marsailema, Etsanatlehi, Pooking
   [Püükon, a god of war], as well as the summaries of the myths
   associated with them, from Frank Cushing's *Zuñi Folk Tales*
   (1901) and the annual reports of the Bureau of Ethnology. The
   mixture of Pueblo Indian beliefs (the fertility cult, with its snake
   dance) and those of the Penitentes (Our Lady, Jesus, Mary) is
   Huxley's invention: in reality "there is no mingling of the two,
   certainly nothing like the fusion that exists in *Brave New World*"
   (Firchow, 1984: Ch. 3).

Linda taught him to read. With a piece of charcoal she drew pictures on the wall – an animal sitting down, a baby inside a bottle; then she wrote letters. THE CAT IS ON THE MAT. THE TOT IS IN THE POT. He learned quickly and easily. When he knew how to read all the words she wrote on the wall, Linda opened her big wooden box and pulled out from under those funny little red trousers she never wore a thin little book. He had often seen it before. 'When you're bigger,' she had said, 'you can read it.' Well, now he was big enough. He was proud. 'I'm afraid you won't find it very exciting,' she said. 'But it's the only thing I have.' She sighed. 'If only you could see the lovely reading machines we used to have in London!' He began reading. *The Chemical and Bacteriological Conditioning of the Embryo. Practical Instructions for Beta Embryo-Store Workers.* It took him a quarter of an hour to read the title alone. He threw the book on the floor. 'Beastly, beastly book!' he said, and began to cry.

The boys still sang their horrible song about Linda. Sometimes, too, they laughed at him for being so ragged. When he tore his clothes, Linda did not know how to mend them. In the Other Place, she told him, people threw away clothes with holes in them and got new ones. 'Rags, rags!' the boys used to shout at him. 'But I can read,' he said to himself, 'and they can't. They don't even know what reading is.' It was fairly easy, if he thought hard enough about the reading, to pretend that he didn't mind when they made fun of him. He asked Linda to give him the book again.

The more the boys pointed and sang, the harder he read. Soon he could read all the words quite well. Even the longest. But what did they mean? He asked Linda; but even when she could answer it didn't seem to make it very clear. And generally she couldn't answer at all.

'What are chemicals?' he would ask.

'Oh, stuff like magnesium salts, and alcohol for keeping the Deltas and Epsilons small and backward, and calcium carbonate for bones, and all that sort of thing.'

'But how do you make chemicals, Linda? Where do they come from?'

'Well, I don't know. You get them out of bottles. And when the bottles are empty, you send up to the Chemical Store for more. It's the Chemical Store people who make them, I suppose. Or else they send to the factory for them. I don't know. I never did any chemistry. My job was always with the embryos.'

It was the same with everything else he asked about. Linda never seemed to know. The old men of the pueblo had much more definite answers.

'The seed of men and all creatures, the seed of the sun and the seed of earth and the seed of the sky – Awonawilona made them all out of the Fog of Increase. Now the world has four wombs; and he laid the seeds in the lowest of the four wombs. And gradually the seeds began to grow . . .'

One day (John calculated later that it must have been soon after his twelfth birthday) he came home and found a book that he had never seen before lying on the floor in the bedroom. It was a thick book and looked very old. The binding had been eaten by mice; some of its pages were loose and crumpled. He picked it up, looked at the title-page: the book was called *The Complete Works of William Shakespeare*.

Linda was lying on the bed, sipping that horrible stinking *mescal* out of a cup. 'Popé brought it,' she said. Her voice was thick and hoarse like somebody else's voice. 'It was lying in one of the chests of the Antelope Kiva.[1] It's supposed to have been there for hundreds of years. I expect it's true, because I looked at it, and it seemed to be full of nonsense. Uncivilized. Still, it'll be

---

1. *Antelope Kiva* : an underground room used for ceremonies, named after the antelope [ˌɑ́nt lɔ p]. Acoma, the place mentioned earlier in John's narrative, possesses seven ceremonial chambers. This pueblo, south-west of Albuquerque in New Mexico, was made a reservation in 1928, and is an independent social, political and ceremonial unit made up of fourteen exogamous clans, each one with its own totem. The Antelope clan traditionally supplies the head of the *cacique*, its ruling body.

good enough for you to practise your reading on.' She took a last sip, set the cup down on the floor beside the bed, turned over on her side, hiccoughed once or twice and went to sleep. He opened the book at random.

> Nay, but to live
> In the rank sweat of an enseamed bed,
> Stew'd in corruption, honeying and making love
> Over the nasty sty . . .[1]

The strange words rolled through his mind; rumbled, like talking thunder; like the drums at the summer dances, if the drums could have spoken; like the men singing the Corn Song, beautiful, beautiful, so that you cried; like old Mitsima saying magic over his feathers and his carved sticks and his bits of bone and stone – *kiathla tsilu silokwe silokwe silokwe. Kiai silu silu, tsithl* – but better than Mitsima's magic, because it meant more, because it talked to *him*; talked wonderfully and only half-understandably, a terrible beautiful magic, about Linda; about Linda lying there snoring, with the empty cup on the floor beside the bed; about Linda and Popé, Linda and Popé.

He hated Popé more and more. A man can smile and smile and be a villain. Remorseless, treacherous, lecherous, kindless villain.[2] What did the words exactly mean? He only half knew. But their magic was strong and went on rumbling in his head, and somehow it was as though he had never really hated Popé before; never really hated him because he had never been able to say how much he hated him. But now he had these words, these

---

1. *Nay ... nasty sty* : Shakespeare, *Hamlet*, III, 4, 91-4. Hamlet is attacking his mother for what he sees as immoral behaviour in marrying Claudius, the brother of his recently dead father: John immediately relates this attack to his own situation.
2. *A man ... kindless villain* : *Hamlet*, I, 5, 108 and II, 2, 609. A villain is an evil-doer; "lecherous" means obsessed with sex; "kindless", meaning unnatural, is archaic. John sees a similarity between Popé and King Claudius.

words like drums and singing and magic. These words and the strange, strange story out of which they were taken (he couldn't make head or tail of it,[1] but it was wonderful, wonderful all the same) – they gave him a reason for hating Popé; and they made his hatred more real; they even made Popé himself more real.

One day, when he came in from playing, the door of the inner room was open, and he saw them lying together on the bed, asleep – white Linda and Popé almost black beside her, with one arm under her shoulders and the other dark hand on her breast, and one of the plaits of his long hair lying across her throat, like a black snake trying to strangle her. Popé's gourd and a cup were standing on the floor near the bed. Linda was snoring.

His heart seemed to have disappeared and left a hole. He was empty. Empty, and cold, and rather sick, and giddy. He leaned against the wall to steady himself. Remorseless, treacherous, lecherous . . . Like drums, like the men singing for the corn, like magic, the words repeated and repeated themselves in his head. From being cold he was suddenly hot. His cheeks burnt with the rush of blood, the room swam and darkened before his eyes. He ground his teeth. 'I'll kill him, I'll kill him, I'll kill him,' he kept saying. And suddenly there were more words.

When he is drunk asleep, or in his rage
Or in the incestuous pleasure of his bed . . .[2]

The magic was on his side, the magic explained and gave orders. He stepped back into the outer room. 'When he is drunk asleep . . .' The knife for the meat was lying on the floor near the fire-place. He picked it up and tiptoed to the door again. 'When he is drunk asleep, drunk asleep . . .' He ran across the room and stabbed – oh, the blood! – stabbed again, as Popé heaved out of

1. *he couldn't make head or tail of it* : he could not make any sense of it (an idiomatic expression referring to the two sides of a coin).
2. *When he is drunk ... his bed* : Hamlet, III, 3, 89. Hamlet is planning when and how to kill Claudius.

his sleep, lifted his hand to stab once more, but found his wrist caught, held and – oh, oh! – twisted. He couldn't move, he was trapped, and there were Popé's small black eyes, very close, staring into his own. He looked away. There were two cuts on Popé's left shoulder. 'Oh, look at the blood!' Linda was crying. 'Look at the blood!' She had never been able to bear the sight of blood. Popé lifted his other hand – to strike him, he thought. He stiffened to receive the blow. But the hand only took him under the chin and turned his face, so that he had to look again into Popé's eyes. For a long time, for hours and hours. And suddenly – he couldn't help it – he began to cry. Popé burst out laughing. 'Go,' he said, in the other Indian words. 'Go, my brave Ahaiyuta.' He ran out into the other room to hide his tears.

'You are fifteen,' said old Mitsima, in the Indian words. 'Now I may teach you to work the clay.'[1]

Squatting by the river, they worked together.

'First of all,' said Mitsima, taking a lump of the wetted clay between his hands, 'we make a little moon.' The old man squeezed the lump into a disk, then bent up the edges; the moon became a shallow cup.

Slowly and unskilfully he imitated the old man's delicate gestures.

'A moon, a cup, and now a snake.' Mitsima rolled out another piece of clay into a long flexible cylinder, hooped it into a circle and pressed it on to the rim of the cup. 'Then another snake. And another. And another.' Round by round, Mitsima built up the sides of the pot; it was narrow, it bulged, it narrowed again towards the neck. Mitsima squeezed and patted, stroked and scraped; and there at last it stood, in shape the familiar water-pot of Malpais, but creamy white instead of black, and still soft to the touch. The crooked [2] parody of Mitsima's, his own stood beside it. Looking at the two pots, he had to laugh.

1. *clay* : material from which pots and cups are made.
2. *crooked* ['krʊkɪd]: twisted and bent.

'But the next one will be better,' he said, and began to moisten another piece of clay.

To fashion, to give form, to feel his fingers gaining in skill and power – this gave him an extraordinary pleasure. 'A, B, C, Vitamin D,' he sang to himself as he worked, 'The fat's in the liver, the cod's in the sea.'[1] And Mitsima also sang – a song about killing a bear. They worked all day, and all day he was filled with an intense, absorbing happiness.

'Next winter,' said old Mitsima, 'I will teach you to make the bow.'

He stood for a long time outside the house; and at last the ceremonies within were finished. The door opened; they came out. Kothlu came first, his right hand outstretched and tightly closed, as though over some precious jewel. Her clenched hand similarly outstretched, Kiakimé followed. They walked in silence, and in silence, behind them, came the brothers and sisters and cousins and all the troop of old people.

They walked out of the pueblo, across the mesa. At the edge of the cliff they halted, facing the early morning sun. Kothlu opened his hand. A pinch of corn meal lay white on the palm; he breathed on it, murmured a few words, then threw it, a handful of white dust, towards the sun. Kiakimé did the same. Then Kiakimé's father stepped forward, and holding up a feathered prayer stick, made a long prayer, then threw the stick after the corn meal.

'It is finished,' said old Mitsima in a loud voice. 'They are married.'

'Well,' said Linda, as they turned away, 'all I can say is, it does seem a lot of fuss to make about so little. In civilized countries, when a boy wants to have a girl, he just . . . But where *are* you going, John?'

1. '*A, B, C, ... in the sea*' : oil extracted from the liver of fish, especially from cod (a large species of sea fish) is frequently given to children as a rich source of vitamins A and D. Linda has taught him a children's rhyme that supports the World State's social health programme.

He paid no attention to her calling, but ran on, away, away, anywhere to be by himself.

It is finished. Old Mitsima's words repeated themselves in his mind. Finished, finished . . . In silence and from a long way off, but violently, desperately, hopelessly, he had loved Kiakimé. And now it was finished. He was sixteen.

At the full moon, in the Antelope Kiva, secrets would be told, secrets would be done and borne.[1] They would go down, boys, into the kiva and come out again, men. The boys were all afraid and at the same time impatient. And at last it was the day. The sun went down, the moon rose. He went with the others. Men were standing, dark, at the entrance to the kiva; the ladder went down into the red lighted depths. Already the leading boys had begun to climb down. Suddenly one of the men stepped forward, caught him by the arm, and pulled him out of the ranks. He broke free and dodged back into his place among the others. This time the man struck him, pulled his hair. 'Not for you, white-hair!' 'Not for the son of the she-dog,' said one of the other men. The boys laughed. 'Go!' And as he still hovered on the fringes of the group, 'Go!' the men shouted again. One of them bent down, took a stone, threw it. 'Go, go, go!' There was a shower of stones. Bleeding, he ran away into the darkness. From the red-lit kiva came the noise of singing. The last of the boys had climbed down the ladder. He was all alone.

All alone, outside the pueblo, on the bare plain of the mesa. The rock was like bleached bones in the moonlight. Down in the valley, the coyotes were howling at the moon. The bruises hurt him, the cuts were still bleeding; but it was not for pain that he sobbed; it was because he was all alone, because he had been driven out, alone, into this skeleton world of rocks and moonlight. At the edge of the precipice he sat down. The moon was behind him; he looked down into the black shadow of the mesa, into the black shadow of death. He had only to take one

---

1. *borne* : endured. (Secret rituals would be done and the initiates would *hear* the pain).

step, one little jump.... He held out his right hand in the moon-light. From the cut on his wrist the blood was still oozing. Every few seconds a drop fell, dark, almost colourless in the dead light. Drop, drop, drop. To-morrow and to-morrow and to-morrow . . .[1] He had discovered Time and Death and God.

'Alone, always alone,' the young man was saying.

The words awoke a plaintive echo in Bernard's mind. Alone, alone . . .'So am I,' he said, on a gush of confidingness.[2] 'Terribly alone.'

'Are you?' John looked surprised. 'I thought that in the Other Place . . . I mean, Linda always said that nobody was ever alone there.'

Bernard blushed uncomfortably. 'You see,' he said, mumbling and with averted eyes, 'I'm rather different from most people, I suppose. If one happens to be decanted different . . .'

'Yes, that's just it.' The young man nodded. 'If one's different, one's bound to be lonely. They're beastly to one. Do you know, they shut me out of absolutely everything? When the other boys were sent out to spend the night on the mountains – you know, when you have to dream which your sacred animal is – they wouldn't let me go with the others; they wouldn't tell me any of the secrets. I did it by myself, though,' he added. 'Didn't eat anything for five days and then went out one night alone into those mountains there.' He pointed.

Patronizingly, Bernard smiled. 'And did you dream of anything?' he asked.

The other nodded. 'But I mustn't tell you what.' He was silent for a little; then, in a low voice, 'Once,' he went on, 'I did something that none of the others did: I stood against a rock in the middle of the day, in summer, with my arms out, like Jesus on the cross.'

'What on earth for?'

1. *Tomorrow and tomorrow and tomorrow* : Shakespeare, *Macbeth*, V, 5, 19.
2. *on a gush of confidingness* [kən'faɪdɪŋnɪs]: suddenly feeling full of trust and wanting to reveal personal secrets.

'I wanted to know what it was like being crucified. Hanging there in the sun . . .'

'But why?'

'Why? Well . . .' He hesitated. 'Because I felt I ought to. If Jesus could stand it. And then, if one has done something wrong . . . Besides, I was unhappy; that was another reason.'

'It seems a funny way of curing your unhappiness,' said Bernard. But on second thoughts he decided that there was, after all, some sense in it. Better than taking *soma* . . .

'I fainted after a time,' said the young man. 'Fell down on my face. Do you see the mark where I cut myself?' He lifted the thick yellow hair from his forehead. The scar showed, pale and puckered,[1] on his right temple.

Bernard looked, and then quickly, with a little shudder, averted his eyes. His conditioning had made him not so much pitiful as profoundly squeamish.[2] The mere suggestion of illness or wounds was to him not only horrifying, but even repulsive and rather disgusting. Like dirt, or deformity, or old age. Hastily he changed the subject.

'I wonder if you'd like to come back to London with us?' he asked, making the first move in a campaign whose strategy he had been secretly elaborating ever since, in the little house, he had realized who the 'father' of this young savage must be. 'Would you like that?'

The young man's face lit up. 'Do you really mean it?'

'Of course; if I can get permission, that is.'

'Linda too?'

'Well . . .' He hesitated doubtfully. That revolting creature! No, it was impossible. Unless, unless . . . It suddenly occurred to Bernard that her very revoltingness might prove an enormous asset. 'But of course!' he cried, making up for his first hesitations with an excess of noisy cordiality.

The young man drew a deep breath. 'To think it should be coming true – what I've dreamt of all my life. Do you remember what Miranda says?'

1. *puckered* : with the skin unevenly stretched and wrinkled.
2. *squeamish* : easily disgusted.

'Who's Miranda?'

But the young man had evidently not heard the question. 'O wonder!'[1] he was saying; and his eyes shone, his face was brightly flushed. 'How many goodly creatures are there here! How beauteous mankind is!' The flush suddenly deepened; he was thinking of Lenina, of an angel in bottle-green viscose, lustrous with youth and skin food, plump, benevolently smiling. His voice faltered. 'O brave new world,' he began, then suddenly interrupted himself; the blood had left his cheeks; he was as pale as paper. 'Are you married to her?' he asked.

'Am I what?'

'Married. You know – for ever. They say "for ever" in the Indian words; it can't be broken.'

'Ford, no!' Bernard couldn't help laughing.

John also laughed, but for another reason – laughed for pure joy.

'O brave new world,' he repeated. 'O brave new world that has such people in it. Let's start at once.'

'You have a most peculiar way of talking sometimes,' said Bernard, staring at the young man in perplexed astonishment. 'And, anyhow, hadn't you better wait till you actually see the new world?'

---

1. *'O wonder!'* : John begins to cite a well-known speech by Miranda in Shakespeare's *The Tempest*: "O wonder! / How many goodly creatures are there here! / How beauteous mankind is! O brave new world, / That has such people in't." (V, 1, 181-184). Miranda has been raised by her father, the magician Prospero, on a small island with only a spirit (Ariel) and an ugly, brutish creature (Caliban) as company; she falls in love with the first young man she sees, Ferdinand, the Prince of Naples, and in the lines John cites she expresses her surprise and delight when she first encounters the other Italian noblemen who were shipwrecked on the island along with Ferdinand. It is one of the most moving moments in the play, but is profoundly ambivalent: Miranda's exclamations are full of emotional truth (in her eyes these are indeed wonderfully attractive creatures); but the audience knows at this point that the world which for her is "brave" is actually a world of treachery and war and is "new" only to her (as her father immediately points out, replying "Tis new to thee"), and that half of these superficially "beauteous" people she now sees are in fact selfish and evil. (Huxley makes use of this dramatic irony, as we shall see.)

Chapter IX

LENINA felt herself entitled, after this day of queerness and horror, to a complete and absolute holiday. As soon as they got back to the rest-house, she swallowed six half-gramme tablets of *soma*, lay down on her bed, and within ten minutes had embarked for lunar eternity. It would be eighteen hours at the least before she was in time again.

Bernard meanwhile lay pensive and wide-eyed in the dark. It was long after midnight before he fell asleep. Long after midnight; but his insomnia had not been fruitless; he had a plan.

Punctually, on the following morning, at ten o'clock, the green-uniformed octoroon stepped out of his helicopter. Bernard was waiting for him among the agaves.[1]

'Miss Crowne's gone on *soma*-holiday,' he explained. 'Can hardly be back before five. Which leaves us seven hours.'

He could fly to Santa Fé, do all the business he had to do, and be in Malpais again long before she woke up.

'She'll be quite safe here by herself?'

'Safe as helicopters,' the octoroon assured him.

---

1. *agaves* [ə'geɪvɪz]: tall fleshy-leaved plants.

They climbed into the machine and started off at once. At ten thirty-four they landed on the roof of the Santa Fé Post Office; at ten thirty-seven Bernard had got through to the World Controller's Office in Whitehall;[1] at ten thirty-nine he was speaking to his fordship's fourth personal secretary; at ten forty-four he was repeating his story to the first secretary, and at ten forty-seven and a half it was the deep, resonant voice of Mustapha Mond himself that sounded in his ears.

'I ventured to think,' stammered Bernard, 'that your fordship might find the matter of sufficient scientific interest . . .'

'Yes, I do find it of sufficient scientific interest,' said the deep voice. 'Bring these two individuals back to London with you.'

'Your fordship is aware that I shall need a special permit . . .'

'The necessary orders,' said Mustapha Mond, 'are being sent to the Warden of the Reservation at this moment. You will proceed at once to the Warden's Office. Good-morning, Mr Marx.'

There was silence. Bernard hung up the receiver and hurried up to the roof.

'Warden's Office,' he said to the Gamma-green octoroon.

At ten fifty-four Bernard was shaking hands with the Warden.

'Delighted, Mr Marx, delighted.' His boom was deferential. 'We have just received special orders . . .'

'I know,' said Bernard, interrupting him. 'I was talking to his fordship on the phone a moment ago.' His bored tone implied that he was in the habit of talking to his fordship every day of the week. He dropped into a chair. 'If you'll kindly take all the necessary steps as soon as possible. As soon as possible,' he emphatically repeated. He was thoroughly enjoying himself.

At eleven three he had all the necessary papers in his pocket.

'So long,'[2] he said patronizingly to the Warden, who had accompanied him as far as the lift gates. 'So long.'

---

1. *Whitehall* : street in central London with many Government offices.
2. *'So long'* : an informal way of saying goodbye to someone.

He walked across to the hotel, had a bath, a vibro-vac massage, and an electrolytic shave, listened in to the morning's news, looked in for half an hour on the televisor, ate a leisured luncheon, and at half-past two flew back with the octoroon to Malpais.

The young man stood outside the rest-house. 'Bernard,' he called. 'Bernard!' There was no answer. Noiseless in his deerskin moccasins, he ran up the steps and tried the door. The door was locked.

They were gone! Gone! It was the most terrible thing that had ever happened to him. She had asked him to come and see them, and now they were gone. He sat down on the steps and cried.

Half an hour later it occurred to him to look through the window. The first thing he saw was a green suit-case, with the initials L. C. painted on the lid. Joy flared up like fire within him. He picked up a stone. The smashed glass tinkled on the floor. A moment later he was inside the room. He opened the green suit- case; and all at once he was breathing Lenina's perfume, filling his lungs with her essential being. His heart beat wildly; for a moment he was almost faint. Then, bending over the precious box, he touched, he lifted into the light, he examined. The zippers on Lenina's spare pair of viscose velveteen shorts were at first a puzzle, then, solved, a delight. Zip,[1] and then zip; zip, and then zip; he was enchanted. Her green slippers were the most beautiful things he had ever seen. He unfolded a pair of zippi-camiknicks,[2] blushed, put them hastily away again; but kissed a perfumed acetate handkerchief and wound a scarf round his neck. Opening a box, he spilt a cloud of scented powder. His hands were floury with the stuff.

---

1. *Zip* : John is pulling up and down the zip fasteners. "Zip" imitates the sound as John opens and closes zips (or "zippers" as Americans still call them).
2. *zippi-camiknicks* : camiknickers are a one-piece undergarment worn by women; these have a zip.

He wiped them on his chest, on his shoulders, on his bare arms. Delicious perfume! He shut his eyes; he rubbed his cheek against his own powdered arm. Touch of smooth skin against his face, scent in his nostrils of musky dust – her real presence. 'Lenina,' he whispered. 'Lenina!'

A noise made him start, made him guiltily turn. He crammed up his thieveries[1] into the suit-case and shut the lid; then listened again, looked. Not a sign of life, not a sound. And yet he had certainly heard something – something like a sigh, something like the creak of a board. He tiptoed to the door and, cautiously opening it, found himself looking on to a broad landing. On the opposite side of the landing was another door, ajar.[2] He stepped out, pushed, peeped.

There, on a low bed, the sheet flung back, dressed in a pair of pink one-piece zippyjamas, lay Lenina, fast asleep and so beautiful in the midst of her curls, so touchingly childish with her pink toes and her grave sleeping face, so trustful in the helplessness of her limp hands and melted limbs, that the tears came to his eyes.

With an infinity of quite unnecessary precautions – for nothing short of a pistol shot could have called Lenina back from her *soma*-holiday before the appointed time – he entered the room, he knelt on the floor beside the bed. He gazed, he clasped his hands, his lips moved. 'Her eyes,' he murmured.

> 'Her eyes, her hair, her cheek, her gait, her voice;
> Handlest in thy discourse, O! that her hand,
> In whose comparison all whites are ink
> Writing their own reproach; to whose soft seizure
> The cygnet's down is harsh . . .'[3]

---

1. *He crammed up his thieveries* : c.f. Shakespeare, *Troilus and Cressida*, IV, 4, 42 ("Injurious Time now with a robber's haste / Crams his rich thievery up, he knows not how.").
2. *ajar* : not completely closed.
3. *Her eyes ... harsh* : *Troilus and Cressida*, I, 1, 54-8.

A fly buzzed round her; he waved it away. 'Flies,' he remembered,

> 'On the white wonder of dear Juliet's hand, may seize
> And steal immortal blessing from her lips,
> Who, even in pure and vestal modesty,
> Still blush, as thinking their own kisses sin.'[1]

Very slowly, with the hesitating gesture of one who reaches forward to stroke a shy and possibly rather dangerous bird, he put out his hand. It hung there trembling, within an inch of those limp fingers, on the verge of contact. Did he dare? Dare to profane with his unworthiest hand that . . .[2] No, he didn't. The bird was too dangerous. His hand dropped back. How beautiful she was ! How beautiful!

Then suddenly he found himself reflecting that he had only to take hold of the zipper at her neck and give one long, strong pull. . . . He shut his eyes, he shook his head with the gesture of a dog shaking its ears as it emerges from the water. Detestable thought! He was ashamed of himself. Pure and vestal modesty . . .

There was a humming in the air. Another fly trying to steal immortal blessings? A wasp? He looked, saw nothing. The humming grew louder and louder, localized itself as being outside the shuttered windows. The plane! In a panic, he scrambled to his feet and ran into the other room, vaulted through the open window, and hurrying along the path between the tall agaves was in time to receive Bernard Marx as he climbed out of the helicopter.

---

1. *On the white ... kisses sin* : Shakespeare, *Romeo and Juliet*, III, 3, 36-9, slightly modified. "Who" refers to Juliet's lips, which "blush", i.e. remain red, as if it were a sin for her two lips to touch each other. Romeo is near Juliet here, but unable to approach her, just like John and Lenina.

2. *profane ... that* : see *Romeo and Juliet*, I, 5, 95 (Romeo, taking Juliet's hand: "If I profane with my unworthiest hand / This holy shrine...").

Chapter X

THE hands of all the four thousand electric clocks in all the Bloomsbury [1] Centre's four thousand rooms marked twenty-seven minutes past two. 'This hive of industry,' as the Director was fond of calling it, was in the full buzz of work. Every one was busy, everything in ordered motion. Under the microscopes, their long tails furiously lashing, spermatozoa were burrowing head first into eggs; and, fertilized, the eggs were expanding, dividing, or if bokanovskified, budding and breaking up into whole populations of separate embryos. From the Social Predestination Room the escalators went rumbling down into the basement, and there, in the crimson darkness, stewingly warm on their cushion of peritoneum and gorged with blood-surrogate and hormones, the fœtuses grew and grew or, poisoned, languished into a stunted Epsilonhood. With a faint hum and rattle the moving racks crawled imperceptibly through the weeks and the recapitulated æons [2] to

1. *Bloomsbury* ['bluːmz͵bəri]: district in central London. (This is the Central London Hatchery and Conditioning Centre again.)
2. *recapitulated æons* ['iːɜnz]: æons (or eons) are enormously long periods of cosmic time. This sentence alludes to the notion that ontogeny recapitulates phylogeny: i.e. the stages of development of the individual embryo (ontogenesis) correspond to, and repeat in miniature, the evolution of the species as a whole (phylogenesis).

where, in the Decanting Room, the newly-unbottled babes uttered their first yell of horror and amazement.

The dynamos purred in the sub-basement, the lifts rushed up and down. On all the eleven floors of Nurseries it was feeding time. From eighteen hundred bottles eighteen hundred carefully labelled infants were simultaneously sucking down their pint of pasteurized external secretion.

Above them, in ten successive layers of dormitory, the little boys and girls who were still young enough to need an afternoon sleep were as busy as every one else, though they did not know it, listening unconsciously to hypnopædic lessons in hygiene and sociability, in class-consciousness and the toddler's [1] love-life. Above these again were the playrooms where, the weather having turned to rain, nine hundred older children were amusing themselves with bricks and clay modelling, hunt-the-slipper, and erotic play.

Buzz, buzz! the hive was humming, busily, joyfully. Blithe was the singing of the young girls over their test-tubes, the Predestinators whistled as they worked, and in the Decanting Room what glorious jokes were cracked [2] above the empty bottles! But the Director's face, as he entered the Fertilizing Room with Henry Foster, was grave, wooden with severity.

'A public example,' he was saying. 'In this room, because it contains more high-caste workers than any other in the Centre. I have told him to meet me here at half-past two.'

'He does his work very well,' put in Henry, with hypocritical generosity.

'I know. But that's all the more reason for severity. His intellectual eminence carries with it corresponding moral responsibilities. The greater a man's talents, the greater his power to lead astray. It is better that one should suffer than that many should be corrupted. Consider the matter dispassionately, Mr Foster, and you will see that no offence is so heinous [3] as

---

1. *toddler's* : of a very small child, who still toddles (walks unsurely).
2. *jokes were cracked* : amusing stories were told. (We "crack jokes".)
3. *heinous* ['heɪnəs]: atrocious, detestable for its wickedness.

unorthodoxy of behaviour. Murder kills only the individual –
and, after all, what is an individual?' With a sweeping gesture
he indicated the rows of microscopes, the test- tubes, the
incubators. 'We can make a new one with the greatest ease – as
many as we like. Unorthodoxy threatens more than the life of a
mere individual; it strikes at Society itself. Yes, at Society itself,'
he repeated. 'Ah, but here he comes.'

Bernard had entered the room and was advancing between
the rows of fertilizers towards them. A veneer of jaunty [1] self-
confidence thinly concealed his nervousness. The voice in which
he said, 'Good-morning, Director,' was absurdly too loud; that
in which, correcting his mistake, he said, 'You asked me to come
and speak to you here,' ridiculously soft, a squeak.

'Yes, Mr Marx,' said the Director portentously. 'I did ask you
to come to me here. You returned from your holiday last night, I
understand.'

'Yes,' Bernard answered.

'Yes-s,' repeated the Director, lingering, a serpent, on the 's.'
Then, suddenly raising his voice, 'Ladies and gentlemen,' he
trumpeted, 'ladies and gentlemen.'

The singing of the girls over their test-tubes, the preoccupied
whistling of the Microscopists, suddenly ceased. There was a
profound silence; every one looked round.

'Ladies and gentlemen,' the Director repeated once more,
'excuse me for thus interrupting your labours. A painful duty
constrains me. The security and stability of Society are in
danger. Yes, in danger, ladies and gentlemen. This man,' he
pointed accusingly at Bernard, 'this man who stands before you
here, this Alpha-Plus to whom so much has been given, and
from whom, in consequence, so much must be expected, this
colleague of yours – or should I anticipate and say this ex-
colleague? – has grossly betrayed the trust imposed in him. By
his heretical views on sport and *soma*, by the scandalous
unorthodoxy of his sex-life, by his refusal to obey the teachings

1.   *jaunty* ['dʒɔːnti]: openly displayed, self-satisfied.

of Our Ford and behave out of office hours "like a babe in a bottle"[1] ' (here the Director made the sign of the T), 'he has proved himself an enemy of Society, a subverter, ladies and gentlemen, of all Order and Stability, a conspirator against Civilization itself. For this reason I propose to dismiss him, to dismiss him with ignominy from the post he has held in this Centre; I propose forthwith [2] to apply for his transference to a Sub-Centre of the lowest order and, that his punishment may serve the best interest of Society, as far as possible removed from any important Centre of population. In Iceland he will have small opportunity to lead others astray by his unfordly example.'[3] The Director paused; then, folding his arms, he turned impressively to Bernard. ' Marx,' he said, 'can you show any reason why I should not now execute the judgment passed upon you?'

'Yes, I can,' Bernard answered in a very loud voice.

Somewhat taken aback, but still majestically, 'Then show it,' said the Director.

'Certainly. But it's in the passage. One moment.' Bernard hurried to the door and threw it open. 'Come in', he commanded, and the reason came in and showed itself.

There was a gasp, a murmur of astonishment and horror; a young girl screamed; standing on a chair to get a better view some one upset two test-tubes full of spermatozoa. Bloated, sagging, and among those firm youthful bodies, those undistorted faces, a strange and terrifying monster of middle-agedness, Linda advanced into the room, coquettishly smiling her broken and discoloured smile, and rolling as she walked, with what was meant to be a voluptuous undulation, her enormous haunches.[4] Bernard walked beside her.

1. *"like a babe in a bottle"* : echoes the Biblical idea that those who listen to Christ's teaching are "babes in Christ" who "desire the sincere milk of the word" of God (I Corinthians 3, 1; I Peter, 2, 2).

2. *forthwith* : without delay, immediately.

3. *lead others ... example* : encourage other people to go the wrong way ("astray") and to adopt uncommendable ("unfordly") ideas and behaviour.

4. *haunches* ['hɔːntʃɪz]: hips (where the leg joins the torso).

'There he is,' he said, pointing at the Director.

'Did you think I didn't recognize him?' Linda asked indignantly; then, turning to the Director, 'Of course I knew you; Tomakin, I should have known you anywhere, among a thousand. But perhaps you've forgotten me. Don't you remember ? Don't you remember, Tomakin ? Your Linda.' She stood looking at him, her head on one side, still smiling, but with a smile that became progressively, in face of the Director's expression of petrified disgust, less and less self-confident, that wavered and finally went out. 'Don't you remember, Tomakin?' she repeated in a voice that trembled. Her eyes were anxious, agonized. The blotched and sagging face twitched grotesquely into the grimace of extreme grief. 'Tomakin !' She held out her arms. Some one began to titter.[1]

'What's the meaning,' began the Director, 'of this monstrous . . .'

'Tomakin!' She ran forward, her blanket trailing behind her, threw her arms round his neck, hid her face on his chest.

A howl of laughter went up irrepressibly.

'. . . this monstrous practical joke,' the Director shouted.

Red in the face, he tried to disengage himself from her embrace. Desperately she clung. 'But I'm Linda, I'm Linda.' The laughter drowned her voice. ' You made me have a baby,' she screamed above the uproar. There was a sudden and appalling hush; eyes floated uncomfortably, not knowing where to look. The Director went suddenly pale, stopped struggling and stood, his hands on her wrists, staring down at her, horrified. 'Yes, a baby – and I was its mother.' She flung the obscenity like a challenge into the outraged silence; then, suddenly breaking away from him, ashamed, ashamed, covered her face with her hands, sobbing. 'It wasn't my fault, Tomakin. Because I always did my drill, didn't I? Didn't I? Always . . . I don't know how . . . If you knew how awful, Tomakin . . . But he was a comfort to me, all the same.' Turning towards the door, 'John!' she called. 'John!'

1. *titter* : giggle, with silly, partially suppressed, little laughs.

He came in at once, paused for a moment just inside the door, looked round, then soft on his moccasined feet strode quickly across the room, fell on his knees in front of the Director, and said in a clear voice: ' My father!'

The word (for 'father' was not so much obscene as – with its connotation of something at one remove from the loathsomeness [1] and moral obliquity of child-bearing – merely gross, a scatological [2] rather than a pornographic impropriety), the comically smutty word relieved what had become a quite intolerable tension. Laughter broke out, enormous, almost hysterical, peal after peal,[3] as though it would never stop. My father – and it was the Director! My *father*! Oh Ford, oh Ford! That was really too good. The whooping and the roaring renewed themselves, faces seemed on the point of disintegration, tears were streaming. Six more test-tubes of spermatozoa were upset. *My father*!

Pale, wild-eyed, the Director glared about him in an agony of bewildered humiliation.

My *father*! The laughter, which had shown signs of dying away, broke out again more loudly than ever. He put his hands over his ears and rushed out of the room.

---

1. *loathsomeness* ['ləʊðsəmnəs]: quality of causing abhorrence and emotional revulsion.
2. *scatological* : dirty (i.e. obscene because disgusting, not because involved with salacious sex, as pornography is).
3. *peal after peal* : one wave, or burst, of laughter followed another.

Chapter XI

AFTER the scene in the Fertilizing Room, all upper-caste London was wild to see this delicious creature who had fallen on his knees before the Director óf Hatcheries and Conditioning – or rather the ex-Director, for the poor man had resigned immediately afterwards and never set foot inside the Centre again – had flopped down and called him (the joke was almost too good to be true!) 'my father.' Linda, on the contrary, cut no ice;[1] nobody had the smallest desire to see Linda. To say one was a mother – that was past a joke: it was an obscenity. Moreover, she wasn't a real savage, had been hatched out of a bottle and conditioned like any one else; so couldn't have really quaint ideas.[2] Finally – and this was by far the strongest reason for people's not wanting to see poor Linda – there was her appearance. Fat; having lost her youth; with bad teeth, and a blotched complexion, and that figure (Ford!) – you simply couldn't look at her without feeling sick, yes, positively sick. So the best people were quite determined *not* to see Linda. And Linda, for her part, had no desire to see them. The return to

---

1. *cut no ice* [with anyone]: did not impress people, had no effect.
2. *quaint ideas* : odd, old-fashioned but pleasing, ideas.

civilization was for her the return to *soma*, was the possibility of lying in bed and taking holiday after holiday, without ever having to come back to a headache or a fit of vomiting, without ever being made to feel as you always felt after *peyotl*, as though you'd done something so shamefully anti-social that you could never hold up your head again. *Soma* played none of these unpleasant tricks. The holiday it gave was perfect and, if the morning after was disagreeable, it was so, not intrinsically, but only by comparison with the joys of the holiday. The remedy was to make the holiday continuous. Greedily she clamoured for ever larger, ever more frequent doses. Dr.Shaw [1] at first demurred;[2] then let her have what she wanted. She took as much as twenty grammes a day.

'Which will finish her off in a month or two,' the doctor confided to Bernard. ' One day the respiratory centre will be paralysed. No more breathing. Finished. And a good thing too. If we could rejuvenate, of course it would be different. But we can't.'

Surprisingly, as every one thought (for on *soma*-holiday Linda was most conveniently out of the way), John raised objections.

'But aren't you shortening her life by giving her so much?'

'In one sense, yes,' Dr. Shaw admitted. 'But in another we're actually lengthening it.' The young man stared, uncomprehending. '*Soma* may make you lose a few years in time,' the doctor went on. 'But think of the enormous, immeasurable durations it can give you out of time. Every *soma*-holiday is a bit of what our ancestors used to call eternity'.

John began to understand. 'Eternity was in our lips and eyes,'[3] he murmured.

'Eh?'

'Nothing.'

---

1. *Dr. Shaw* : see note 1, p. 42.
2. *demurred* [dɪ'mɜːd]: was unwilling, refused to comply.
3. *'Eternity was in our lips and eyes'* : Shakespeare, *Antony and Cleopatra*, I, 3, 35.

'Of course,' Dr. Shaw went on, 'you can't allow people to go popping off [1] into eternity if they've got any serious work to do. But as she hasn't got any serious work . . .'

'All the same,' John persisted, 'I don't believe it's right.'

The doctor shrugged his shoulders. 'Well, of course, if you prefer to have her screaming mad all the time . . .'

In the end John was forced to give in. Linda got her *soma*. Thenceforward she remained in her little room on the thirty-seventh floor of Bernard's apartment house, in bed, with the radio and television always on, and the patchouli [2] tap just dripping, and the *soma* tablets within reach of her hand – there she remained; and yet wasn't there at all, was all the time away, infinitely far away, on holiday; on holiday in some other world, where the music of the radio was a labyrinth of sonorous colours, a sliding, palpitating labyrinth, that led (by what beautifully inevitable windings) to a bright centre of absolute conviction; where the dancing images of the television box were the performers in some indescribably delicious all-singing feely; where the dripping patchouli was more than scent – was the sun, was a million sexophones, was Popé making love, only much more so, incomparably more, and without end.

'No, we can't rejuvenate. But I'm very glad,' Dr. Shaw had concluded, 'to have had this opportunity to see an example of senility in a human being. Thank you so much for calling me in.' He shook Bernard warmly by the hand.

It was John, then, they were all after.[3] And as it was only through Bernard, his accredited guardian, that John could be seen, Bernard now found himself, for the first time in his life, treated not merely normally, but as a person of outstanding importance. There was no more talk of the alcohol in his blood-surrogate, no gibes [4] at his personal appearance. Henry Foster

---

1. *popping off* : going away (usually suddenly, for reasons of the moment: here it sounds incongruous and funny).
2. *patchouli* [pæ'tʃuli]: perfume (from a South-East Asian plant).
3. *were all after* : they all wanted to reach.
4. *gibes* [dʒaɪbz]: provoking remarks, mocking comments.

went out of his way to be friendly; Benito Hoover made him a present of six packets of sex-hormone chewing-gum; the Assistant Predestinator came and cadged [1] almost abjectly for an invitation to one of Bernard's evening parties. As for the women, Bernard had only to hint at the possibility of an invitation, and he could have whichever of them he liked.

'Bernard's asked me to meet the Savage next Wednesday,' Fanny announced triumphantly.

'I'm so glad,' said Lenina. 'And now you must admit that you were wrong about Bernard. Don't you think he's really rather sweet ?'

Fanny nodded. 'And I must say,' she said, 'I was quite agreeably surprised.'

The Chief Bottler, the Director of Predestination, three Deputy Assistant Fertilizer-Generals, the Professor of Feelies in the College of Emotional Engineering, the Dean of the Westminster Community Singery, the Supervisor of Bokanovskification – the list of Bernard's notabilities was interminable.

'And I had six girls last week,' he confided to Helmholtz Watson. 'One on Monday, two on Tuesday, two more on Friday, and one on Saturday. And if I'd had the time or the inclination, there were at least a dozen more who were only too anxious . . .'

Helmholtz listened to his boastings in a silence so gloomily disapproving that Bernard was offended.

'You're envious,' he said.

Helmholtz shook his head. 'I'm rather sad, that's all,' he answered.

Bernard went off in a huff.[2] Never, he told himself, never would he speak to Helmholtz again.

The days passed. Success went fizzily to Bernard's head,[3] and in the process completely reconciled him (as any good

1. *cadged* : tried to get by entreating, begged.
2. *in a huff* : feeling irritated, with a burst of a bad temper.
3. *Success went fizzily to Bernard's head* : he became big-headed, with an exaggerated sense of his own importance, as if he had been made light-headed by a fizzy wine. (Huxley combines both the common uses of this idiom.)

intoxicant should do) to a world which, up till then, he had found very unsatisfactory. In so far as it recognized him as important, the order of things was good. But, reconciled by his success, he yet refused to forgo the privilege of criticizing this order. For the act of criticizing heightened his sense of importance, made him feel larger. Moreover, he did genuinely believe that there were things to criticize. (At the same time, he genuinely liked being a success and having all the girls he wanted.) Before those who now, for the sake of the Savage, paid their court to him, Bernard would parade a carping unorthodoxy.[1] He was politely listened to. But behind his back people shook their heads. ' That young man will come to a bad end,' they said, prophesying the more confidently in that they themselves would in due course personally see to it that the end was bad. ' He won't find another Savage to help him out a second time,' they said. Meanwhile, however, there was the first Savage; they were polite. And because they were polite, Bernard felt positively gigantic – gigantic and at the same time light with elation, lighter than air.

'Lighter than air,' said Bernard, pointing upwards.

Like a pearl in the sky, high, high above them, the Weather Department's captive balloon shone rosily in the sunshine.

'. . . the said [2] Savage,' so ran Bernard's instructions, 'to be shown civilized life in all its aspects . . .'

He was being shown a bird's-eye view of it at present, a bird's-eye view from the platform of the Charing-T Tower. The Station Master and the Resident Meteorologist were acting as guides. But it was Bernard who did most of the talking. Intoxicated, he was behaving as though, at the very least, he were a visiting World Controller. Lighter than air.

1. *parade a carping unorthodoxy* : make a show of his differences of opinion by complaining all the time about all sorts of things.
2. *the said* : the previously mentioned. (Formal, bureaucratic language.)

The Bombay Green Rocket dropped out of the sky. The passengers alighted. Eight identical Dravidian [1] twins in khaki looked out of the eight portholes of the cabin – the stewards.

'Twelve hundred and fifty kilometres an hour,' said the Station Master impressively. 'What do you think of that, Mr Savage?'

John thought it very nice. 'Still,' he said, 'Ariel could put a girdle round the earth in forty minutes.'[2]

'The Savage,' wrote Bernard in his report to Mustapha Mond, 'shows surprisingly little astonishment at, or awe of, civilized inventions. This is partly due, no doubt, to the fact that he has heard them talked about by the woman Linda, his m——.'

(Mustapha Mond frowned. 'Does the fool think I'm too squeamish to see the word written out at full length?')

'Partly on his interest being focused on what he calls "the soul," which he persists as regarding as an entity independent of the physical environment; whereas, as I tried to point out to him . . .'

The Controller skipped the next sentences and was just about to turn the page in search of something more interestingly concrete, when his eye was caught by a series of quite extraordinary phrases. ' . . . though I must admit,' he read, ' that I agree with the Savage in finding civilized infantility too easy or, as he puts it, not expensive enough; and I would like to take this opportunity of drawing your fordship's attention to . . .'

Mustapha Mond's anger gave place almost at once to mirth. The idea of this creature solemnly lecturing him – *him* – about the social order was really too grotesque. The man must have gone mad. 'I ought to give him a lesson,' he said to himself; then threw back his head and laughed aloud. For the moment, at any rate, the lesson would not be given.

---

1. *Dravidian* : belonging to the dark-skinned race found in southern India.
2. *'Ariel ... forty minutes.'* : John makes a slight mistake, it is not Ariel but another spirit, Puck, who promises to "put a girdle round about the earth / In forty minutes", in Shakespeare's *A Midsummer-Night's Dream*, II, 1, 175.

It was a small factory of lighting-sets for helicopters, a branch of the Electrical Equipment Corporation. They were met on the roof itself (for that circular letter of recommendation from the Controller was magical in its effects) by the Chief Technician and the Human Element Manager.[1] They walked downstairs into the factory.

'Each process,' explained the Human Element Manager, 'is carried out, so far as possible, by a single Bokanovsky Group.'

And, in effect, eighty-three almost noseless black brachycephalic Deltas were cold-pressing.[2] The fifty-six four-spindle chucking and turning machines were being manipulated by fifty-six aquiline and ginger Gammas. One hundred and seven heat-conditioned Epsilon Senegalese were working in the foundry. Thirty-three Delta females, long-headed, sandy, with narrow pelvises, and all within 20 millimetres of 1 metre 69 centimetres tall, were cutting screws. In the assembling room, the dynamos were being put together by two sets of Gamma-Plus dwarfs. The two low work-tables faced one another; between them crawled the conveyor with its load of separate parts; forty-seven blond heads were confronted by forty-seven brown ones. Forty-seven snubs by forty-seven hooks;[3] forty-seven receding by forty-seven prognathous [4] chins. The completed mechanisms were inspected by eighteen identical curly auburn girls in Gamma green, packed in crates by thirty-four short-legged, left-handed male Delta-Minuses, and loaded into the waiting trucks and lorries by sixty-three blue-eyed, flaxen [5] and freckled [6] Epsilon Semi-Morons.

1. *Human Element Manager* : personnel manager. (The "human element" today generally means the unpredictable and fallible aspect of human nature; to have a "manager" of this is strongly ironic.)
2. *cold-pressing* : carrying out an industrial process for shaping steel.
3. *Forty-seven ... hooks* : short (snub) noses faced by long curved (hooked) noses.
4. *prognathous* ['prɒgnəθəs] or [ˌprɒg'neɪθəs]: projecting (the opposite of a receding chin).
5. *flaxen* ['flæksn]: pale yellow, like flax (the fibres used in linen).
6. *freckled* : with light brown spots on the skin.

'O brave new world . . .' By some malice of his memory the Savage found himself repeating Miranda's words. 'O brave new world that has such people in it.'

'And I assure you,' the Human Element Manager concluded, as they left the factory, 'we hardly ever have any trouble with our workers. We always find . . .'

But the Savage had suddenly broken away from his companions and was violently retching,[1] behind a clump of laurels, as though the solid earth had been a helicopter in an air pocket.

'The Savage,' wrote Bernard, 'refuses to take *soma*, and seems much distressed because the woman Linda, his m——, remains permanently on holiday. It is worthy of note that, in spite of his m——'s senility and the extreme repulsiveness of her appearance, the Savage frequently goes to see her and appears to be much attached to her – an interesting example of the way in which early conditioning can be made to modify and even run counter to natural impulses (in this case, the impulse to recoil from an unpleasant object).'

At Eton [2] they alighted on the roof of Upper School. On the opposite side of School Yard, the fifty-two stories of Lupton's Tower [3] gleamed white in the sunshine. College on their left and, on their right, the School Community Singery reared their venerable piles of ferro-concrete and vita-glass.[4] In the centre of the quadrangle stood the quaint old chrome-steel statue of Our Ford.

1. *retching* : vomiting (as with sea- or airsickness).
2. *Eton* : Eton College; the most renowned English public school, founded in 1440 by Henry VI. Huxley was a pupil there from 1908 to 1911 and a teacher from 1917 to 1919. ("Public schools" are private.)
3. *Lupton's Tower* : named after one of the first Provosts (head of the school).
4. *vita-glass* : trademark (1925) of a special type of glass that lets through ultra-violet rays. Although the buildings described correspond to the actually existing ones (with the famous Chapel re-named a Singery), the materials mentioned are not those of the truly "venerable" buildings of today, made of red brick and stained glass.

Dr. Gaffney, the Provost, and Miss Keate,[1] the Head Mistress, received them as they stepped out of the plane.

'Do you have many twins here?' the Savage asked rather apprehensively, as they set out on their tour of inspection.

'Oh no,' the Provost answered. 'Eton is reserved exclusively for upper-caste boys and girls. One egg, one adult. It makes education more difficult, of course. But as they'll be called upon to take responsibilities and deal with unexpected emergencies, it can't be helped.' He sighed.

Bernard, meanwhile, had taken a strong fancy to [2] Miss Keate. 'If you're free any Monday, Wednesday, or Friday evening,' he was saying. Jerking his thumb towards the Savage, 'He's curious, you know,' Bernard added. ' Quaint.'

Miss Keate smiled (and her smile was really charming, he thought); said Thank you; would be delighted to come to one of his parties. The Provost opened a door.

Five minutes in that Alpha-Double-Plus classroom left John a trifle bewildered.

'What is elementary relativity?' he whispered to Bernard. Bernard tried to explain, then thought better of it and suggested that they should go to some other classroom.

From behind a door in the corridor leading to the Beta-Minus geography room, a ringing soprano voice called, 'One, two, three, four,' and then, with a weary impatience, 'As you were.'

'Malthusian Drill,' explained the Head Mistress. 'Most of our girls are freemartins, of course. I'm a freemartin myself.' She smiled at Bernard. 'But we have about eight hundred unsterilized ones who need constant drilling.'

In the Beta-Minus geography room John learnt that 'a savage reservation is a place which, owing to unfavourable climatic or geological conditions, or poverty of natural resources, has not been worth the expense of civilizing.' A click; the room was darkened; and suddenly, on the screen above the Master's head,

1. *Dr Gaffney ... Keate* : names from recent Eton College history that Huxley remembered from his own contacts with the school.
2. *taken . . . fancy to* : begun to feel very attracted by.

there were the *Penitentes* of Acoma prostrating themselves before Our Lady,[1] and wailing as John had heard them wail, confessing their sins before Jesus on the cross, before the eagle image of Pookong. The young Etonians fairly shouted with laughter. Still wailing, the *Penitentes* rose to their feet, stripped off their upper garments and, with knotted whips, began to beat themselves, blow after blow. Redoubled, the laughter drowned even the amplified record of their groans.

'But why do they laugh?' asked the Savage in a pained bewilderment.

'Why?' The Provost turned towards him a still broadly grinning face. '*Why*?' But because it's so extraordinarily funny.'

In the cinematographic twilight, Bernard risked a gesture which, in the past, even total darkness would hardly have emboldened him to make. Strong in his new importance, he put his arm round the Head Mistress's waist. It yielded, willowily.[2] He was just about to snatch a kiss or two and perhaps a gentle pinch,[3] when the shutters clicked open again.

'Perhaps we had better go on,' said Miss Keate, and moved towards the door.

'And this,' said the Provost a moment later, 'is the Hypnopædic Control Room.'

Hundreds of synthetic music boxes, one for each dormitory, stood ranged in shelves round three sides of the room, pigeon-holed on the fourth were the paper sound-track rolls on which the various hypnopædic lessons were printed.

1. *Penitentes of Acoma ... Our Lady* : the Penitentes are a sect of religious zealots to be found among the Spanish communities in New Mexico; their practice of self-flagellation, particularly in Holy Week, may derive from the Flagellants of medieval Spain. Huxley seems to want his Savage to be influenced equally by the Indian religious traditions (at Acoma this means *kachina* - the masked god cult, and ceremonies for summer rain, the corn harvest and so on) and Roman Catholic beliefs (taken over from the Spanish).

2. *willowily* ['wɪləʊɪli]: with grace and flexibility.

3. *snatch . . . pinch* : quickly get himself the pleasure of kissing her and of squeezing her body between his fingers.

'You slip the roll in here,' explained Bernard, interrupting Dr. Gaffney, 'press down this switch . . .'

'No, that one,' corrected the Provost, annoyed.

'That one, then. The roll unwinds. The selenium [1] cells transform the light impulses into sound waves, and . . .'

'And there you are,' Dr. Gaffney concluded.

'Do they read Shakespeare? ' asked the Savage as they walked, on their way to the Biochemical Laboratories, past the School Library.

'Certainly not,' said the Head Mistress, blushing.

'Our library,' said Dr. Gaffney, ' contains only books of reference. If our young people need distraction, they can get it at the feelies. We don't encourage them to indulge in any solitary amusements.'

Five bus-loads of boys and girls, singing or in a silent embracement, rolled past them over the vitrified highway.

'Just returned,' explained Dr. Gaffney, while Bernard, whispering, made an appointment with the Head Mistress for that very evening, 'from the Slough Crematorium. Death conditioning begins at eighteen months. Every tot [2] spends two mornings a week in a Hospital for the Dying. All the best toys are kept there, and they get chocolate cream on death days. They learn to take dying as a matter of course.'

'Like any other physiological process,' put in the Head Mistress professionally.

Eight o'clock at the Savoy.[3] It was all arranged.

On their way back to London they stopped at the Television Corporation's factory at Brentford.

'Do you mind waiting here a moment while I go and telephone?' asked Bernard.

---

1. *selenium* [ˌsɪˈliːnɪəm]: non-metallic element, atomic no. 34.
2. *tot* : very small child.
3. *Eight o'clock at the Savoy* : Bernard will meet Miss Keate at this high-class London restaurant and hotel.

The Savage waited and watched. The Main Day-Shift was just going off duty. Crowds of lower-caste workers were queued up in front of the monorail station – seven or eight hundred Gamma, Delta and Epsilon men and women, with not more than a dozen faces and statures between them. To each of them, with his or her ticket, the booking clerk pushed over a little cardboard pill-box. The long caterpillar of men and women moved slowly forward.

'What's in those' (remembering *The Merchant of Venice*), 'those caskets?'[1] the Savage enquired when Bernard had rejoined him.

'The day's *soma* ration,' Bernard answered, rather indistinctly, for he was masticating a piece of Benito Hoover's chewing-gum. 'They get it after their work's over. Four half-gramme tablets. Six on Saturdays.'

He took John's arm affectionately and they walked back towards the helicopter.

Lenina came singing into the Changing Room.

'You seem very pleased with yourself,' said Fanny.

'I *am* pleased,' she answered. Zip! 'Bernard rang up half an hour ago.' Zip, zip! She stepped out of her shorts. 'He has an unexpected engagement.' Zip! 'Asked me if I'd take the Savage to the feelies this evening. I must fly.'[2] She hurried away towards the bathroom.

'She's a lucky girl,' Fanny said to herself as she watched Lenina go.

There was no envy in the comment; good-natured Fanny was merely stating a fact. Lenina *was* lucky; lucky in having shared with Bernard a generous portion of the Savage's immense celebrity, lucky in reflecting from her insignificant person the

1. *caskets* : small decorative box, usually made of wood or metal; the word is inappropriate for little cardboard boxes (which would not be seen on the Reservations). Three caskets play an important part in Shakespeare's play *The Merchant of Venice*.
2. *I must fly* : I must hurry (a present-day idiom).

moment's supremely fashionable glory. Had not the Secretary of the Young Women's Fordian Association [1] asked her to give a lecture about her experiences ? Had she not been invited to the Annual Dinner of the Aphroditæum Club? Had she not already appeared in the Feelytone News [2] – visibly, audibly and tactually appeared to countless millions all over the planet?

Hardly less flattering had been the attentions paid her by conspicuous individuals. The Resident World Controller's Second Secretary had asked her to dinner and breakfast. She had spent one week-end with the Ford Chief-Justice, and another with the Arch-Community-Songster of Canterbury. The President of the Internal and External Secretions Corporation was perpetually on the phone, and she had been to Deauville [3] with the Deputy-Governor of the Bank of Europe.

'It's wonderful, of course. And yet in a way,' she had confessed to Fanny, 'I feel as though I were getting something on false pretences. Because, of course, the first thing they all want to know is what it's like to make love to a Savage. And I have to say I don't know.' She shook her head. 'Most of the men don't believe me, of course. But it's true. I wish it weren't,' she added sadly, and sighed. 'He's terribly good-looking; don't you think so?'

'But doesn't he like you?' asked Fanny.

'Sometimes I think he does and sometimes I think he doesn't. He always does his best to avoid me; goes out of the room when I come in; won't touch me; won't even look at me. But sometimes if I turn round suddenly, I catch him staring; and then – well, you know how men look when they like you.'

Yes, Fanny knew.

'I can't make it out,' said Lenina.

---

1. *Young Women's Fordian Association* : (later, Y.W.F.A.) recalls today's Young Women's Christian Association.

2. *Feelytone News* : by analogy with Movietone news, cinema news programmes, introduced in Britain in 1929 and of considerable importance until television news took over.

3. *Deauville* : fashionable resort in France, on the Normandy coast.

She couldn't make it out; and not only was bewildered; was also rather upset.

'Because, you see, Fanny, *I* like him.'

Liked him more and more. Well, now there'd be a real chance, she thought, as she scented herself after her bath. Dab, dab, dab [1] – a real chance. Her high spirits overflowed in song.

'Hug me till you drug me, honey;
Kiss me till I'm in a coma:
Hug me, honey, snuggly bunny;
Love's as good as *soma*.'

The scent organ was playing a delightfully refreshing Herbal Capriccio – rippling arpeggios of thyme and lavender, of rosemary, basil, myrtle, tarragon;[2] a series of daring modulations through the spice keys into ambergris; and a slow return through sandalwood, camphor, cedar and new-mown hay (with occasional subtle touches of discord – a whiff of kidney pudding, the faintest suspicion of pig's dung) back to the simple aromatics with which the piece began. The final blast of thyme died away; there was a round of applause; the lights went up. In the synthetic music machine the sound-track roll began to unwind. It was a trio for hyper-violin, super-'cello and oboe-surrogate that now filled the air with its agreeable languor. Thirty or forty bars – and then, against this instrumental background, a much more than human voice began to warble; now throaty, now from the head, now hollow as a flute, now charged with yearning harmonics, it effortlessly passed from Gaspard Forster's [3] low record on the very frontiers of musical tone to a trilled bat-note high above the highest C to which (in 1770, at the Ducal opera of

---

1. *Dab, dab, dab* : she is dabbing (making light applications of) perfume on her body.
2. *thyme, ... myrtle, tarragon* : aromatic plants.
3. *Gaspard Forster* : Kaspar Forster (1617-73) was a German composer and singer, with an extraordinary ability for singing very low notes.

Parma, and to the astonishment of Mozart) Lucrezia Ajugari, alone of all the singers in history, once piercingly gave utterance. Sunk in their pneumatic stalls,[1] Lenina and the Savage sniffed and listened. It was now the turn also for eyes and skin. The house lights went down; fiery letters stood out solid and as though self-supported in the darkness. THREE WEEKS IN A HELICOPTER.[2] AN ALL-SUPER-SINGING, SYNTHETIC-TALKING, COLOURED, STEREOSCOPIC FEELY. WITH SYNCHRONIZED SCENT-ORGAN ACCOMPANIMENT.

'Take hold of those metal knobs on the arms of your chair,' whispered Lenina. 'Otherwise you won't get any of the feely effects.'

The Savage did as he was told.

Those fiery letters, meanwhile, had disappeared; there were ten seconds of complete darkness; then suddenly, dazzling and incomparably more solid-looking than they would have seemed in actual flesh and blood, far more real than reality, there stood the stereoscopic images, locked in one another's arms, of a gigantic negro and a golden-haired young brachycephalic Beta-Plus female.

The Savage started. That sensation on his lips! He lifted a hand to his mouth; the titillation ceased; let his hand fall back on the metal knob; it began again. The scent organ, meanwhile, breathed pure musk.[3] Expiringly, a sound-track super-dove cooed 'Oo-ooh'; and vibrating only thirty-two times a second, a deeper than African bass made answer: 'Aa-aah.' 'Ooh-ah! Ooh-ah!' the stereoscopic lips came together again, and once more the facial erogenous zones of the six thousand spectators in the Alhambra tingled with almost intolerable galvanic pleasure. 'Ooh . . .'

---

1   *stalls* : the usual name for seats at the lower level in an auditorium.

2.   *Three weeks ... helicopter* : this title alludes to the novel *Three Weeks* (1907), best known of the 21 romantic novels published by Elinor Glyn (1864-1943); it had become famous because of its erotic scenes.

3.   *musk* : strong-smelling substance used in perfumes.

The plot of the film was extremely simple. A few minutes after the first Ooh's and Aah's (a duet having been sung and a little love made on that famous bearskin, every hair of which – the Assistant Predestinator was perfectly right – could be separately and distinctly felt), the negro had a helicopter accident, fell on his head. Thump! what a twinge [1] through the forehead! A chorus of *ow's* and *aie's* went up from the audience.

The concussion knocked all the negro's conditioning into a cocked hat. He developed for the Beta blonde an exclusive and maniacal passion. She protested. He persisted. There were struggles, pursuits, an assault on a rival, finally a sensational kidnapping. The Beta blonde was ravished away into the sky and kept there, hovering, for three weeks in a wildly anti-social *tête-à-tête* with the black madman. Finally, after a whole series of adventures and much aerial acrobacy, three handsome young Alphas succeeded in rescuing her. The negro was packed off to an Adult Re-conditioning Centre and the film ended happily and decorously, with the Beta blonde becoming the mistress of all her three rescuers. They interrupted themselves for a moment to sing a synthetic quartet, with full super-orchestral accompaniment and gardenias on the scent organ. Then the bearskin made a final appearance and, amid a blare [2] of sexophones, the last stereoscopic kiss faded into darkness, the last electric titillation died on the lips like a dying moth that quivers, quivers, ever more feebly, ever more faintly, and at last is quite, quite still.

But for Lenina the moth did not completely die. Even after the lights had gone up, while they were shuffling slowly along with the crowd towards the lifts, its ghost still fluttered against her lips, still traced fine shuddering roads of anxiety and pleasure across her skin. Her cheeks were flushed, her eyes

---

1. *twinge* : a momentary pain. (Generally not a terrible, unbearable one.)
2. *amid a blare* [bleər]: accompanied by the unpleasantly loud noise.

dewily ¹ bright, her breath came deeply. She caught hold of the Savage's arm and pressed it, limp, against her side. He looked down at her for a moment, pale, pained, desiring, and ashamed of his desire. He was not worthy, not . . . Their eyes for a moment met. What treasures hers promised! A queen's ransom ² of temperament. Hastily he looked away, disengaged his imprisoned arm. He was obscurely terrified lest she should cease to be something he could feel himself unworthy of.

'I don't think you ought to see things like that,' he said, making haste to transfer from Lenina herself to the surrounding circumstances the blame for any past or possible future lapse from perfection.

'Things like what, John?'

'Like this horrible film.'

'Horrible?' Lenina was genuinely astonished. 'But I thought it was lovely.'

'It was base,'³ he said indignantly, 'it was ignoble.'

She shook her head. 'I don't know what you mean.' Why was he so queer? Why did he go out of his way to spoil things?

In the taxicopter he hardly even looked at her. Bound by strong vows that had never been pronounced, obedient to laws that had long since ceased to run, he sat averted and in silence. Sometimes, as though a finger had plucked at some taut,⁴ almost breaking string, his whole body would shake with a sudden nervous start.

The taxicopter landed on the roof of Lenina's apartment house. 'At last,' she thought exultantly as she stepped out of the cab. At last – even though he *had* been so queer just now. Standing under a lamp, she peered into her hand-mirror. At last. Yes, her nose *was* a bit shiny. She shook the loose powder from

---

1. *dewily* ['djuːɪli]: as if shining with dew, the tiny drops of water that form on cool surfaces in the night.

2. *A queen's ransom* : a vast amount, a great wealth (an idiom).

3. *base* : mean, low-principled.

4. *taut* [tɔːt]: tightly stretched. (She is very tense.)

her puff. While he was paying off the taxi – there would just be time. She rubbed at the shininess, thinking: 'He's terribly good-looking. No need for him to be shy like Bernard. And yet . . . Any other man would have done it long ago. Well, now at last.' That fragment of a face in the little round mirror suddenly smiled at her.

'Good-night,' said a strangled voice behind her. Lenina wheeled round. He was standing in the doorway of the cab, his eyes fixed, staring; had evidently been staring all this time while she was powdering her nose, waiting – but what for? or hesitating, trying to make up his mind, and all the time thinking, thinking – she could not imagine what extraordinary thoughts. 'Good-night, Lenina,' he repeated, and made a strange grimacing attempt to smile.

'But, John . . . I thought you were . . . I mean, aren't you . . .?'

He shut the door and bent forward to say something to the driver. The cab shot up into the air.

Looking down through the window in the floor, the Savage could see Lenina's upturned face, pale in the bluish light of the lamps. The mouth was open, she was calling. Her foreshortened figure rushed away from him; the diminishing square of the roof seemed to be falling through the darkness.

Five minutes later he was back in his room. From its hiding-place he took out his mouse-nibbled volume, turned with religious care its stained and crumpled pages, and began to read *Othello*. Othello, he remembered, was like the hero of *Three Weeks in a Helicopter* – a black man.

Drying her eyes, Lenina walked across the roof to the lift. On her way down to the twenty-seventh floor she pulled out her *soma* bottle. One gramme, she decided, would not be enough; hers had been more than a one-gramme affliction. But if she took two grammes, she ran the risk of not waking up in time tomorrow morning. She compromised and, into her cupped left palm, shook out three half-gramme tablets.

Chapter XII

BERNARD had to shout through the locked door; the Savage would not open. 'But everybody's there, waiting for you.' 'Let them wait,' came back the muffled voice through the door.

'But you know quite well, John' (how difficult it is to sound persuasive at the top of one's voice!), 'I asked them on purpose to meet you.'

'You ought to have asked me first whether I wanted to meet *them*.'

'But you always came before, John.'

'That's precisely why I don't want to come again.'

'Just to please me,' Bernard bellowingly wheedled.[1] 'Won't you come to please me?'

'No.'

'Do you seriously mean it?'

'Yes.'

Despairingly, 'But what shall I do?' Bernard wailed.

'Go to hell!' bawled the exasperated voice from within.

1. *bellowingly wheedled* ['beləʊ(w)iŋli 'wiːdld]: coaxing, trying to sound pleasant and endearing, but having to shout in a deep voice (bellowing) to be heard through the door – an oxymoron.

'But the Arch-Community-Songster of Canterbury is there tonight.' Bernard was almost in tears.

'*Ai yaa tákwa!*' It was only in Zuñi that the Savage could adequately express what he felt about the Arch-Community-Songster. '*Háni!*' he added as an afterthought; and then (with what derisive ferocity!): '*Sons éso tse-ná.*' And he spat on the ground, as Popé might have done.

In the end Bernard had to slink back,[1] diminished, to his rooms and inform the impatient assembly that the Savage would not be appearing that evening. The news was received with indignation. The men were furious at having been tricked into behaving politely to this insignificant fellow with the unsavoury reputation and the heretical opinions. The higher their position in the hierarchy, the deeper their resentment.

'To play such a joke on me,' the Arch-Songster kept repeating, 'on *me!*'

As for the women, they indignantly felt that they had been had on false pretences – had by a wretched little man who had had alcohol poured into his bottle by mistake – by a creature with a Gamma-Minus physique. It was an outrage, and they said so, more and more loudly. The Head Mistress of Eton was particularly scathing.[2]

Lenina alone said nothing. Pale, her blue eyes clouded with an unwonted [3] melancholy, she sat in a corner, cut off from those who surrounded her by an emotion which they did not share. She had come to the party filled with a strange feeling of anxious exultation. 'In a few minutes,' she had said to herself, as she entered the room, 'I shall be seeing him, talking to him, telling him' (for she had come with her mind made up) 'that I like him – more than anybody I've ever known. And then perhaps he'll say. . .'

What would he say ? The blood had rushed to her cheeks.

1. *slink back* : return quietly, without attracting attention to himself.
2. *scathing* ['skeɪðɪŋ]: severe, harsh.
3. *unwonted* [ʌn'wəʊntɪd]: not usual for her, not customary.

'Why was he so strange the other night, after the feelies? So queer. And yet I'm absolutely sure he really does rather like me. I'm sure . . .'

It was at this moment that Bernard had made his announcement; the Savage wasn't coming to the party.

Lenina suddenly felt all the sensations normally experienced at the beginning of a Violent Passion Surrogate [1] treatment – a sense of dreadful emptiness, a breathless apprehension, a nausea. Her heart seemed to stop beating.

'Perhaps it's because he doesn't like me,' she said to herself. And at once this possibility became an established certainty: John had refused to come because he didn't like her. He didn't like her....

'It really is a bit *too* thick,'[2] the Head Mistress of Eton was saying to the Director of Crematoria and Phosphorus Reclamation. 'When I think that I actually . . .'

'Yes,' came the voice of Fanny Crowne, 'it's absolutely true about the alcohol. Some one I know knew some one who was working in the Embryo Store at the time. She said to my friend, and my friend said to me . . .'

'Too bad, too bad,' said Henry Foster, sympathizing with the Arch-Community-Songster. 'It may interest you to know that our ex-Director was on the point of transferring him to Iceland.'

Pierced by every word that was spoken, the tight balloon of Bernard's happy self-confidence was leaking from a thousand wounds. Pale, distraught,[3] abject and agitated, he moved among his guests, stammering incoherent apologies, assuring them that next time the Savage would certainly be there, begging them to sit down and take a carotine sandwich, a slice of vitamin A *pâté*, a glass of champagne-surrogate. They duly ate, but ignored him;

---

1. *Violent Passion Surrogate* : (later V.P.S.) a treatment involving hormones and drugs that produces effects in the body like those connected with strong emotions but without any mental crisis.
2. *a bit too thick* : a little too insensitive to others to be tolerated (referring to Bernard's change of plan).
3. *distraught* [dɪˈstrɔːt]: mentally very disturbed and upset.

drank and were either rude to his face or talked to one another
about him, loudly and offensively as though he had not been
there.

'And now, my friends,' said the Arch-Community-Songster
of Canterbury, in that beautiful ringing voice with which he led
the proceedings at Ford's Day Celebrations, 'Now, my friends, I
think perhaps the time has come . . .' He rose, put down his
glass, brushed from his purple viscose waistcoat the crumbs of a
considerable collation, and walked towards the door.

Bernard darted forward to intercept him.

'Must you really, Arch-Songster ? . . . It's very early still. I'd
hoped you would . . .'

Yes, what hadn't he hoped, when Lenina confidentially told
him that the Arch-Community-Songster would accept an
invitation if it were sent. 'He's really rather sweet, you know.'
And she had shown Bernard the little golden zipper-fastening in
the form of a T which the Arch-Songster had given her as a
memento of the week-end she had spent at the Diocesan
Singery. *To meet the Arch-Community-Songster of Canterbury and
Mr Savage.* Bernard had proclaimed his triumph on every
invitation card. But the Savage had chosen this evening of all
evenings to lock himself up in his room, to shout '*Háni!*' and
even (it was lucky that Bernard didn't understand Zuñi) '*Sons
éso tse-ná!*' What should have been the crowning moment of
Bernard's whole career had turned out to be the moment of his
greatest humiliation.

'I'd so much hoped . . .' he stammeringly [1] repeated, looking
up at the great dignitary with pleading and distracted eyes.

'My young friend,' said the Arch-Community-Songster in a
tone of loud and solemn severity; there was a general silence. 'Let
me give you a word of advice.' He wagged his finger at Bernard.

---

1. *stammeringly* : saying the words with hesitations and repetitions
    caused by emotional tension. (The use of unusual adverbial
    constructions like this one is characteristic of Huxley's style; c.f.
    "bewilderedly" [p. 212], or the phrase "dithyrhambically
    chanted", used in an essay in *Music at Night* [1931]).

'Before it's too late. A word of good advice.' (His voice became sepulchral.) 'Mend your ways,[1] my young friend, mend your ways.' He made the sign of the T over him and turned away. 'Lenina, my dear,' he called in another tone. 'Come with me.'

Obediently, but unsmiling and (wholly insensible of the honour done to her) without elation, Lenina walked after him, out of the room. The other guests followed at a respectful interval. The last of them slammed the door. Bernard was all alone.

Punctured, utterly deflated,[2] he dropped into a chair and, covering his face with his hands, began to weep. A few minutes later, however, he thought better of it and took four tablets of *soma*.

Upstairs in his room the Savage was reading *Romeo and Juliet*.

Lenina and the Arch-Community-Songster stepped out on to the roof of the Singery. 'Hurry up, my young friend – I mean, Lenina,' called the Arch-Songster impatiently from the lift gates. Lenina, who had lingered for a moment to look at the moon, dropped her eyes and came hurrying across the roof to rejoin him.

'A New Theory of Biology' was the title of the paper which Mustapha Mond had just finished reading. He sat for some time, meditatively frowning, then picked up his pen and wrote across the title-page. 'The author's mathematical treatment of the conception of purpose is novel and highly ingenious, but heretical and, so far as the present social order is concerned, dangerous and potentially subversive. *Not to be published*.' He underlined the words. 'The author will be kept under

1. *Mend your ways* : improve your habits. He sounds like a prophet in the Old Testament: e.g. "Therefore now amend your ways and your doings, and obey the voice of the Lord your God" (Jeremiah, XXVI, 13).

2. *deflated* [dɪˈfleɪtɪd]: emptied out (referring back to the metaphor of Bernard as a balloon inflated with self-confidence); without spirit.

supervision. His transference to the Marine Biological Station of St. Helena [1] may become necessary.' A pity, he thought, as he signed his name. It was a masterly piece of work. But once you began admitting explanations in terms of purpose – well, you didn't know what the result might be. It was the sort of idea that might easily decondition the more unsettled minds among the higher castes – make them lose their faith in happiness as the Sovereign Good and take to believing, instead, that the goal was somewhere beyond, somewhere outside the present human sphere; that the purpose of life was not the maintenance of well-being, but some intensification and refining of consciousness, some enlargement of knowledge. Which was, the Controller reflected, quite possibly true. But not, in the present circumstances, admissible. He picked up his pen again, and under the words 'Not to be published' drew a second line, thicker and blacker than the first; then sighed. 'What fun it would be,' he thought, 'if one didn't have to think about happiness!'

With closed eyes, his face shining with rapture, John was softly declaiming to vacancy:[2]

> 'O, she doth teach the torches to burn bright!
> It seems she hangs upon the cheek of night
> Like a rich jewel in an Ethiop's ear;
> Beauty too rich for use, for earth too dear. . .'[3]

The golden T lay shining on Lenina's bosom. Sportively, the Arch-Community-Songster caught hold of it, sportively he pulled, pulled. 'I think,' said Lenina suddenly, breaking a long silence, 'I'd better take a couple of grammes of *soma*.'

---

1. *St. Helena* : an extremely isolated island in the South Atlantic Ocean.
2. *declaiming to vacancy* : reciting alone, in an empty room.
3. *O, she doth teach . . . too dear* : Romeo and Juliet, I, 5, 45-8. (For John, it is Lenina who, like Juliet, stands out like a bright jewel in a dim world.)

Bernard, by this time, was fast asleep and smiling at the private paradise of his dreams. Smiling, smiling. But inexorably, every thirty seconds, the minute hand of the electric clock above his bed jumped forward with an almost imperceptible click. Click, click, click, click . . . And it was morning. Bernard was back among the miseries of space and time. It was in the lowest spirits that he taxied across to his work at the Conditioning Centre. The intoxication of success had evaporated; he was soberly his old self; and by contrast with the temporary balloon of these last weeks, the old self seemed unprecedentedly heavier than the surrounding atmosphere.

To this deflated Bernard the Savage showed himself unexpectedly sympathetic.

'You're more like what you were at Malpais,' he said, when Bernard had told him his plaintive story. 'Do you remember when we first talked together? Outside the little house. You're like what you were then.'

'Because I'm unhappy again; that's why.'

'Well, I'd rather be unhappy than have the sort of false, lying happiness you were having here.'

'I like that,' said Bernard bitterly. 'When it's you who were the cause of it all. Refusing to come to my party and so turning them all against me!' He knew that what he was saying was absurd in its injustice; he admitted inwardly, and at last even aloud, the truth of all that the Savage now said about the worthlessness of friends who could be turned upon so slight a provocation into persecuting enemies. But in spite of this knowledge and these admissions, in spite of the fact that his friend's support and sympathy were now his only comfort, Bernard continued perversely to nourish, along with his quite genuine affection, a secret grievance against the Savage, to meditate a campaign of small revenges to be wreaked [1] upon him. Nourishing a grievance against the Arch-Community-Songster was useless; there was no possibility of being revenged on the Chief Bottler or the Assistant Predestinator. As a victim,

1. *wreaked* [riːkt]: made to have effect, carried out.

the Savage possessed, for Bernard, this enormous superiority over the others: that he was accessible. One of the principal functions of a friend is to suffer (in a milder and symbolic form) the punishments that we should like, but are unable, to inflict upon our enemies.

Bernard's other victim-friend was Helmholtz. When, discomfited,[1] he came and asked once more for the friendship which in his prosperity he had not thought it worth his while to preserve, Helmholtz gave it; and gave it without a reproach, without a comment, as though he had forgotten that there had ever been a quarrel. Touched, Bernard felt himself at the same time humiliated by this magnanimity – a magnanimity the more extraordinary and therefore the more humiliating in that it owed nothing to *soma* and everything to Helmholtz's character. It was the Helmholtz of daily life who forgot and forgave, not the Helmholtz of a half-gramme holiday. Bernard was duly grateful (it was an enormous comfort to have his friend again) and also duly resentful (it would be a pleasure to take some revenge on Helmholtz for his generosity).

At their first meeting after the estrangement, Bernard poured out the tale of his miseries and accepted consolation. It was not till some days later that he learned, to his surprise and with a twinge of shame, that he was not the only one who had been in trouble. Helmholtz had also come into conflict with Authority.

'It was over some rhymes,' he explained. 'I was giving my usual course of Advanced Emotional Engineering for Third Year Students. Twelve lectures, of which the seventh is about rhymes. "On the Use of Rhymes in Moral Propaganda and Advertisement," to be precise. I always illustrate my lecture with a lot of technical examples. This time I thought I'd give them one I'd just written myself. Pure madness, of course; but I

---

1. *discomfited* [dɪsˈkʌmfɪtɪd]: defeated, very confused and disconcerted.

couldn't resist it.' He laughed. 'I was curious to see what their reactions would be. Besides,' he added more gravely, 'I wanted to do a bit of propaganda; I was trying to engineer them into feeling as I'd felt when I wrote the rhymes. Ford!' He laughed again. 'What an outcry there was! The Principal had me up and threatened to hand me the immediate sack.[1] I'm a marked man.'[2]

'But what were your rhymes?' Bernard asked.

'They were about being alone.'

Bernard's eyebrows went up.

'I'll recite them to you, if you like.' And Helmholtz began:

'Yesterday's committee,
Sticks, but a broken drum,
Midnight in the City,
Flutes in a vacuum,
Shut lips, sleeping faces,
Every stopped machine,
The dumb and littered places
Where crowds have been –
All silences rejoice,
Weep (loudly or low),
Speak – but with the voice
Of whom, I do not know.

Absence, say, of Susan's,
Absence of Egeria's
Arms and respective bosoms,
Lips and, ah, posteriors,
Slowly form a presence;
Whose? and, I ask, of what
So absurd an essence,
That something, which is not,

1. *hand me the immediate sack* : dismiss me (give me the sack) at once.
2. *a marked man* : someone who is under suspicion and being observed.

Nevertheless should populate
Empty night more solidly
Than that with which we copulate,
Why should it seem so squalidly?

Well, I gave them that as an example, and they reported me
to the Principal.'

'I'm not surprised,' said Bernard. 'It's flatly against all their
sleep-teaching. Remember, they've had at least a quarter of a
million warnings against solitude.'

'I know. But I thought I'd like to see what the effect would be.'

'Well, you've seen now.'

Helmholtz only laughed. 'I feel,' he said, after a silence, 'as
though I were just beginning to have something to write about.
As though I were beginning to be able to use that power I feel
I've got inside me – that extra, latent power. Something seems to
be coming to me.' In spite of all his troubles, he seemed, Bernard
thought, profoundly happy.

Helmholtz and the Savage took to one another at once. So
cordially indeed that Bernard felt a sharp pang of jealousy. In all
these weeks he had never come to so close an intimacy with the
Savage as Helmholtz immediately achieved. Watching them,
listening to their talk, he found himself sometimes resentfully
wishing that he had never brought them together. He was
ashamed of his jealousy and alternately made efforts of will and
took *soma* to keep himself from feeling it. But the efforts were
not very successful; and between the soma-holidays there were,
of necessity, intervals. The odious sentiment kept on returning.

At his third meeting with the Savage, Helmholtz recited his
rhymes on Solitude.

'What do you think of them?' he asked when he had done.

The Savage shook his head. 'Listen to *this*,' was his answer;
and unlocking the drawer in which he kept his mouse-eaten
book, he opened and read:

> Let the bird of loudest lay,
> On the sole Arabian tree,
> Herald sad and trumpet be . . .'[1]

Helmholtz listened with a growing excitement. At 'sole Arabian tree' he started;[2] at 'thou shrieking harbinger' he smiled with sudden pleasure; at 'every fowl of tyrant wing' the blood rushed up into his cheeks; but at 'defunctive music' he turned pale and trembled with an unprecedented emotion. The Savage read on:

> 'Property was thus appall'd,
> That the self was not the same;
> Single nature's double name
> Neither two nor one was call'd.

> Reason in itself confounded
> Saw division grow together . . .'

'Orgy-porgy!' said Bernard, interrupting the reading with a loud, unpleasant laugh. 'It's just a Solidarity Service hymn.' He was revenging himself on his two friends for liking one another more than they liked him.

In the course of their next two or three meetings he frequently repeated this little act of vengeance. It was simple and, since both Helmholtz and the Savage were dreadfully pained by the shattering and defilement of a favourite poetic crystal, extremely effective. In the end, Helmholtz threatened to

---

1. *Let the bird . . . trumpet be* : the first lines of Shakespeare's poem "The Phoenix and the Turtle". Other phrases from the poem follow (the "shrieking harbinger" is the screech-owl, said to warn of coming death) and then stanzas 10 and 11 – which Bernard interrupts, confusing the metaphysical loss of separate identity (the phoenix and the turtledove in love are "neither two nor one"), with the only too physical loss of separation in a Solidarity Service orgy.

2. *started* : made a sudden involuntary movement (of surprised pleasure).

kick him out of the room if he dared to interrupt again. And yet, strangely enough, the next interruption, the most disgraceful of all, came from Helmholtz himself.

The Savage was reading *Romeo and Juliet* aloud – reading (for all the time he was seeing himself as Romeo and Lenina as Juliet) with an intense and quivering passion. Helmholtz had listened to the scene of the lovers' first meeting with a puzzled interest. The scene in the orchard had delighted him with its poetry; but the sentiments expressed had made him smile. Getting into such a state about having a girl – it seemed rather ridiculous. But, taken detail by verbal detail, what a superb piece of emotional engineering! 'That old fellow,' he said, 'he makes our best propaganda technicians look absolutely silly.' The Savage smiled triumphantly and resumed his reading. All went tolerably well until, in the last scene of the third act, Capulet and Lady Capulet began to bully Juliet to marry Paris. [1] Helmholtz had been restless throughout the entire scene; but when, pathetically mimed by the Savage, Juliet cried out:

> 'Is there no pity sitting in the clouds,
> That sees into the bottom of my grief?
> O, sweet my mother, cast me not away!
> Delay this marriage for a month, a week;
> Or, if you do not, make the bridal bed
> In that dim monument where Tybalt lies . . .' [2]

when Juliet said this, Helmholtz broke out in an explosion of uncontrollable guffawing. [3]

The mother and father (grotesque obscenity) forcing the daughter to have someone she didn't want! And the idiotic girl

1. *bully Juliet to marry Paris* : Paris is the young Count that Juliet's parents, the Capulets, want to force (bully) her into marrying against her will.
2. *Is there no . . . Tybalt lies* : *Romeo and Juliet*, III, 5, 198-203. Tybalt is her cousin who has just been killed, so Juliet's last lines here mean "I'll die if I have to marry Paris immediately".
3. *guffawing* [ˌgʌˈfɔːɪŋ]: noisy, unrestrained laughing.

not saying that she was having some one else whom (for the moment, at any rate) she preferred! In its smutty absurdity the situation was irresistibly comical. He had managed, with a heroic effort, to hold down the mounting pressure of his hilarity; but 'sweet mother' (in the Savage's tremulous tone of anguish) and the reference to Tybalt lying dead, but evidently uncremated and wasting his phosphorus on a dim monument, were too much for him. He laughed and laughed till the tears streamed down his face – quenchlessly [1] laughed while, pale with a sense of outrage, the Savage looked at him over the top of his book and then, as the laughter still continued, closed it indignantly, got up and, with the gesture of one who removes his pearl from before swine,[2] locked it away in its drawer.

'And yet,' said Helmholtz when, having recovered breath enough to apologize, he had mollified the Savage into listening to his explanations, 'I know quite well that one needs ridiculous, mad situations like that; one can't write really well about anything else. Why was that old fellow such a marvellous propaganda technician? Because he had so many insane, excruciating things to get excited about. You've got to be hurt and upset; otherwise you can't think of the really good, penetrating, X-rayish [3] phrases. But fathers and mothers!' He shook his head. 'You can't expect me to keep a straight face about fathers and mothers. And who's going to get excited about a boy having a girl or not having her?' (The Savage winced; but Helmholtz, who was staring pensively at the floor, saw nothing.) 'No,' he concluded, with a sigh, 'it won't do. We need some other kind of madness and violence. But what? What? Where can one find it ?' He was silent; then, shaking his head, 'I don't know,' he said at last, 'I don't know.'

1. *quenchlessly* : in un unstoppable, never finished way.
2. *removes his pearl from before swine* : takes back something too precious to be appreciated by such unrefined minds. Alludes to a well-known saying that derives from Christ's injunction in the Bible: "neither cast ye your pearls before swine [pigs], lest they trample them under their feet" (from the "Sermon on the Mount": Matthew, 7, 6).
3. *X-rayish* ['eks'reɪjɪʃ]: probing, like X-rays.

Chapter XIII

ENRY FOSTER loomed up [1] through the twilight of the Embryo Store. 'Like to come to a feely this evening?' Lenina shook her head without speaking.

'Going out with some one else?' It interested him to know which of his friends was being had by which other. 'Is it Benito?' he questioned.

She shook her head again.

Henry detected the weariness in those purple eyes, the pallor beneath that glaze of lupus, the sadness at the corners of the unsmiling crimson mouth. 'You're not feeling ill, are you?' he asked, a trifle [2] anxiously, afraid that she might be suffering from one of the few remaining infectious diseases.

Yet once more Lenina shook her head. 'Anyhow, you ought to go and see the doctor,' said Henry. 'A doctor a day keeps the jim-jams away,'[3] he added heartily, driving home his

---

1. *loomed up* : appeared, at first indistinctly, then suddenly very large.
2. *a trifle* [traɪfl]: a little bit, slightly.
3. *'A doctor . . . jim-jams away'* : recalls the present-day saying, "An apple a day keeps the doctor away"; the jimjams is a brain disorder (delirium tremens) indicating a bad physical condition.

hypnopædic adage with a clap on the shoulder. 'Perhaps you need a Pregnancy Substitute,' he suggested. 'Or else an extra-strong V.P.S. treatment. Sometimes, you know, the standard passion-surrogate isn't quite . . .'

'Oh, for Ford's sake,' said Lenina, breaking her stubborn silence, 'shut up!' And she turned back to her neglected embryos.

A V.P.S. treatment [1] indeed! She would have laughed, if she hadn't been on the point of crying. As though she hadn't got enough V.P. of her own! She sighed profoundly as she refilled her syringe. 'John,' she murmured to herself, 'John . . .' Then 'My Ford,' she wondered, 'have I given this one its sleeping-sickness injection, or haven't I?' She simply couldn't remember. In the end, she decided not to run the risk of letting it have a second dose, and moved down the line to the next bottle.

Twenty-two years eight months and four days from that moment, a promising young Alpha-Minus administrator at Mwanza-Mwanza [2] was to die of trypanosomiasis – the first case for over half a century. Sighing, Lenina went on with her work.

An hour later, in the Changing Room, Fanny was energetically protesting. 'But it's absurd to let yourself get into a state like this. Simply absurd,' she repeated. 'And what about? A man – *one* man.'

'But he's the one I want.'

'As though there weren't millions of other men in the world.'

'But I don't want them.'

'How can you know till you've tried?'

'I have tried.'

'But how many?' asked Fanny, shrugging her shoulders contemptuously. 'One, two?'

'Dozens. But,' shaking her head, 'it wasn't any good,' she added.

---

1. *V.P.S. treatment* : see note 1, p. 184.

2. *Mwanza-Mwanza* : a town on Lake Victoria in Tanzania (or, when Huxley wrote *BNW*, in the British colony of Tanganyika Territory).

'Well, you must persevere,' said Fanny sententiously. But it was obvious that her confidence in her own prescriptions had been shaken. 'Nothing can be achieved without perseverance.'

'But meanwhile . . .'

'Don't think of him.'

'I can't help it.'

'Take *soma*, then.'

'I do.'

'Well, go on.'

'But in the intervals I still like him. I shall always like him.'

'Well, if that's the case,' said Fanny, with decision, 'why don't you just go and take him. Whether he wants it or no.'

'But if you knew how terribly *queer* he was!'

'All the more reason for taking a firm line.'

'It's all very well to say that.'

'Don't stand any nonsense. Act.' Fanny's voice was a trumpet; she might have been a Y.W.F.A. lecturer giving an evening talk to adolescent Beta-Minuses. 'Yes, act – at once. Do it now.'

'I'd be scared,' said Lenina.

'Well, you've only got to take half a gramme of *soma* first. And now I'm going to have my bath.' She marched off, trailing her towel.

The bell rang, and the Savage, who was impatiently hoping that Helmholtz would come that afternoon (for having at last made up his mind to talk to Helmholtz about Lenina, he could not bear to postpone his confidences a moment longer), jumped up and ran to the door.

'I had a premonition it was you, Helmholtz,' he shouted as he opened.

On the threshold, in a white acetate-satin sailor suit, and with a round white cap rakishly tilted [1] over her left ear, stood Lenina.

---

1. *rakishly tilted* ['reɪkɪʃli 'tɪltɪd]: sloping down playfully, jauntily.

'Oh!' said the Savage, as though some one had struck him a heavy blow.

Half a gramme had been enough to make Lenina forget her fears and her embarrassments. 'Hullo, John,' she said, smiling, and walked past him into the room. Automatically he closed the door and followed her. Lenina sat down. There was a long silence.

'You don't seem very glad to see me, John,' she said at last.

'Not glad?' The Savage looked at her reproachfully; then suddenly fell on his knees before her and, taking Lenina's hand, reverently kissed it. 'Not glad? Oh, if you only knew,' he whispered, and, venturing to raise his eyes to her face, 'Admired Lenina,' he went on, 'indeed the top of admiration, worth what's dearest in the world.'[1] She smiled at him with a luscious [2] tenderness. 'Oh, you so perfect' (she was leaning towards him with parted lips), 'so perfect and so peerless are created' (nearer and nearer) 'of every creature's best.'[3] Still nearer. The Savage suddenly scrambled to his feet. 'That's why,' he said, speaking with averted face, 'I wanted to do something first . . . I mean, to show I was worthy of you. Not that I could ever really be that. But at any rate to show I wasn't absolutely unworthy. I wanted to do something.'

'Why should you think it necessary . . .' Lenina began, but left the sentence unfinished. There was a note of irritation in her voice. When one has leant forward, nearer and nearer, with parted lips – only to find oneself, quite suddenly, as a clumsy oaf [4] scrambles to his feet, leaning towards nothing at all – well, there is a reason, even with half a gramme of soma circulating in one's blood-stream, a genuine reason for annoyance.

1. 'Admired Lenina . . . dearest in the world' : Shakespeare, The Tempest, III, 1, 37-39. (With "Lenina" instead of "Miranda"; the first of several references to Ferdinand's courting of Miranda.)

2. luscious ['lʌʃəs]: suggesting sensual delights, attractively inviting.

3. 'Oh, you . . . creature's best' : The Tempest, III, 1, 46-8. Ferdinand finds Miranda without equals ("peerless").

4. clumsy oaf [əuf]: awkward lout, roughly-behaved, unaccomplished person (Lenina's opinion of John).

'At Malpais,' the Savage was incoherently mumbling, 'you had to bring her the skin of a mountain lion – I mean, when you wanted to marry some one. Or else a wolf.'

'There aren't any lions in England,' Lenina almost snapped.

'And even if there were,' the Savage added, with sudden contemptuous resentment, 'people would kill them out of helicopters, I suppose, with poison gas or something. I wouldn't do *that*, Lenina.' He squared his shoulders, he ventured to look at her and was met with a stare of annoyed incomprehension. Confused, 'I'll do anything,' he went on, more and more incoherently. 'Anything you tell me. There be some sports are painful – you know. But their labour delight in them sets off. [1] That's what I feel. I mean I'd sweep the floor if you wanted.'

'But we've got vacuum cleaners here,' said Lenina in bewilderment. 'It isn't necessary.'

'No, of course it isn't *necessary*. But some kinds of baseness are nobly undergone.[2] I'd like to undergo something nobly. Don't you see?'

'But if there *are* vacuum cleaners . . .'

'That's not the point.'

'And Epsilon Semi-Morons to work them,' she went on, 'well, really, *why?*'

'Why? But for you, for *you* Just to show that I . . .'

'And what on earth vacuum cleaners have got to do with lions . . .'

'To show how much . . .'

'Or lions with being glad to see *me* . . .' She was getting more and more exasperated.

---

1. *There be some sports . . . delight in them sets off*: The Tempest, III, 1, 1-2. (Slightly modified; the meaning is 'Although certain activities are arduous, the pleasure of doing them compensates for [sets off] the difficulties they involve'. Prospero tests Ferdinand's love for his daughter by making him work hard at piling wood.)

2. *some kinds of baseness are nobly undergone* : the continuation of Ferdinand's speech. ("Baseness" refers to something too undignified for a nobleman to do; John had earlier used the word "base" in more strongly pejorative, modern sense – see above, p. 180, n. 3).

'How much I love you, Lenina,' he brought out almost desperately.

An emblem of the inner tide of startled elation,[1] the blood rushed up into Lenina's cheeks. 'Do you mean it, John?'

'But I hadn't meant to say so,' cried the Savage, clasping his hands in a kind of agony. 'Not until . . . Listen, Lenina; in Malpais people get married.'

'Get what?' The irritation had begun to creep back into her voice. What was he talking about now?

'For always. They make a promise to live together for always.'

'What a horrible idea!' Lenina was genuinely shocked.

'Outliving beauty's outward, with a mind that doth renew swifter than blood decays.'[2]

'*What?*'

'It's like that in Shakespeare too. "If thou dost break her virgin knot before all sanctimonious ceremonies may with full and holy rite . . ."'[3]

'For Ford's sake, John, talk sense. I can't understand a word you say. First it's vacuum cleaners; then it's knots. You're driving me crazy.' She jumped up and, as though afraid that he might run away from her physically, as well as with his mind, caught him by the wrist. 'Answer me this question: do you really like me, or don't you?'

There was a moment's silence; then, in a very low voice, 'I love you more than anything in the world,' he said.

'Then why on earth didn't you say so?' she cried, and so intense was her exasperation that she drove her sharp nails into

---

1. *startled elation* ['stɑːtld ɪ'leɪ ʃn]: exaltation mixed with shock and surprise.

2. *'Outliving beauty's . . . decays'* : Shakespeare, *Troilus and Cressida*, III, 2, 169-70. (Lasting longer than outward beauties.)

3. *If thou dost break . . . rite . . . '* : *The Tempest*, IV, 1, 15. (Prospero is warning Ferdinand against having pre-marital sexual intercourse with Miranda).

the skin of his wrist. 'Instead of drivelling away [1] about knots and vacuum cleaners and lions, and making me miserable for weeks and weeks.'

She released his hand and flung it angrily away from her.

'If I didn't like you so much,' she said, 'I'd be furious with you.'

And suddenly her arms were round his neck; he felt her lips soft against his own. So deliciously soft, so warm and electric that inevitably he found himself thinking of the embraces in *Three Weeks in a Helicopter*. Ooh! ooh! the stereoscopic blonde and aah! the more than real blackamoor.[2] Horror, horror, horror . . . he tried to disengage himself; but Lenina tightened her embrace.

'Why didn't you say so?' she whispered, drawing back her face to look at him. Her eyes were tenderly reproachful.

'The murkiest den, the most opportune place' (the voice of conscience thundered poetically), 'the strongest suggestion our worser genius can, shall never melt mine honour into lust. Never, never!'[3] he resolved.

'You silly boy!' she was saying. 'I wanted you so much. And if you wanted me too, why didn't you . . .?'

'But, Lenina . . .' he began protesting; and as she immediately untwined [4] her arms, as she stepped away from him, he thought, for a moment, that she had taken his unspoken hint. But when she unbuckled her white patent cartridge belt and hung it carefully over the back of a chair, he began to suspect that he had been mistaken.

'Lenina!' he repeated apprehensively.

---

1. *drivelling away* ['drɪvlɪŋ ə'weɪ]: talking a lot of silly nonsense.
2. *blackamoor* ['blæk(ə)mʊəʳ]: a black Moor, i.e. a black person.
3. *'The murkiest den . . . Never, never!'* : *The Tempest*, IV, 1, 25-26. (Ferdinand asserts that he will not give way to lust, even if he finds himself alone with Miranda in a dark, out-of-the-way place.)
4. *untwined* [ˌʌn'twaɪnd]: loosened and separated, opened.

She put her hand to her neck and gave a long vertical pull; her white sailor's blouse was ripped to the hem; suspicion condensed into a too, too solid certainty.[1] 'Lenina, what *are* you doing?'

Zip, zip! Her answer was wordless. She stepped out of her bell-bottomed trousers. Her zippicamiknicks were a pale shell pink. The Arch-Community-Songster's golden T dangled at her breast.

'For those milk paps that through the window bars bore at men's eyes . . .'[2] The singing, thundering, magical words made her seem doubly dangerous, doubly alluring. Soft, soft, but how piercing! boring and drilling [3] into reason, tunnelling through resolution. 'The strongest oaths are straw to the fire i' the blood. Be more abstemious, or else . . .'[4]

Zip! The rounded pinkness fell apart like a neatly divided apple. A wriggle of the arms, a lifting first of the right foot, then the left: the zippicamiknicks were lying lifeless and as though deflated on the floor.

Still wearing her shoes and socks, and her rakishly tilted round white cap, she advanced towards him. 'Darling. *Darling*! If only you'd said so before !' She held out her arms.

But instead of also saying 'Darling!' and holding out his arms, the Savage retreated in terror, flapping his hands at her as though he were trying to scare away some intruding and dangerous animal. Four backward steps, and he was brought to bay against the wall.

1. *a too, too solid certainty* : alludes to *Hamlet*, I, 2, 129 – "O that this too too sullied [or solid] flesh would melt".
2. *'For those milk paps . . . men's eyes . . .'* : Shakespeare, *Timon of Athens*, IV, 3, 116. ("Window bars" because of the lattice-work common at the time on a woman's dress above her breasts.)
3. *boring and drilling* : literally, forcing a hole; describing the effects of Lenina's sexual attractiveness.
4. *'The strongest oaths . . . or else . . . '* : *The Tempest*, IV, 1, 52-4. A further warning by Prospero: your virtuous resolutions will be too weak if your passion ("the fire in the blood") get heated.

'Sweet!' said Lenina and, laying her hands on his shoulders, pressed herself against him. 'Put your arms round me,' she commanded. 'Hug me till you drug me, honey.' She too had poetry at her command, knew words that sang and were spells and beat drums. 'Kiss me'; she closed her eyes, she let her voice sink to a sleepy murmur, 'kiss me till I'm in a coma. Hug me, honey, snuggly . . .'

The Savage caught her by the wrists, tore her hands from his shoulders, thrust her roughly away at arm's length.

'Ow, you're hurting me, you're . . . oh!' She was suddenly silent. Terror had made her forget the pain. Opening her eyes, she had seen his face – no, not *his* face, a ferocious stranger's, pale, distorted, twitching with some insane, inexplicable fury. Aghast,[1] 'But what is it, John?' she whispered. He did not answer, but only stared into her face with those mad eyes. The hands that held her wrists were trembling. He breathed deeply and irregularly. Faint almost to imperceptibility, but appalling, she suddenly heard the grinding of his teeth. 'What is it ?' she almost screamed.

And as though awakened by her cry he caught her by the shoulders and shook her. 'Whore!' he shouted. 'Whore! Impudent strumpet!'[2]

'Oh, don't, do-on't,' she protested in a voice made grotesquely tremulous by his shaking.

'Whore !'

'Plea-ease.'

'Damned whore !'

'A gra-amme is be-etter . . .' she began.

The Savage pushed her away with such force that she staggered and fell. 'Go,' he shouted, standing over her menacingly, 'get out of my sight or I'll kill you.' He clenched his fists.

Lenina raised her arm to cover her face. 'No, please don't, John . . .'

1. *Aghast* [ɔ'gɑːst]: suddenly filled with a strong feeling of shock.
2. *Whore! Impudent strumpet!* : Shakespeare, *Othello*, IV, 2, 81. Unpleasant words meaning "prostitute".

'Hurry up. Quick!'

One arm still raised, and following his every movement with a terrified eye, she scrambled to her feet, and still crouching, still covering her head, made a dash for the bathroom.

The noise of that prodigious slap by which her departure was accelerated was like a pistol-shot.

'Ow!'[1] Lenina bounded forward.

Safely locked into the bathroom, she had leisure to take stock of [2] her injuries. Standing with her back to the mirror, she twisted her head. Looking over her left shoulder she could see the imprint of an open hand standing out distinct and crimson on the pearly flesh. Gingerly she rubbed the wounded spot.

Outside, in the other room, the Savage was striding up and down, marching, marching to the drums and music of magical words. 'The wren goes to't, and the small gilded fly does lecher in my sight.'[3] Maddeningly they rumbled in his ears. 'The fitchew nor the soiled horse goes to't with a more riotous appetite. Down from the waist they are Centaurs, though women all above. But to the girdle do the gods inherit. Beneath is all the fiends'. There's hell, there's darkness, there is the sulphurous pit, burning, scalding, stench, consumption; fie, fie, fie, pah, pah! Give me an ounce of civet, good apothecary, to sweeten my imagination.'[4]

1. *Ow!* [aʊ]: an exclamation expressing pain.

2. *take stock of*: carefully count up and evaluate.

3. *'The wren . . . my sight'* : Shakespeare, *King Lear*, IV, 6, 114-5. The wren copulates; golden flies give way to their sexual appetites. The king, wild with fury, inveighs against the low nature of the desires, especially sexual desires, that govern humankind.

4. *'The fitchew . . . my imagination'* : continuation of the same speech, *King Lear*, IV, 6, 124-33. Not even animals like the polecat ("fitchew": a small carnivorous mammal) or the horse have a greater sexual appetite than an apparently impeccable old woman. It is the familiar accusation that women, or women's bodies from the waist ("girdle") down, lead men to sexual acts for which they will go to hell, to the devils ("fiends"); the king demands a strong-smelling scent ("civet") to drive from his mind the smell of hell.

'John!' ventured a small ingratiating voice from the bathroom. 'John!'

'O thou weed, who art so lovely fair and smell'st so sweet that the sense aches at thee. Was this most goodly book made to write "whore" upon? Heaven stops the nose at it . . .'[1] But her perfume still hung about him, his jacket was white with the powder that had scented her velvety body. 'Impudent strumpet, impudent strumpet, impudent strumpet.' The inexorable rhythm beat itself out. 'Impudent . . .'

'John, do you think I might have my clothes?'

He picked up the bell-bottomed trousers, the blouse, the zippicamiknicks.

'Open!' he ordered, kicking the door.

'No, I won't.' The voice was frightened and defiant.

'Well, how do you expect me to give them to you ?'

'Push them through the ventilator over the door.'

He did what she suggested and returned to his uneasy pacing of the room. 'Impudent strumpet, impudent strumpet. The devil Luxury with his fat rump and potato finger . . .'[2]

'John.'

He would not answer. 'Fat rump and potato finger.'

'John.'

'What is it?' he asked gruffly.

'I wonder if you'd mind giving me my Malthusian belt.'

Lenina sat listening to the footsteps in the other room, wondering, as she listened, how long he was likely to go tramping up and down like that; whether she would have to wait until he left the flat; or if it would be safe, after allowing his madness a reasonable time to subside, to open the bathroom door and make a dash for it.[3]

She was interrupted in the midst of these uneasy speculations by the sound of the telephone bell ringing in the

---

1. 'O thou weed . . . stops the nose at it' : see Othello, IV, 2, 66-67.
2. The devil . . . finger . . . : Troilus and Cressida, V, 2, 56.
3. make a dash for it : run quickly away from there (an idiom).

other room. Abruptly the tramping ceased. She heard the voice
of the Savage parleying [1] with silence.

'Hullo.'

. . . . . .

'Yes.'

. . . . . .

'If I do not usurp myself, I am.'[2]

. . . . . .

'Yes, didn't you hear me say so? Mr Savage speaking.'

. . . . . .

'What? Who's ill? Of course it interests me.'

. . . . . .

'But is it serious? Is she really bad? I'll go at once....'

. . . . . .

'Not in her rooms any more? Where has she been taken?'

. . . . . .

'Oh, my God! What's the address ?'

. . . . . .

'Three Park Lane [3] – is that it? Three? Thanks.'

Lenina heard the click of the replaced receiver, then hurrying
steps. A door slammed. There was silence. Was he really gone?

With an infinity of precautions [4] she opened the door a
quarter of an inch; peeped through the crack; was encouraged
by the view of emptiness; opened a little further, and put her
whole head out; finally tiptoed into the room; stood for a few
seconds with strongly beating heart, listening, listening; then
darted to the front door, opened, slipped through, slammed,
ran. It was not till she was in the lift and actually dropping
down the well that she began to feel herself secure.

1. *parleying* ['paːlɪɪn] *with silence* : discussing something with
someone whose voice could not be heard.
2. *'If I do not usurp myself, I am.'* : Shakespeare, *Twelfth Night*, I, 5,
198. (That is "If I am not an impostor": "usurp" [juː'zɜːp] means
to take a position which does not belong to you.)
3. *Park Lane* : a wide avenue next to Hyde Park, an expensive and
very exclusive area in the West End of London.
4. *with an infinity of precautions* : this phrase is repeated from page
156.

Chapter XIV

THE Park Lane Hospital for the Dying was a sixty-story tower of primrose tiles. As the Savage stepped out of his taxicopter a convoy of gaily-coloured aerial hearses [1] rose whirring from the roof and darted away across the Park, westwards, bound for the Slough Crematorium. At the lift gates the presiding porter gave him the information he required, and he dropped down to Ward 81 (a Galloping Senility ward,[2] the porter explained) on the seventeenth floor.

It was a large room bright with sunshine and yellow paint, and containing twenty beds, all occupied. Linda was dying in company – in company and with all the modern conveniences. The air was continuously alive with gay synthetic melodies. At the foot of every bed, confronting its moribund occupant, was a television box. Television was left on, a running tap, from morning till night. Every quarter of an hour the prevailing perfume of the room was automatically changed. 'We try,'

---

1. *aerial hearses* : flying vehicles for carrying away the dead for cremation. Their rotor blades whirr [wɜːr] like those of helicopters as they ascend.

2. *Galloping Senility ward* : large room for patients becoming senile increasingly rapidly and uncontrollably.

explained the nurse, who had taken charge of the Savage at the door, 'we try to create a thoroughly pleasant atmosphere here – something between a first-class hotel and a feely-palace, if you take my meaning.'

'Where is she?' asked the Savage, ignoring these polite explanations.

The nurse was offended. 'You *are* in a hurry,' she said.

'Is there any hope?' he asked.

'You mean, of her not dying?' (He nodded.) 'No, of course there isn't. When somebody's sent here, there's no . . .' Startled by the expression of distress on his pale face, she suddenly broke off. 'Why, whatever is the matter?' she asked. She was not accustomed to this kind of thing in visitors. (Not that there were many visitors anyhow: or any reason why there should be many visitors.) 'You're not feeling ill, are you?'

He shook his head. 'She's my mother,' he said in a scarcely audible voice.

The nurse glanced at him with startled, horrified eyes; then quickly looked away. From throat to temple [1] she was all one hot blush.

'Take me to her,' said the Savage, making an effort to speak in an ordinary tone.

Still blushing, she led the way down the ward. Faces still fresh and unwithered (for senility galloped so hard that it had no time to age the cheeks – only the heart and brain) turned as they passed. Their progress was followed by the blank, incurious eyes of second infancy. The Savage shuddered as he looked.

Linda was lying in the last of the long row of beds, next to the wall. Propped up on pillows, she was watching the Semi-finals of the South American Riemann-Surface Tennis Championship, which were being played in silent and diminished reproduction on the screen of the television box at the foot of the bed. Hither and thither [2] across their square of

---

1. *temple* : either side of the forehead.
2. *Hither and thither* : here and there, from side to side.

illumined glass the little figures noiselessly darted, like fish in an aquarium – the silent but agitated inhabitants of another world.

Linda looked on, vaguely and uncomprehendingly smiling. Her pale, bloated face wore an expression of imbecile happiness. Every now and then her eyelids closed, and for a few seconds she seemed to be dozing. Then with a little start she would wake up again – wake up to the aquarium antics of the Tennis Champions, to the Super-Vox-Wurlitzeriana rendering [1] of 'Hug me till you drug me, honey,' to the warm draught of verbena [2] that came blowing through the ventilator above her head – would wake to these things, or rather to a dream of which these things, transformed and embellished by the *soma* in her blood, were the marvellous constituents, and smile once more her broken and discoloured smile of infantile contentment.

'Well, I must go,' said the nurse. 'I've got my batch of children coming. Besides, there's Number 3.' She pointed up the ward. 'Might go off any minute now. Well, make yourself comfortable.' She walked briskly away.

The Savage sat down beside the bed.

'Linda,' he whispered, taking her hand.

At the sound of her name, she turned Her vague eyes brightened with recognition. She squeezed his hand, she smiled, her lips moved; then quite suddenly her head fell forward. She was asleep. He sat watching her – seeking through the tired flesh, seeking and finding that young, bright face which had stooped over his childhood in Malpais, remembering (and he closed his eyes) her voice, her movements, all the events of their life together. 'Streptocock-Gee to Banbury-T . . .' How beautiful her singing had been! And those childish rhymes, how magically strange and mysterious!

1. *Super-Vox-Wurlitzeriana rendering* : played on a large electric organ made by the American Rudolf Wurlitzer Company; the "Mighty Wurlitzer", as it was often referred to, came to be widely used in cinemas. (The Wurlitzer trademark dates from 1926.)

2. *verbena* [vɜːˈbiːnə]: herbaceous plants; probably Huxley has in mind lemon-scented verbena (Lippia citriodora).

A, B, C, vitamin D:
The fat's in the liver, the cod's in the sea.

He felt the hot tears welling up behind his eyelids as he recalled the words and Linda's voice as she repeated them. And then the reading lessons; The tot is in the pot, the cat is on the mat; and the Elementary Instructions for Beta Workers in the Embryo Store. And long evenings by the fire or, in summer time, on the roof of the little house, when she told him those stories about the Other Place, outside the Reservation: that beautiful, beautiful Other Place, whose memory, as of a heaven, a paradise of goodness and loveliness, he still kept whole and intact, undefiled by contact with the reality of this real London, these actual civilized men and women.

A sudden noise of shrill voices made him open his eyes and, after hastily brushing away the tears, look round. What seemed an interminable stream of identical eight-year-old male twins was pouring into the room. Twin after twin, twin after twin, they came – a nightmare. Their faces, their repeated face – for there was only one between the lot of them – puggishly [1] stared, all nostrils and pale goggling eyes. Their uniform was khaki. All their mouths hung open. Squealing and chattering they entered. In a moment, it seemed, the ward was maggoty with them. They swarmed between the beds, clambered over, crawled under, peeped into the television boxes, made faces at the patients.

Linda astonished and rather alarmed them. A group stood clustered at the foot of her bed, staring with the frightened and stupid curiosity of animals suddenly confronted by the unknown.

'Oh, look, look!' They spoke in low, scared voices. 'Whatever is the matter with her? Why is she so fat?'

They had never seen a face like hers before – had never seen a face that was not youthful and taut-skinned, a body that had ceased to be slim and upright. All these moribund sexagenarians [2]

---

1. *puggishly* ['pʌgɪʃli]: with short, flattened, upturned noses – their faces look squashed, like that of the pug-dog.
2. *sexagenarians* : people between the ages of sixty and seventy.

had the appearance of childish girls. At forty-four, Linda seemed, by contrast, a monster of flaccid and distorted senility.

'Isn't she awful?' came the whispered comments. 'Look at her teeth!'

Suddenly from under the bed a pug-faced twin popped up between John's chair and the wall, and began peering into Linda's sleeping face.

'I say . . .' he began; but his sentence ended prematurely in a squeal. The Savage had seized him by the collar, lifted him clear over the chair and, with a smart box on the ears, sent him howling away.

His yells brought the Head Nurse hurrying to the rescue.

'What have you been doing to him?' she demanded fiercely. 'I won't have you striking the children.'

'Well, then, keep them away from this bed.' The Savage's voice was trembling with indignation. 'What are these filthy little brats doing here at all? It's disgraceful!'

'Disgraceful? But what do you mean? They're being death-conditioned. And I tell you,' she warned him truculently,[1] 'if I have any more of your interference with their conditioning, I'll send for the porters and have you thrown out.'

The Savage rose to his feet and took a couple of steps towards her. His movements and the expression on his face were so menacing that the nurse fell back in terror. With a great effort he checked himself and, without speaking, turned away and sat down again by the bed.

Reassured, but with a dignity that was a trifle shrill and uncertain, 'I've warned you,' said the nurse, 'so mind.'[2] Still, she led the too inquisitive twins away and made them join in the game of hunt-the-zipper,[3] which had been organized by one of her colleagues at the other end of the room.

'Run along now and have your cup of caffeine solution, dear,' she said to the other nurse. The exercise of authority

---

1. *truculently* : aggressively, as if ready for contestation.
2. *so mind* : so take care, make sure what you do follows the rules.
3. *hunt-the-zipper* : by analogy with the game of hunt-the-slipper (mentioned on p. 159).

restored her confidence, made her feel better. 'Now, children!' she called.

Linda had stirred uneasily, had opened her eyes for a moment, looked vaguely around, and then once more dropped off to sleep. Sitting beside her, the Savage tried hard to recapture his mood of a few minutes before. 'A, B, C, vitamin D,' he repeated to himself, as though the words were a spell that would restore the dead past to life. But the spell was ineffective. Obstinately the beautiful memories refused to rise; there was only a hateful resurrection of jealousies and uglinesses and miseries. Popé with the blood trickling down from his cut shoulder; and Linda hideously asleep, and the flies buzzing round the spilt *mescal* on the floor beside the bed; and the boys calling those names as she passed. . . . Ah, no, no! He shut his eyes, he shook his head in strenuous denial of these memories. 'A, B, C, vitamin D . . .' He tried to think of those times when he sat on her knees and she put her arms about him and sang, over and over again, rocking him, rocking him to sleep. 'A, B, C, vitamin D, vitamin D, vitamin D. . .'

The Super-Vox-Wurlitzeriana had risen to a sobbing crescendo; and suddenly the verbena gave place, in the scent-circulating system, to an intense patchouli. Linda stirred, woke up, stared for a few seconds bewilderedly [1] at the Semi-finalists, then, lifting her face, sniffed once or twice at the newly perfumed air and suddenly smiled – a smile of childish ecstasy.

'Popé!' she murmured, and closed her eyes. 'Oh, I do so like it, I do . . .' She sighed and let herself sink back into the pillows.

'But, Linda!' The Savage spoke imploringly. 'Don't you know me?' He had tried so hard, had done his very best; why wouldn't she allow him to forget? He squeezed her limp hand almost with violence, as though he would force her to come back from this dream of ignoble pleasures, from these base and hateful memories – back into the present, back into reality; the appalling present, the awful reality – but sublime, but

---

1. *bewilderedly* [bɪˈwɪldədli]: in a state of confused incomprehension. ("In bewilderment" would have been more normal).

significant, but desperately important precisely because of the imminence of that which made them so fearful. 'Don't you know me, Linda?'

He felt the faint answering pressure of her hand. The tears started into his eyes. He bent over her and kissed her.

Her lips moved. 'Popé!' she whispered again, and it was as though he had had a pailful of ordure [1] thrown in his face.

Anger suddenly boiled up in him. Balked [2] for the second time, the passion of his grief had found another outlet, was transformed into a passion of agonized rage.

'But I'm John!' he shouted. 'I'm John !' And in his furious misery he actually caught her by the shoulder and shook her.

Linda's eyes fluttered open; she saw him, knew him – 'John !' – but situated the real face, the real and violent hands, in an imaginary world – among the inward and private equivalents of patchouli and the Super-Wurlitzer, among the transfigured memories and the strangely transposed sensations that constituted the universe of her dream. She knew him for John, her son, but fancied him an intruder into that paradisal Malpais where she had been spending her *soma*-holiday with Popé. He was angry because she liked Popé, he was shaking her because Popé was there in the bed – as though there were something wrong, as though all civilized people didn't do the same? 'Every one belongs to every . . .' Her voice suddenly died into an almost inaudible breathless croaking: her mouth fell open: she made a desperate effort to fill her lungs with air. But it was as though she had forgotten how to breathe. She tried to cry out – but no sound came; only the terror of her staring eyes revealed what she was suffering. Her hands went to her throat, then clawed at the air [3] – the air she could no longer breathe, the air that, for her, had ceased to exist.

The Savage was on his feet, bent over her. 'What is it, Linda? What is it?' His voice was imploring; it was as though he were begging to be reassured.

---

1. *pailful of ordure* ['ɔːdjʊəʳ]: full bucket of excrement.
2. *Balked* [bɔːkt]: ignored, frustrated in his aims.
3. *clawed at the air* : repeatedly reached out, as if trying with the fingers to take hold of the air.

The look she gave him was charged with an unspeakable terror – with terror and, it seemed to him, reproach. She tried to raise herself in bed, but fell back on to the pillows. Her face was horribly distorted, her lips blue.

The Savage turned and ran up the ward.

'Quick, quick!' he shouted. 'Quick!'

Standing in the centre of a ring of zipper-hunting twins, the Head Nurse looked round. The first moment's astonishment gave place almost instantly to disapproval. 'Don't shout! Think of the little ones,' she said, frowning. 'You might decondition . . . But what are you doing?' He had broken through the ring. 'Be careful!' A child was yelling.

'Quick, quick!' He caught her by the sleeve, dragged her after him. 'Quick! Something's happened. I've killed her.'

By the time they were back at the end of the ward Linda was dead.

The Savage stood for a moment in frozen silence, then fell on his knees beside the bed and, covering his face with his hands, sobbed uncontrollably.

The nurse stood irresolute, looking now at the kneeling figure by the bed (the scandalous exhibition!) and now (poor children!) at the twins who had stopped their hunting of the zipper and were staring from the other end of the ward, staring with all their eyes and nostrils at the shocking scene that was being enacted round Bed 20. Should she speak to him? try to bring him back to a sense of decency? remind him of where he was? of what fatal mischief he might do to these poor innocents? Undoing all their wholesome [1] death-conditioning with this disgusting outcry – as though death were something terrible, as though any one mattered as much as all that! It might give them the most disastrous ideas about the subject,

---

1. *wholesome* : beneficial. (Satirical: we are expected to be amused by the nurse's unquestioned assumption that "death-conditioning" is good for your personality and 'moral health', partly because the word "wholesome" is exclusively applied to things with strongly positive connotations in our world, like fresh air or healthy food.)

might upset them into reacting in the entirely wrong, the utterly anti-social way.

She stepped forward, she touched him on the shoulder. 'Can't you behave?' she said in a low, angry voice. But, looking round, she saw that half a dozen twins were already on their feet and advancing down the ward. The circle was disintegrating. In another moment . . . No, the risk was too great; the whole Group might be put back six or seven months in its conditioning. She hurried back towards her menaced charges.

'Now, who wants a chocolate éclair?'[1] she asked in a loud, cheerful tone.

'Me!' yelled the entire Bokanovsky Group in chorus. Bed 20 was completely forgotten.

'Oh, God, God, God . . .' the Savage kept repeating to himself. In the chaos of grief and remorse that filled his mind it was the one articulate word. 'God!' he whispered it aloud. 'God . . .'

'Whatever is he saying?' said a voice, very near, distinct and shrill through the warblings of the Super-Wurlitzer.

The Savage violently started and, uncovering his face, looked round. Five khaki twins, each with the stump of a long éclair in his right hand, and their identical faces variously smeared with liquid chocolate, were standing in a row, puggily goggling[2] at him.

They met his eyes and simultaneously grinned. One of them pointed with his éclair butt.

'Is she dead?' he asked.

The Savage stared at them for a moment in silence. Then, in silence he rose to his feet, in silence slowly walked towards the door.

'Is she dead?' repeated the inquisitive twin, trotting at his side. The Savage looked down at him and still without speaking pushed him away. The twin fell on the floor and at once began to howl. The Savage did not even look round.

1. *chocolate éclair* : a small cake with a long, thin cream-filled puff-pastry case, topped with chocolate.
2. *puggily goggling* ['pʌgɪli 'gɒglɪŋ]: staring, so their prominent round eyes and snub noses were particulary evident.

Chapter XV

THE menial staff of the Park Lane Hospital for the Dying consisted of one hundred and sixty-two Deltas divided into two Bokanovsky Groups of eighty-four red-headed female and seventy-eight dark dolichocephalic [1] male twins, respectively. At six, when their working day was over, the two Groups assembled in the vestibule of the Hospital and were served by the Deputy Sub-Bursar [2] with their *soma* ration.

From the lift the Savage stepped out into the midst of them. But his mind was elsewhere – with death, with his grief, and his remorse; mechanically, without consciousness of what he was doing, he began to shoulder his way through the crowd.

'Who are you pushing? Where do you think you're going?'

High, low, from a multitude of separate throats, only two voices squeaked or growled. Repeated indefinitely, as though by a train of mirrors, two faces, one a hairless and freckled moon haloed [3] in orange, the other a thin, beaked bird-mask, stubbly

---

1. *dolichocephalic* [ˌdɒlɪkəɪsʊˈfælɪk]: long-headed.
2. *Deputy Sub-Bursar* : a minor cash-keeper.
3. *haloed* [ˈheɪləʊd]: with a circle (of orange-coloured hair) around their faces, like the halo on angel has around its head.

with two days' beard, turned angrily towards him. Their words
and, in his ribs, the sharp nudging of elbows, broke through his
unawareness. He woke once more to external reality, looked
round him, knew what he saw – knew it, with a sinking sense of
horror and disgust, for the recurrent delirium of his days and
nights, the nightmare of swarming indistinguishable sameness.
Twins, twins . . . Like maggots [1] they had swarmed defilingly
over the mystery of Linda's death. Maggots again, but larger,
full grown, they now crawled across his grief and his
repentance. He halted and, with bewildered and horrified eyes,
stared round him at the khaki mob, in the midst of which,
overtopping it by a full head, he stood. 'How many goodly
creatures are there here!' The singing words mocked him
derisively. 'How beauteous mankind is! O brave new world . . .'

'*Soma* distribution!' shouted a loud voice. 'In good order,
please. Hurry up there.'

A door had been opened, a table and chair carried into the
vestibule. The voice was that of a jaunty young Alpha, who had
entered carrying a black iron cash-box. A murmur of satisfaction
went up from the expectant twins. They forgot all about the
Savage. Their attention was now focussed on the black cash-box,
which the young man had placed on the table, and was now in
process of unlocking. The lid was lifted.

'Oo-oh!' said all the hundred and sixty-two simultaneously,
as though they were looking at fireworks.

The young man took out a handful of tiny pill-boxes. 'Now,'
he said peremptorily, 'step forward, please. One at a time, and
no shoving.'[2]

One at a time, with no shoving, the twins stepped forward.
First two males, then a female, then another male, then three
females, then . . .

The Savage stood looking on. 'O brave new world, O brave
new world . . .' In his mind the singing words seemed to change

---

1. *maggots* : see note 1, p. 80.
2. *no shoving* [ʃʌvɪŋ]: (colloquial) no pushing or prodding.

their tone. They had mocked him through his misery and remorse, mocked him with how hideous a note of cynical derision! Fiendishly laughing, they had insisted on the low squalor, the nauseous ugliness of the nightmare. Now, suddenly, they trumpeted a call to arms. 'O brave new world!' Miranda was proclaiming the possibility of loveliness, the possibility of transforming even the nightmare into something fine and noble. 'O brave new world !' It was a challenge, a command.

'No shoving there, now !' shouted the Deputy Sub-Bursar in a fury. He slammed down the lid of his cash-box. 'I shall stop the distribution unless I have good behaviour.'

The Deltas muttered, jostled one another a little, and then were still. The threat had been effective. Deprivation of *soma* – appalling thought !

'That's better,' said the young man, and re-opened his cash-box.

Linda had been a slave, Linda had died; others should live in freedom, and the world be made beautiful. A reparation, a duty. And suddenly it was luminously clear to the Savage what he must do; it was as though a shutter had been opened, a curtain drawn back.

'Now,' said the Deputy-Bursar.

Another khaki female stepped forward.

'Stop!' called the Savage in a loud and ringing voice. 'Stop!'

He pushed his way to the table; the Deltas stared at him with astonishment.

'Ford!' said the Deputy Sub-Bursar below his breath. 'It's the Savage.' He felt scared.

'Listen, I beg you,' cried the Savage earnestly. 'Lend me your ears . . .'[1] He had never spoken in public before, and found it very difficult to express what he wanted to say. 'Don't take that horrible stuff. It's poison, it's poison.'

---

1. *'Lend me your ears . . .'* : Shakespeare, *Julius Caesar*, III, 2, 78. (From the start of the most memorable example of public speech-making in Shakespeare: Mark Antony's funeral oration for Caesar.)

'I say, Mr Savage,' said the Deputy Sub-Bursar, smiling propitiatingly. 'Would you mind letting me . . .'

'Poison to soul as well as body.'

'Yes, but let me get on with my distribution, won't you? There's a good fellow.' With the cautious tenderness of one who strokes a notoriously vicious animal, he patted the Savage's arm. 'Just let me . . .'

'Never!' cried the Savage.

'But look here, old man . . .'[1]

'Throw it all away, that horrible poison.'

The words 'Throw it all away' pierced through the enfolding layers of incomprehension to the quick [2] of the Deltas' consciousness. An angry murmur went up from the crowd.

'I come to bring you freedom,' said the Savage, turning back towards the twins. 'I come . . .'

The Deputy Sub-Bursar heard no more; he had slipped out of the vestibule and was looking up a number in the telephone book.

'Not in his own rooms,' Bernard summed up. 'Not in mine, not in yours. Not at the Aphroditæum; not at the Centre or the College. Where can he have got to?'

Helmholtz shrugged his shoulders. They had come back from their work expecting to find the Savage waiting for them at one or other of their usual meeting-places, and there was no sign of the fellow. Which was annoying, as they had meant to nip [3] across to Biarritz in Helmholtz's four-seater sporticopter. They'd be late for dinner if he didn't come soon.

'We'll give him five more minutes,' said Helmholtz. 'If he doesn't turn up by then, we'll . . .'

1. *old man* ... : form of address expressing familiarity, here condescension.
2. *pierced . . . to the quick* : penetrated to the most sensitive, vital part.
3. *nip* : go quickly. (Satirical parody: normally used in informal speech, with a variety of prepositions, for easy, quick trips, whereas London to Biarritz, in 1931, would have been long and tiring).

The ringing of the telephone bell interrupted him. He picked up the receiver. 'Hullo. Speaking.' Then, after a long interval of listening, 'Ford in Flivver!' he swore. 'I'll come at once.'

'What is it?' Bernard asked.

'A fellow I know at the Park Lane Hospital,' said Helmholtz. 'The Savage is there. Seems to have gone mad. Anyhow, it's urgent. Will you come with me?'

Together they hurried along the corridor to the lifts.

'But do you like being slaves?' the Savage was saying as they entered the Hospital. His face was flushed, his eyes bright with ardour and indignation. 'Do you like being babies? Yes, babies. Mewling and puking,'[1] he added, exasperated by their bestial stupidity into throwing insults at those he had come to save. The insults bounced off their carapace [2] of thick stupidity; they stared at him with a blank expression of dull and sullen resentment in their eyes. 'Yes, puking!' he fairly shouted. Grief and remorse, compassion and duty – all were forgotten now and, as it were, absorbed into an intense overpowering hatred of these less than human monsters. 'Don't you want to be free and men? Don't you even understand what manhood and freedom are?' Rage was making him fluent; the words came easily, in a rush. 'Don't you?' he repeated, but got no answer to his question. 'Very well, then,' he went on grimly. 'I'll teach you; I'll *make* you be free whether you want to or not.' And pushing open a window that looked on to the inner court of the Hospital, he began to throw the little pill-boxes of *soma* tablets in handfuls out into the area.

For a moment the khaki mob was silent, petrified, at the spectacle of this wanton [3] sacrilege, with amazement and horror.

'He's mad,' whispered Bernard, staring with wide open eyes. 'They'll kill him. They'll . . .' A great shout suddenly went up

1. *Mewling* ['mjuːlɪŋ] *and puking* ['pjuːkɪŋ]: Shakespeare, *As You Like It*, III, 7, 144. (The first of the "seven ages" of man described in this famous speech: the baby, crying and vomiting in its nurse's arms.)
2. *carapace* ['kærəpeɪs]: hard protective shell.
3. *wanton* : purposeless, wasteful and yet non-accidental.

from the mob; a wave of movement drove it menacingly towards the Savage. 'Ford help him!' said Bernard, and averted his eyes.

'Ford helps those who help themselves.'[1] And with a laugh, actually a laugh of exultation, Helmholtz Watson pushed his way through the crowd.

'Free, free!' the Savage shouted, and with one hand continued to throw the *soma* into the area while, with the other, he punched the indistinguishable faces of his assailants. 'Free!' And suddenly there was Helmholtz at his side – 'Good old Helmholtz!' – also punching – 'Men at last!' – and in the interval also throwing the poison out by handfuls through the open window. 'Yes, men! men!' and there was no more poison left. He picked up the cash-box and showed them its black emptiness. 'You're free!'

Howling, the Deltas charged with a redoubled fury.

Hesitant on the fringes of the battle, 'They're done for,' said Bernard and, urged by a sudden impulse, ran forward to help them; then thought better of it and halted; then, ashamed, stepped forward again; then again thought better of it, and was standing in an agony of humiliated indecision – thinking that *they* might be killed if he didn't help them, and that *he* might be killed if he did – when (Ford be praised!), goggle-eyed and swine-snouted [2] in their gas-masks, in ran the police.

Bernard dashed to meet them. He waved his arms; and it was action, he was doing something. He shouted 'Help!' several times, more and more loudly so as to give himself the illusion of helping. 'Help! *Help! HELP!'*

The policemen pushed him out of the way and got on with their work. Three men with spraying machines buckled to their shoulders pumped thick clouds of *soma* vapour into the air. Two

---

1. *'Ford . . . themselves'* : this proverb, in the form we have known since the sixteenth century, begins "God helps . . ."

2. *swine-snouted* ['swaɪn'snaʊtɪd]: (with the protruding gas-masks on) having snouts (noses) like a pig's.

more were busy round the portable Synthetic Music Box. Carrying water pistols charged with a powerful anæsthetic, four others had pushed their way into the crowd and were methodically laying out, squirt by squirt,[1] the more ferocious of the fighters.

'Quick, quick!' yelled Bernard. 'They'll be killed if you don't hurry. They'll . . . Oh!' Annoyed by his chatter, one of the policemen had given him a shot from his water pistol. Bernard stood for a second or two wambling [2] unsteadily on legs that seemed to have lost their bones, their tendons, their muscles, to have become mere sticks of jelly, and at last not even jelly – water: he tumbled in a heap on the floor.

Suddenly, from out of the Synthetic Music Box a Voice began to speak. The Voice of Reason, the Voice of Good Feeling. The sound-track roll was unwinding itself in Synthetic Anti-Riot Speech Number Two (Medium Strength). Straight from the depths of a non-existent heart, 'My friends, my friends !' said the Voice so pathetically, with a note of such infinitely tender reproach that, behind their gas-masks, even the policemen's eyes were momentarily dimmed with tears, 'what is the meaning of this? Why aren't you all being happy and good together. Happy and good,' the Voice repeated. 'At peace, at peace.' It trembled, sank into a whisper and momentarily expired. 'Oh, I do want you to be happy,' it began, with a yearning earnestness. 'I do so want you to be good! Please, please be good and . . .'

Two minutes later the Voice and the soma vapour had produced their effect. In tears, the Deltas were kissing and hugging one another – half a dozen twins at a time in a comprehensive embrace. Even Helmholtz and the Savage were almost crying. A fresh supply of pill-boxes was brought in from the Bursary; a new distribution was hastily made and, to the sound of the Voice's richly affectionate, baritone valedictions,

---

1. *laying out, squirt by squirt* : putting out of action, using one spray of anaesthetic after another.
2. *wambling* ['wɒmblɪŋ]: staggering, wobbling around, tottering.

the twins dispersed, blubbering as though their hearts would break. 'Good-bye, my dearest, dearest friends, Ford keep you ! Good-bye, my dearest, dearest friends, Ford keep you. Good-bye, my dearest, dearest . . .'

When the last of the Deltas had gone the policeman switched off the current. The angelic Voice fell silent.

'Will you come quietly?' asked the Sergeant, 'or must we anæsthetize?' He pointed his water pistol menacingly.

'Oh, we'll come quietly,' the Savage answered, dabbing alternately a cut lip, a scratched neck, and a bitten left hand.

Still keeping his handkerchief to his bleeding nose, Helmholtz nodded in confirmation.

Awake and having recovered the use of his legs, Bernard had chosen this moment to move as inconspicuously as he could towards the door.

'Hi, you there,' called the Sergeant, and a swine-masked policeman hurried across the room and laid a hand on the young man's shoulder.

Bernard turned with an expression of indignant innocence. Escaping? He hadn't dreamed of such a thing. 'Though what on earth you want *me* for,' he said to the Sergeant, 'I really can't imagine.'

'You're a friend of the prisoners, aren't you?'

'Well . . .' said Bernard, and hesitated. No, he really couldn't deny it. 'Why shouldn't I be?' he asked.

'Come on, then,' said the Sergeant, and led the way towards the door and the waiting police car.

Chapter XVI

THE room into which the three were ushered was the Controller's study. 'His fordship will be down in a moment.' The Gamma butler left them to themselves.

Helmholtz laughed aloud.

'It's more like a caffeine-solution party [1] than a trial,' he said, and let himself fall into the most luxurious of the pneumatic armchairs. 'Cheer up, Bernard,' he added, catching sight of his friend's green unhappy face. But Bernard would not be cheered; without answering, without even looking at Helmholtz, he went and sat down on the most uncomfortable chair in the room, carefully chosen in the obscure hope of somehow deprecating the wrath [2] of the higher powers.

The Savage meanwhile wandered restlessly round the room, peering with a vague superficial inquisitiveness at the books in the shelves, at the sound-track rolls and the reading-machine bobbins

---

1. *caffeine-solution party* : the *BNW* equivalent of a coffee party (when friends get together, drink coffee and chat); the active ingredients (here, caffeine ['kæfiːn]) of today's foods are retained in products specially synthesized as functionally-reduced substitutes.
2. *deprecating the wrath* [rɒθ]: averting or keeping away the anger.

in their numbered pigeon-holes.[1] On the table under the window lay a massive volume bound in limp black leather-surrogate, and stamped with large golden T's. He picked it up and opened it. MY LIFE AND WORK, BY OUR FORD. The book had been published at Detroit [2] by the Society for the Propagation of Fordian Knowledge.[3] Idly [4] he turned the pages, read a sentence here, a paragraph there, and had just come to the conclusion that the book didn't interest him, when the door opened, and the Resident World Controller for Western Europe walked briskly into the room.

Mustapha Mond shook hands with all three of them; but it was to the Savage that he addressed himself. 'So you don't much like civilization, Mr Savage,' he said.

The Savage looked at him. He had been prepared to lie, to bluster,[5] to remain sullenly unresponsive; but, reassured by the good-humoured intelligence of the Controller's face, he decided to tell the truth, straightforwardly. 'No.' He shook his head.

Bernard started and looked horrified. What would the Controller think ? To be labelled as the friend of a man who said that he didn't like civilization – said it openly and, of all people, to the Controller – it was terrible. 'But, John,' he began. A look from Mustapha Mond reduced him to an abject silence.

'Of course,' the Savage went on to admit, 'there are some very nice things. All that music in the air, for instance . . .'

'Sometimes a thousand twangling instruments will hum about my ears, and sometimes voices.'[6]

---

1. *pigeon-holes* ['pɪdʒɪn‚həʊlz]: rows of small, open, labelled compartments used, in this case, for filing the rolls of microfilm.

2. *Detroit* : American city, home of the Ford Motor Company.

3. *Society for the Propagation of Fordian Knowledge* : by analogy with today's Society for the Propagation of Christian Knowledge.

4. *Idly* ['aɪdli]: just to pass the time, without particular effort or purpose.

5. *bluster* [blʌstəʳ]: to speak out forcefully and assertively.

6. *'Sometimes . . . sometimes voices'* : The Tempest, III, 2, 146. (On hearing that the island is full of delightful "sounds and sweet airs", one of the newcomers replies, "This will prove a brave kingdom to me, where I shall have my music for nothing".)

The Savage's face lit up with a sudden pleasure. 'Have you read it too?' he asked. 'I thought nobody knew about that book here, in England.'

'Almost nobody. I'm one of the very few. It's prohibited, you see. But as I make the laws here, I can also break them. With impunity, Mr Marx,' he added, turning to Bernard. 'Which I'm afraid you *can't* do.'

Bernard sank into a yet more hopeless misery.

'But why is it prohibited ?' asked the Savage. In the excitement of meeting a man who had read Shakespeare he had momentarily forgotten everything else.

The Controller shrugged his shoulders. 'Because it's old; that's the chief reason. We haven't any use for old things here.'

'Even when they're beautiful?'

'Particularly when they're beautiful. Beauty's attractive, and we don't want people to be attracted by old things. We want them to like the new ones.'

'But the new ones are so stupid and horrible. Those plays, where there's nothing but helicopters flying about and you *feel* the people kissing.' He made a grimace. 'Goats and monkeys!' [1] Only in Othello's words could he find an adequate vehicle for his contempt and hatred.

'Nice tame animals, anyhow,' the Controller murmured parenthetically.

'Why don't you let them see *Othello* instead?'

'I've told you; it's old. Besides, they couldn't understand it.'

Yes, that was true. He remembered how Helmholtz had laughed at *Romeo and Juliet*. 'Well, then,' he said, after a pause, 'something new that's like *Othello*, and that they could understand.'

'That's what we've all been wanting to write,' said Helmholtz, breaking a long silence.

'And it's what you never will write,' said the Controller. 'Because, if it were really like *Othello* nobody could understand

---

1. *'Goats and monkeys!'* : *Othello*, IV, 1, 274. (Othello uses this phrase to express his disgust at lustful sexual acts between humans.)

it, however new it might be. And if it were new, it couldn't possibly be like *Othello.'*

'Why not?'

'Yes, why not?' Helmholtz repeated. He too was forgetting the unpleasant realities of the situation. Green with anxiety and apprehension, only Bernard remembered them; the others ignored him. 'Why not?'

'Because our world is not the same as Othello's world. You can't make flivvers without steel – and you can't make tragedies without social instability. The world's stable now. People are happy; they get what they want, and they never want what they can't get. They're well off; they're safe; they're never ill; they're not afraid of death; they're blissfully ignorant of passion and old age; they're plagued with no mothers or fathers; they've got no wives, or children, or lovers to feel strongly about; they're so conditioned that they practically can't help behaving as they ought to behave. And if anything should go wrong, there's *soma.* Which you go and chuck out of the window in the name of liberty, Mr Savage. *Liberty!'* He laughed. 'Expecting Deltas to know what liberty is ! And now expecting them to understand *Othello!* My good boy!'

The Savage was silent for a little. 'All the same,' he insisted obstinately, '*Othello's* good, *Othello's* better than those feelies.'

'Of course it is,' the Controller agreed. 'But that's the price we have to pay for stability. You've got to choose between happiness and what people used to call high art. We've sacrificed the high art. We have the feelies and the scent organ instead.'

'But they don't mean anything.'

'They mean themselves; they mean a lot of agreeable sensations to the audience.'

'But they're . . . they're told by an idiot.'[1]

---

1. *told by an idiot* : Shakespeare, *Macbeth,* V, 5, 27. (Life, says Macbeth, "is a tale / Told by an idiot, full of sound and fury, / Signifying nothing." This much-admired speech was referred to earlier – see p.150, n. 1. The title of Huxley's essay "Tomorrow and tomorrow and tomorrow", comes from its opening line and that of his story collection *Brief Candles* is also borrowed from it.)

The Controller laughed. 'You're not being very polite to your friend, Mr Watson. One of our most distinguished Emotional Engineers . . .'

'But he's right,' said Helmholtz gloomily. 'Because it *is* idiotic. Writing when there's nothing to say . . .'

'Precisely. But that requires the most enormous ingenuity. You're making flivvers out of the absolute minimum of steel – works of art out of practically nothing but pure sensation.'

The Savage shook his head. 'It all seems to me quite horrible.'

'Of course it does. Actual happiness always looks pretty squalid in comparison with the over-compensations for misery. And, of course, stability isn't nearly so spectacular as instability. And being contented has none of the glamour of a good fight against misfortune, none of the picturesqueness of a struggle with temptation, or a fatal overthrow by passion or doubt. Happiness is never grand.'

'I suppose not,' said the Savage after a silence. 'But need it be quite so bad as those twins?' He passed his hand over his eyes as though he were trying to wipe away the remembered image of those long rows of identical midgets at the assembling tables, those queued-up twin-herds ¹ at the entrance to the Brentford monorail station, those human maggots swarming round Linda's bed of death, the endlessly repeated face of his assailants. He looked at his bandaged left hand and shuddered. 'Horrible!'

'But how useful! I see you don't like our Bokanovsky Groups; but, I assure you, they're the foundation on which everything else is built. They're the gyroscope ² that stabilizes

1. *queued-up twin-herds* ['kjuːdʌp 'twɪnˌhɜːdz]: this refers back to the masses of lower-caste workers John had seen lined up waiting to receive their soma ration in Chapter 11; the crowds of nearly identical Bokanovsky groups looked like groups of animals (though a "cowherd", for example, is usually the name for the person who looks after them and not the name for the herd of cows).

2. *gyroscope* ['dʒaɪrəskəup]: a stabilising device with a spinning wheel.

the rocket plane of state on its unswerving course.' The deep voice thrillingly vibrated; the gesticulating hand implied all space and the onrush of the irresistible machine. Mustapha Mond's oratory was almost up to synthetic standards.

'I was wondering,' said the Savage, 'why you had them at all – seeing that you can get whatever you want out of those bottles. Why don't you make everybody an Alpha Double Plus while you're about it?'

Mustapha Mond laughed. 'Because we have no wish to have our throats cut,' he answered. 'We believe in happiness and stability. A society of Alphas couldn't fail to be unstable and miserable. Imagine a factory staffed by Alphas – that is to say by separate and unrelated individuals of good heredity and conditioned so as to be capable (within limits) of making a free choice and assuming responsibilities. Imagine it!' he repeated.

The Savage tried to imagine it, not very successfully.

'It's an absurdity. An Alpha-decanted, Alpha-conditioned man would go mad if he had to do Epsilon Semi-Moron work – go mad, or start smashing things up. Alphas can be completely socialized – but only on condition that you make them do Alpha work. Only an Epsilon can be expected to make Epsilon sacrifices, for the good reason that for him they aren't sacrifices; they're the line of least resistance. His conditioning has laid down rails along which he's got to run. He can't help himself; he's foredoomed.[1] Even after decanting, he's still inside a bottle – an invisible bottle of infantile and embryonic fixations. Each one of us, of course,' the Controller meditatively continued, 'goes through life inside a bottle. But if we happen to be Alphas, our bottles are, relatively speaking, enormous. We should suffer acutely if we were confined in a narrower space. You cannot pour upper-caste champagne-surrogate into lower-caste bottles. It's obvious theoretically. But it has also been proved in actual practice. The result of the Cyprus experiment was convincing.'

'What was that?' asked the Savage.

---

1. *he's foredoomed* : what will happen to him is determined at the start of his life.

Mustapha Mond smiled. 'Well, you can call it an experiment in rebottling if you like. It began in A.F. 473. The Controllers had the island of Cyprus cleared of all its existing inhabitants and re-colonized with a specially prepared batch of twenty-two thousand Alphas. All agricultural and industrial equipment was handed over to them and they were left to manage their own affairs. The result exactly fulfilled all the theoretical predictions. The land wasn't properly worked; there were strikes in all the factories; the laws were set at naught,[1] orders disobeyed; all the people detailed for a spell of low-grade work were perpetually intriguing for high-grade jobs, and all the people with high-grade jobs were counter-intriguing at all costs to stay where they were. Within six years they were having a first-class civil war. When nineteen [2] out of the twenty-two thousand had been killed, the survivors unanimously petitioned the World Controllers to resume the government of the island. Which they did. And that was the end of the only society of Alphas that the world has ever seen.'

The Savage sighed, profoundly.

'The optimum population,' said Mustapha Mond, 'is modelled on the iceberg – eight-ninths below the water line, one-ninth above.'

'And they're happy below the water line?'

'Happier than above it. Happier than your friends here, for example.' He pointed.

'In spite of that awful work?'

'Awful? *They* don't find it so. On the contrary, they like it. It's light, it's childishly simple. No strain on the mind or the muscles. Seven and a half hours of mild, unexhausting labour, and then the *soma* ration and games and unrestricted copulation and the feelies. What more can they ask for? True,' he added, 'they might ask for shorter hours. And of course we could give them shorter hours. Technically, it would be perfectly simple to

1. *set at naught* [nɔːt]: (or, nought) reduced to nothing, made ineffectual (as if no laws existed).
2. *nineteen* : this means nineteen thousand.

reduce all lower-caste working hours to three or four a day. But would they be any the happier for that? No, they wouldn't. The experiment was tried, more than a century and a half ago. The whole of Ireland was put on to the four-hour day. What was the result? Unrest and a large increase in the consumption of *soma*; that was all. Those three and a half hours of extra leisure were so far from being a source of happiness, that people felt constrained to take a holiday from them. The Inventions Office is stuffed with plans for labour-saving processes. Thousands of them.' Mustapha Mond made a lavish gesture. 'And why don't we put them into execution? For the sake of the labourers; it would be sheer cruelty to afflict them with excessive leisure. It's the same with agriculture. We could synthesize every morsel of food, if we wanted to. But we don't. We prefer to keep a third of the population on the land. For their own sakes – because it takes *longer* to get food out of the land than out of a factory. Besides, we have our stability to think of. We don't want to change. Every change is a menace to stability. That's another reason why we're so chary ¹ of applying new inventions. Every discovery in pure science is potentially subversive; even science must sometimes be treated as a possible enemy. Yes, even science.'

Science? The Savage frowned. He knew the word. But what it exactly signified he could not say. Shakespeare and the old men of the pueblo had never mentioned science, and from Linda he had only gathered the vaguest hints: science was something you made helicopters with, something that caused you to laugh at the Corn Dances, something that prevented you from being wrinkled and losing your teeth. He made a desperate effort to take the Controller's meaning.

'Yes,' Mustapha Mond was saying, 'that's another item in the cost of stability. It isn't only art that's incompatible with happiness; it's also science. Science is dangerous; we have to keep it most carefully chained and muzzled.'²

1. *chary* [tʃeəri]: wary, cautious about.
2. *chained and muzzled* [mʌzld]: under strict control, like a dangerous dog held with a chain and with a guard over the mouth.

'What?' said Helmholtz, in astonishment. 'But we're always saying that science is everything. It's a hypnopædic platitude.'
'Three times a week between thirteen and seventeen,' put in Bernard.
'And all the science propaganda we do at the College . . .'
'Yes; but what sort of science?' asked Mustapha Mond sarcastically. 'You've had no scientific training, so you can't judge. I was a pretty good physicist in my time. Too good – good enough to realize that all our science is just a cookery book, with an orthodox theory of cooking that nobody's allowed to question, and a list of recipes that mustn't be added to except by special permission from the head cook. I'm the head cook now. But I was an inquisitive young scullion [1] once. I started doing a bit of cooking on my own. Unorthodox cooking, illicit cooking. A bit of real science, in fact.' He was silent.
'What happened?' asked Helmholtz Watson.
The Controller sighed. 'Very nearly what's going to happen to you young men. I was on the point of being sent to an island.'
The words galvanized Bernard into a violent and unseemly [2] activity. 'Send *me* to an island?' He jumped up, ran across the room, and stood gesticulating in front of the Controller. 'You can't send *me*. I haven't done anything. It was the others. I swear it was the others.' He pointed accusingly to Helmholtz and the Savage. 'Oh, please don't send me to Iceland. I promise I'll do what I ought to do. Give me another chance. Please give me another chance.' The tears began to flow. 'I tell you, it's their fault,' he sobbed. 'And not to Iceland. Oh, please, your fordship, please . . .' And in a paroxysm of abjection he threw himself on his knees before the Controller. Mustapha Mond tried to make him get up; but Bernard persisted in his grovelling;[3] the stream of words poured out inexhaustibly. In the end the Controller had to ring for his fourth secretary.

1. *scullion* ['skʌlɪən]: a kitchen boy for unskilled tasks (a job that has largely disappeared since Huxley wrote this).
2. *unseemly* : to be ashamed of, not suited to the situation.
3. *grovelling* : crawling on the floor and pleading, self-abasement.

'Bring three men,' he ordered, 'and take Mr Marx into a bedroom. Give him a good *soma* vaporization and then put him to bed and leave him.'

The fourth secretary went out and returned with three green-uniformed twin footmen. Still shouting and sobbing, Bernard was carried out.

'One would think he was going to have his throat cut,' said the Controller, as the door closed. 'Whereas, if he had the smallest sense, he'd understand that his punishment is really a reward. He's being sent to an island. That's to say, he's being sent to a place where he'll meet the most interesting set of men and women to be found anywhere in the world. All the people who, for one reason or another, have got too self-consciously individual to fit into community-life. All the people who aren't satisfied with orthodoxy, who've got independent ideas of their own. Every one, in a word, who's any one. I almost envy you, Mr Watson.'

Helmholtz laughed. 'Then why aren't you on an island yourself?'

'Because, finally, I preferred this,' the Controller answered. 'I was given the choice: to be sent to an island, where I could have got on with my pure science, or to be taken on to the Controllers' Council with the prospect of succeeding in due course to an actual Controllership. I chose this and let the science go.' After a little silence, 'Sometimes,' he added, 'I rather regret the science. Happiness is a hard master – particularly other people's happiness. A much harder master, if one isn't conditioned to accept it unquestionably, than truth.' He sighed, fell silent again, then continued in a brisker tone. 'Well, duty's duty. One can't consult one's own preferences. I'm interested in truth, I like science. But truth's a menace, science is a public danger. As dangerous as it's been beneficent. It has given us the stablest equilibrium in history. China's was hopelessly insecure by comparison; even the primitive matriarchies weren't steadier than we are. Thanks, I repeat, to science. But we can't allow science to undo its own good work. That's why we so carefully limit the scope of its researches – that's why I almost got sent to an island. We don't allow it to deal with any but the most immediate problems of the moment. All other enquiries are most sedulously discouraged. It's curious,' he went on after a little pause, 'to read what people in the time of Our Ford used to write about scientific progress. They seemed to have imagined that it could be allowed to go on indefinitely, regardless of everything else. Knowledge was the highest good, truth the supreme value; all the rest was secondary and subordinate. True, ideas were beginning to change even then. Our Ford himself did a great deal to shift the emphasis from truth and beauty to comfort and happiness. Mass production demanded the shift. Universal happiness keeps the wheels steadily turning; truth and beauty can't. And, of course, whenever the masses seized political power, then it was happiness rather than truth and beauty that mattered. Still, in spite of everything, unrestricted scientific research was still permitted. People still went on talking about truth and beauty as though they were the sovereign goods. Right up to the time of the Nine Years' War. *That* made them change their tune [1] all right. What's the point of truth or beauty or knowledge when the anthrax bombs are popping all around you ? That was when science first began to be controlled – after the Nine Years' War. People were ready to have even their appetites controlled then. Anything for a quiet life. We've gone on controlling ever since. It hasn't been very good for truth, of course. But it's been very good for happiness. One can't have something for nothing. Happiness has got to be paid for. You're paying for it, Mr Watson – paying because you happen to be too much interested in beauty. I was too much interested in truth; I paid too.'

'But *you* didn't go to an island,' said the Savage, breaking a long silence.

The Controller smiled. 'That's how I paid. By choosing to serve happiness. Other people's – not mine. It's lucky,' he added, after a pause, 'that there are such a lot of islands in the

---

1. *change their tune* : (idiom) adopt a different attitude.

world. I don't know what we should do without them. Put you
all in the lethal chamber, I suppose. By the way, Mr Watson,
would you like a tropical climate? The Marquesas, for example;
or Samoa?[1] Or something rather more bracing?'[2]

Helmholtz rose from his pneumatic chair. 'I should like a
thoroughly bad climate,' he answered. 'I believe one would
write better if the climate were bad. If there were a lot of wind
and storms, for example . . .'

The Controller nodded his approbation. 'I like your spirit,
Mr Watson. I like it very much indeed. As much as I officially
disapprove of it.' He smiled. 'What about the Falkland Islands ?'

'Yes, I think that will do,' Helmholtz answered. 'And now, if
you don't mind, I'll go and see how poor Bernard's getting on.'

1. *Marquesas . . . Samoa* : islands in the South Pacific.
2. *bracing* : that builds up your strength (because it needs
   resistance).

Chapter XVII

ART, science – you seem to have paid a fairly high price for your happiness,' said the Savage, when they were alone. 'Anything else?' 'Well, religion, of course,' replied the Controller. 'There used to be something called God – before the Nine Years' War. But I was forgetting; you know all about God, I suppose.'

'Well . . .' The Savage hesitated. He would have liked to say something about solitude, about night, about the mesa lying pale under the moon, about the precipice, the plunge into shadowy darkness, about death. He would have liked to speak; but there were no words. Not even in Shakespeare.

The Controller, meanwhile, had crossed to the other side of the room and was unlocking a large safe let into the wall between the bookshelves. The heavy door swung open. Rummaging in the darkness within, 'It's a subject,' he said, 'that has always had a great interest for me.' He pulled out a thick black volume. 'You've never read this, for example.'

The Savage took it. '*The Holy Bible, containing the Old and New Testaments,*' he read aloud from the title-page.

'Nor this.' It was a small book and had lost its cover.

'The Imitation of Christ.'[1]

'Nor this.' He handed out another volume.

'The Varieties of Religious Experience. By William James.'[2]

'And I've got plenty more,' Mustapha Mond continued, resuming his seat. 'A whole collection of pornographic old books. God in the safe and Ford on the shelves.' He pointed with a laugh to his avowed library – to shelves of books, the racks full of reading-machine bobbins and sound-track rolls.

'But if you know about God, why don't you tell them?' asked the Savage indignantly. 'Why don't you give them these books about God ?'

'For the same reason as we don't give them *Othello*: they're old; they're about God hundreds of years ago. Not about God now.'

'But God doesn't change.'

'Men do, though.'

'What difference does that make ?'

'All the difference in the world,' said Mustapha Mond. He got up again and walked to the safe. 'There was a man called Cardinal Newman,'[3] he said. 'A cardinal,' he exclaimed parenthetically, 'was a kind of Arch-Community-Songster.'

1. *The Imitation of Christ* : the *Imitatio Christi* is a devotional work in the tradition of Western mysticism that instructs Christians, in language of great limpidity, how to follow Christ's example. It is said to be the work of a German Augustinian canon known as Thomas à Kempis (c. 1380-1471) and to have been translated into more languages than any other book except the Bible.

2. *William James* : (1842-1910), an American psychologist and a leading figure in pragmatism in philosophy. In the Gifford Lectures, published in 1902, he endeavoured to deal seriously with the varieties of religious experiences using an empirical, scientifically acceptable approach – just as Huxley himself was later to do.

3. *Cardinal Newman* : John Henry Newman (1801-90), an English cardinal, responsible for a series of writings presented as *Tracts for the Times* (between 1833 and 1841), the aim of which was to secure a clear basis of doctrine for the Anglican Church; his work for the Tractarian (or Oxford) Movement led him, however, towards the Roman Catholic Church, into which he was received in 1845.

'"I, Pandulph, of fair Milan cardinal."[1] I've read about them in Shakespeare.'

'Of course you have. Well, as I was saying, there was a man called Cardinal Newman. Ah, here's the book.' He pulled it out. 'And while I'm about it I'll take this one too. It's by a man called Maine de Biran.[2] He was a philosopher, if you know what that was.'

'A man who dreams of fewer things than there are in heaven and earth,'[3] said the Savage promptly.

'Quite so. I'll read you one of the things he did dream of in a moment. Meanwhile, listen to what this old Arch-Community-Songster said.' He opened the book at the place marked by a slip of paper and began to read. '"We are not our own [4] any more than what we possess is our own. We did not make ourselves, we cannot be supreme over ourselves. We are not our own masters. We are God's property. Is it not our happiness thus to view the matter? Is it any happiness, or any comfort, to consider that we *are* our own? It may be thought so by the young and prosperous. These may think it a great thing to have everything, as they suppose, their own way – to depend on no one – to have to think of nothing out of sight, to be without the irksomeness [5] of continual acknowledgement, continual prayer, continual reference of what they do to the will of another. But as time goes on, they, as all men, will find that independence was not made

---

1. *"I Pandulph, . . . cardinal"* : Shakespeare, *King John*, III, 1, 138.

2. *Maine de Biran* : French philosopher (1766-1824) who stressed the role of will and self-reflection in our perception of the physical world. Huxley was to write – a long essay about de Biran, published in *Themes and Variations* (1950).

3. *'A man who dreams . . . earth'* : Huxley's joke at the expense of philosophers refers to Hamlet's famous reflection, "There are more things in heaven and earth, Horatio, / Than are dreamt of in your philosophy" – *Hamlet*, 1, 5, 166-7.

4. *"We are not our own . . . to the end . . ."* : quoted (with some cuts) from Sermon 6 in Newman's *Parochial and Plain Sermons*, Volume 5.

5. *irksomeness* ['ɜːksəmnəs]: annoying and tiresome condition.

for man – that it is an unnatural state – will do for a while, but will not carry us on safely to the end . . .'" Mustapha Mond paused, put down the first book and, picking up the other, turned over the pages. 'Take this, for example,' he said, and in his deep voice once more began to read: '"A man grows old;[1] he feels in himself that radical sense of weakness, of listlessness,[2] of discomfort, which accompanies the advance of age; and, feeling thus, imagines himself merely sick, lulling his fears with the notion that this distressing condition is due to some particular cause, from which, as from an illness, he hopes to recover. Vain imaginings ! That sickness is old age; and a horrible disease it is. They say that it is the fear of death and of what comes after death that makes men turn to religion as they advance in years. But my own experience has given me the conviction that, quite apart from any such terrors or imaginings, the religious sentiment tends to develop as we grow older; to develop because, as the passions grow calm, as the fancy and sensibilities are less excited and less excitable, our reason becomes less troubled in its working, less obscured by the images, desires and distractions, in which it used to be absorbed; whereupon God emerges as from behind a cloud; our soul feels, sees, turns towards the source of all light; turns naturally and inevitably; for now that all that gave to the world of sensations its life and charm has begun to leak away from us, now that phenomenal existence is no more bolstered up [3] by impressions from within or from without, we feel the need to lean on something that abides, something that will never play us false – a reality, an absolute and everlasting truth. Yes, we inevitably turn to God; for this religious sentiment is of its nature so pure, so delightful to the soul that experiences it, that it makes up to us for all our other losses.'" Mustapha Mond shut the book and leaned back

1. *"A man grows old . . . our other losses"* : from Maine de Biran's *Intimate Journal*, the entry for 6th and 7th June 1818 (modified by Huxley).

2. *listlessness* : not having the energy or desire to do anything.

3. *bolstered up* : given needed support.

in his chair. 'One of the numerous things in heaven and earth that these philosophers didn't dream about was this' (he waved his hand), 'us, the modern world. "You can only be independent of God while you've got youth and prosperity; independence won't take you safely to the end." Well, we've now got youth and prosperity right up to the end. What follows? Evidently, that we can be independent of God. "The religious sentiment will compensate us for all our losses." But there aren't any losses for us to compensate; religious sentiment is superfluous. And why should we go hunting for a substitute for youthful desires, when youthful desires never fail ? A substitute for distractions, when we go on enjoying all the old fooleries [1] to the very last? What need have we of repose when our minds and bodies continue to delight in activity? of consolation, when we have *soma*? of something immovable, when there is the social order?'

'Then you think there is no God?'

'No, I think there quite probably is one.'

'Then why . . . ?'

Mustapha Mond checked him. 'But he manifests himself in different ways to different men. In pre-modern times he manifested himself as the being that's described in these books. Now . . .'

'How does he manifest himself now?' asked the Savage.

'Well, he manifests himself as an absence; as though he weren't there at all.'

'That's your fault.'

'Call it the fault of civilization. God isn't compatible with machinery and scientific medicine and universal happiness. You must make your choice. Our civilization has chosen machinery and medicine and happiness. That's why I have to keep these books locked up in the safe. They're smut. People would be shocked if . . .'

The Savage interrupted him. 'But isn't it *natural* to feel there's a God?'

---

1. *fooleries* : habitual follies (here, the familiar ways of amusing oneself). The phrase "bygone fooleries" occurs in Shakespeare, *The Winter's Tale*, III, 2, 184.

'You might as well ask if it's natural to do up one's trousers with zippers,' said the Controller sarcastically. 'You remind me of another of those old fellows called Bradley.[1] He defined philosophy as the finding of bad reasons for what one believes by instinct. As if one believed anything by instinct! One believes things because one has been conditioned to believe them. Finding bad reasons for what one believes for other bad reasons – that's philosophy. People believe in God because they've been conditioned to believe in God.'

'But all the same,' insisted the Savage, 'it is natural to believe in God when you're alone – quite alone, in the night, thinking about death . . .'

'But people never are alone now,' said Mustapha Mond. 'We make them hate solitude; and we arrange their lives so that it's almost impossible for them ever to have it.'

The Savage nodded gloomily. At Malpais he had suffered because they had shut him out from the communal activities of the pueblo, in civilized London he was suffering because he could never escape from those communal activities, never be quietly alone.

'Do you remember that bit in *King Lear?*' said the Savage at last: '"The gods are just, and of our pleasant vices make instruments to plague us; the dark and vicious place where thee he got cost him his eyes," and Edmund answers – you remember, he's wounded, he's dying – "Thou hast spoken right; 'tis true. The wheel is come full circle; I am here."[2] What about

1. *Bradley* : Francis Herbert Bradley (1846-1924), a British philosopher whose absolute idealism, as expounded in *Appearance and Reality* (1893), contends that reality can only be known in terms of immediate feeling – beyond that, everything we think is fallible. In the "Preface" Bradley wrote that "Metaphysics is the finding of bad reasons for what we believe upon instinct".

2. *"The gods . . . I am here."* : *King Lear*, V, 3, 170-4. (Edmund, the bastard son of the Earl of Gloucester, represents the "dark and vicious place" of his father's adultery, so there is a kind of justice in the fact that it was Edmund who incriminated his father as a traitor and stood by when Gloucester was punished by having his eyes put out; the wheel of fortune has turned round completely, "the gods are just", and now it is Edmund's turn to be punished.)

that, now? Doesn't there seem to be a God managing things, punishing, rewarding?'

'Well, does there?' questioned the Controller in his turn. 'You can indulge in any number of pleasant vices with a freemartin and run no risks of having your eyes put out by your son's mistress. "The wheel is come full circle; I am here." But where would Edmund be nowadays? Sitting in a pneumatic chair, with his arm round a girl's waist, sucking away at his sex-hormone chewing-gum and looking at the feelies. The gods are just. No doubt. But their code of law is dictated, in the last resort, by the people who organize society; Providence takes its cue [1] from men.'

'Are you sure?' asked the Savage. 'Are you quite sure that the Edmund in that pneumatic chair hasn't been just as heavily punished as the Edmund who's wounded and bleeding to death? The gods are just. Haven't they used his pleasant vices as an instrument to degrade him?'

'Degrade him from what position? As a happy, hard-working, goods-consuming citizen he's perfect. Of course, if you choose some other standard than ours, then perhaps you might say he was degraded. But you've got to stick to one set of postulates. You can't play Electro-magnetic Golf according to the rules of Centrifugal Bumble-puppy.'

'But value dwells not in particular will,' said the Savage. 'It holds his estimate and dignity as well wherein 'tis precious of itself as in the prizer.' [2]

'Come, come,' protested Mustapha Mond, 'that's going rather far, isn't it?'

'If you allowed yourselves to think of God, you wouldn't allow yourselves to be degraded by pleasant vices. You'd have a reason for bearing things patiently, for doing things with courage. I've seen it with the Indians.'

---

1. *takes its cue* [kjuː]: receives its instructions, is put into effect.
2. *'But value dwells . . . the prizer'* : *Troilus and Cressida*, II, 2, 56. (People or things are not valuable simply because someone says they are: they must have some intrinsic qualities that support the estimate).

'I'm sure you have,' said Mustapha Mond. 'But then we aren't Indians. There isn't any need for a civilized man to bear anything that's seriously unpleasant. And as for doing things – Ford forbid that he should get the idea into his head. It would upset the whole social order if men started doing things on their own.'

'What about self-denial, then? If you had a God, you'd have a reason for self-denial.'

'But industrial civilization is only possible when there's no self-denial. Self-indulgence up to the very limits imposed by hygiene and economics. Otherwise the wheels stop turning.'

'You'd have a reason for chastity!' said the Savage, blushing a little as he spoke the words.

'But chastity means passion, chastity means neurasthenia.[1] And passion and neurasthenia mean instability. And instability means the end of civilization. You can't have a lasting civilization without plenty of pleasant vices.'

'But God's the reason for everything noble and fine and heroic. If you had a God . . .'

'My dear young friend,' said Mustapha Mond, 'civilization has absolutely no need of nobility or heroism. These things are symptoms of political inefficiency. In a properly organized society like ours, nobody has any opportunities for being noble or heroic. Conditions have got to be thoroughly unstable before the occasion can arise. Where there are wars, where there are divided allegiances, where there are temptations to be resisted, objects of love to be fought for or defended – there, obviously, nobility and heroism have some sense. But there aren't any wars nowadays. The greatest care is taken to prevent you from loving any one too much. There's no such thing as a divided allegiance; you're so conditioned that you can't help doing what you ought to do. And what you ought to do is on the whole so pleasant, so

1. *neurasthenia* [ˌnjʊərəsˈθiːnɪə]: (obsolete term) form of neurosis characterised by extreme inability to act. (Satirical: the condition of being in love and not having one's love confirmed or fulfilled is reduced to its physiological symptoms and given a 'scientific' label.)

many of the natural impulses are allowed free play, that there really aren't any temptations to resist. And if ever, by some unlucky chance, anything unpleasant should somehow happen, why, there's always *soma* to give you a holiday from the facts. And there's always *soma* to calm your anger, to reconcile you to your enemies, to make you patient and long-suffering. In the past you could only accomplish these things by making a great effort and after years of hard moral training. Now, you swallow two or three half-gramme tablets, and there you are. Anybody can be virtuous now. You can carry at least half your morality about in a bottle. Christianity without tears – that's what *soma* is.'

'But the tears are necessary. Don't you remember what Othello said? "If after every tempest come such calms, may the winds blow till they have wakened death."[1] There's a story one of the old Indians used to tell us, about the Girl of Mátsaki. The young men who wanted to marry her had to do a morning's hoeing [2] in her garden. It seemed easy; but there were flies and mosquitoes, magic ones. Most of the young men simply couldn't stand the biting and stinging. But the one that could – he got the girl.'

'Charming ! But in civilized countries,' said the Controller, 'you can have girls without hoeing for them; and there aren't any flies or mosquitoes to sting you. We got rid of [3] them all centuries ago.'

The Savage nodded, frowning. 'You got rid of them. Yes, that's just like you. Getting rid of everything unpleasant instead of learning to put up with it. Whether 'tis nobler in the mind to suffer the slings and arrows of outrageous fortune, or to take arms against a sea of troubles and by opposing end them. . .[4] But

---

1. *"If after every tempest . . . death"* : *Othello*, II, 1, 187.
2. *hoeing* : working with a hoe, loosening the soil.
3. *got rid of* : eliminated, removed (something unwanted). Here it contrasts with "putting up with" (learning to accept) unpleasant things.
4. *Whether 'tis nobler . . . end them* : *Hamlet*, III, 1, 57-60. (The famous "To be or not to be" soliloquy.)

you don't do either. Neither suffer nor oppose. You just abolish the slings and arrows. It's too easy.'

He was suddenly silent, thinking of his mother. In her room on the thirty-seventh floor, Linda had floated in a sea of singing lights and perfumed caresses – floated away, out of space, out of time, out of the prison of her memories, her habits, her aged and bloated body. And Tomakin, ex-Director of Hatcheries and Conditioning, Tomakin was still on holiday – on holiday from humiliation and pain, in a world where he could not hear those words, that derisive laughter, could not see that hideous face, feel those moist and flabby arms round his neck, in a beautiful world . . .

'What you need,' the Savage went on, 'is something *with* tears for a change. Nothing costs enough here.'

('Twelve and a half million dollars,' Henry Foster had protested when the Savage told him that. 'Twelve and a half million – that's what the new Conditioning Centre cost. Not a cent less.')

'Exposing what is mortal and unsure to all that fortune, death and danger dare, even for an egg-shell.[1] Isn't there something in that?' he asked, looking up at Mustapha Mond. 'Quite apart from God – though of course God would be a reason for it. Isn't there something in living dangerously?'

'There's a great deal in it,' the Controller replied. 'Men and women must have their adrenals [2] stimulated from time to time.'

'What?' questioned the Savage, uncomprehending.

'It's one of the conditions of perfect health. That's why we've made the V.P.S. treatments compulsory.'

'V.P.S.?'

'Violent Passion Surrogate. Regularly once a month. We flood the whole system with adrenin. It's the complete

---

1. *'Exposing . . . egg-shell.* : Hamlet, IV, 4, 51-3. (Hamlet reflects that human honour requires us to be prepared to risk our life for what we consider important.)
2. *adrenals* [ə'driːnlz]: that is, the adrenal glands, ductless glands near the kidneys which produce the hormone adrenalin.

physiological equivalent of fear and rage. All the tonic effects of murdering Desdemona and being murdered by Othello, without any of the inconveniences.'

'But I like the inconveniences.'

'We don't,' said the Controller 'We prefer to do things comfortably.'

'But I don't want comfort. I want God, I want poetry, I want real danger, I want freedom, I want goodness. I want sin.'

'In fact,' said Mustapha Mond, 'you're claiming the right to be unhappy.'

'All right, then,' said the Savage defiantly, 'I'm claiming the right to be unhappy.'

'Not to mention the right to grow old and ugly and impotent; the right to have syphilis and cancer; the right to have too little to eat; the right to be lousy;[1] the right to live in constant apprehension of what may happen to-morrow; the right to catch typhoid; the right to be tortured by unspeakable pains of every kind.'

There was a long silence.

'I claim them all,' said the Savage at last.

Mustapha Mond shrugged his shoulders. 'You're welcome,' he said.

---

1. *lousy* ['lauzi]: infested with lice.

Chapter XVIII

THE door was ajar; they entered.

'John!'

From the bathroom came an unpleasant and characteristic sound.

'Is there anything the matter?' Helmholtz called.

There was no answer. The unpleasant sound was repeated, twice; there was silence. Then, with a click, the bathroom door opened and, very pale, the Savage emerged.

'I say,' Helmholtz exclaimed solicitously, 'you do look ill, John!'

'Did you eat something that didn't agree with you?' asked Bernard.

The Savage nodded. 'I ate civilization.'

'What?'

'It poisoned me; I was defiled.[1] And then,' he added, in a lower tone, 'I ate my own wickedness.'

'Yes, but what exactly . . . ? I mean, just now you were . . .'

'Now I am purified,' said the Savage. 'I drank some mustard [2] and warm water.'

---

1. *defiled* [dɪˈfaɪld]: made impure (but not used for food poisoning, so not explicable in relation to his vomiting.)

2. *mustard* : a pungent condiment, here used as an emetic.

The others stared at him in astonishment. 'Do you mean to say that you were doing it on purpose?' asked Bernard.

'That's how the Indians always purify themselves.' He sat down and, sighing, passed his hand across his forehead. 'I shall rest for a few minutes,' he said. 'I'm rather tired.'

'Well, I'm not surprised,' said Helmholtz. After a silence, 'We've come to say good-bye,' he went on in another tone. 'We're off to-morrow morning.'

'Yes, we're off to-morrow,' said Bernard, on whose face the Savage remarked a new expression of determined resignation. 'And by the way, John,' he continued, leaning forward in his chair and laying a hand on the Savage's knee, 'I want to say how sorry I am about everything that happened yesterday.' He blushed. 'How ashamed,' he went on, in spite of the unsteadiness of his voice, 'how really . . .'

The Savage cut him short and, taking his hand, affectionately pressed it.

'Helmholtz was wonderful to me,' Bernard resumed, after a little pause. 'If it hadn't been for him, I should . . .'

'Now, now,' Helmholtz protested.

There was a silence. In spite of their sadness – because of it, even; for their sadness was the symptom of their love for one another – the three young men were happy.

'I went to see the Controller this morning,' said the Savage at last.

'What for?'

'To ask if I mightn't go to the islands with you.'

'And what did he say?' asked Helmholtz eagerly.

The Savage shook his head. 'He wouldn't let me.'

'Why not?'

'He said he wanted to go on with the experiment. But I'm damned,' the Savage added, with sudden fury, 'I'm damned if I'll go on being experimented with. Not for all the Controllers in the world. I shall go away to-morrow too.'

'But where?' the others asked in unison.

The Savage shrugged his shoulders. 'Anywhere. I don't care. So long as I can be alone.'

From Guildford the down-line [1] followed the Wey valley to Godalming, then, over Milford and Witley, proceeded to Haslemere and on through Petersfield towards Portsmouth. Roughly parallel to it, the up-line passed over Worplesden, Tongham, Puttenham, Elstead and Grayshott. Between the Hog's Back [2] and Hindhead there were points where the two lines were not more than six or seven kilometres apart. The distance was too small for careless flyers – particularly at night and when they had taken half a gramme too much. There had been accidents. Serious ones. It had been decided to deflect the up-line a few kilometres to the west. Between Grayshott and Tongham four abandoned air-lighthouses [3] marked the course of the old Portsmouth-to-London road. The skies above them were silent and deserted. It was over Selborne, Borden and Farnham that the helicopters now ceaselessly hummed and roared.

The Savage had chosen as his hermitage the old lighthouse which stood on the crest of the hill between Puttenham and Elstead. The building was of ferro-concrete and in excellent condition – almost too comfortable, the Savage had thought when he first explored the place, almost too civilizedly luxurious. He pacified his conscience by promising himself a compensatingly harder self-discipline, purifications the more complete and thorough. His first night in the hermitage was, deliberately, a sleepless one. He spent the hours on his knees praying, now to that Heaven from which the guilty Claudius [4] had begged forgiveness, now in Zuñi to Awonawilona, now to

1. *down-line* : the air traffic lane going south-west from London, passing over the towns listed down to Portsmouth, on the South Coast; the "up-line" is for traffic returning to London. (Words borrowed from railway terminology.)
2. *the Hog's Back* : a hill in Surrey. It is the name given to a ridge of the North Downs between Guildford and Farnham, with marvellous views over the open fields and woods. Huxley was born in Godalming and lived in this area as a boy.
3. *air-lighthouses* : towers with lights at the top to guide air traffic.
4. *Claudius* : in *Hamlet*, III, 3, King Claudius, who is guilty of murder, is unable to pray – "My words fly up, my thoughts remain below".

Jesus and Pookong, now to his own guardian animal, the eagle. From time to time he stretched out his arms as though he were on the cross, and held them thus through long minutes of an ache that gradually increased till it became a tremulous and excruciating agony; held them, in voluntary crucifixion, while he repeated, through clenched teeth (the sweat, meanwhile, pouring down his face), 'Oh, forgive me! Oh, make me pure! Oh, help me to be good!' again and again, till he was on the point of fainting from the pain.

When morning came, he felt he had earned the right to inhabit the lighthouse; yes, even though there still *was* glass in most of the windows, even though the view from the platform *was* so fine. For the very reason why he had chosen the lighthouse had become almost instantly a reason for going somewhere else. He had decided to live there because the view was so beautiful, because, from his vantage point, he seemed to be looking out on to the incarnation of a divine being. But who was he to be pampered with the daily and hourly sight of loveliness? Who was he to be living in the visible presence of God? All he deserved to live in was some filthy sty,[1] some blind hole in the ground. Stiff and still aching after his long night of pain, but for that very reason inwardly reassured, he climbed up to the platform of his tower, he looked out over the bright sunrise world which he had regained the right to inhabit. On the north the view was bounded by the long chalk ridge of the Hog's Back, from behind whose eastern extremity rose the towers of the seven skyscrapers which constituted Guildford. Seeing them, the Savage made a grimace; but he was to become reconciled to them in course of time; for at night they twinkled gaily with geometrical constellations, or else, flood-lighted,[2] pointed their luminous fingers (with a gesture whose significance nobody in England but the Savage now understood) solemnly towards the plumbless [3] mysteries of heaven.

1. *sty* : a building for pigs.
2. *flood-lighted* : illuminated from a distance by large lamps.
3. *plumbless* ['plʌmləs]: that cannot be measured, unfathomable.

In the valley which separated the Hog's Back from the sandy hill on which the lighthouse stood, Puttenham was a modest little village nine stories high, with silos, a poultry farm, and a small vitamin-D factory. On the other side of the lighthouse, towards the south, the ground fell away in long slopes of heather to a chain of ponds.

Beyond them, above the intervening woods, rose the fourteen-story tower of Elstead. Dim in the hazy English air, Hindhead and Selborne invited the eye into a blue romantic distance. But it was not alone the distance that had attracted the Savage to his lighthouse; the near was as seductive as the far. The woods, the open stretches of heather and yellow gorse, the clumps of Scotch firs, the shining ponds with their overhanging birch trees, their water lilies, their beds of rushes [1] – these were beautiful and, to an eye accustomed to the aridities of the American desert, astonishing. And then the solitude! Whole days passed during which he never saw a human being. The lighthouse was only a quarter of an hour's flight from the Charing-T Tower; but the hills of Malpais were hardly more deserted than this Surrey heath. The crowds that daily left London left it only to play Electro-magnetic Golf or Tennis. Puttenham possessed no links,[2] the nearest Riemann-surfaces were at Guildford. Flowers and a landscape were the only attractions here. And so, as there was no good reason for coming, nobody came. During the first days the Savage lived alone and undisturbed.

Of the money which, on his first arrival, John had received for his personal expenses, most had been spent on his equipment. Before leaving London he had bought four viscose-woollen blankets, rope and string, nails, glue, a few tools, matches (though he intended in due course to make a fire drill),[3]

1. *beds of rushes* : areas filled with plants of the family Juncaceae, with small flowers, long stems and grasslike cylindrical leaves, and which grow in wet places.
2. *links* : golf courses. (The word means areas of flat ground.)
3. *fire drill* : in this case, a stick which will generate fire when spun between the hands in a suitable hole with some dry material.

some pots and pans, two dozen packets of seeds, and ten kilogrammes of wheat flour. 'No, *not* synthetic starch and cotton-waste flour-substitute,' he had insisted. 'Even though it is more nourishing.' But when it came to pan-glandular [1] biscuits and vitaminized beef-surrogate, he had not been able to resist the shopman's persuasion. Looking at the tins now, he bitterly reproached himself for his weakness. Loathsome civilized stuff! He had made up his mind that he would never eat it, even if he were starving. 'That'll teach them,' he thought vindictively. It would also teach him.

He counted his money. The little that remained would be enough, he hoped, to tide him over [2] the winter. By next spring, his garden would be producing enough to make him independent of the outside world. Meanwhile, there would always be game.[3] He had seen plenty of rabbits, and there were water-fowl on the ponds. He set to work at once to make a bow and arrows.

There were ash trees near the lighthouse and, for arrow shafts, a whole copse [4] full of beautifully straight hazel saplings. He began by felling a young ash,[5] cut out six feet of unbranched stem, stripped off the bark and, paring by paring,[6] shaved away the white wood, as old Mitsima had taught him, until he had a stave [7] of his own height, stiff at the thickened centre, lively and quick at the slender tips. The work gave him an intense pleasure. After those weeks of idleness in London, with nothing to do, whenever he wanted anything, but to press a switch or

1. *pan-glandular* : containing secretions from many glands.
2. *tide him over* : enable him to survive until the end of.
3. *game* : wild animals that can be hunted for food.
4. *copse . . . hazel saplings* : a small wood of young, periodically cut, hazel trees.
5. *ash* : tree (genus, *Fraxinus*) with hard, tough wood suitable for making a bow.
6. *paring by paring* ['peərɪŋ]: cutting away thin strips of wood one after another.
7. *stave* ['steɪv]: a strong, straight piece of wood.

turn a handle, it was pure delight to be doing something that demanded skill and patience.

He had almost finished whittling [1] the stave into shape, when he realized with a start that he was singing – *singing!* It was as though, stumbling upon himself from the outside, he had suddenly caught himself out, taken himself flagrantly at fault. Guiltily he blushed. After all, it was not to sing and enjoy himself that he had come here. It was to escape further contamination by the filth of civilized life; it was to be purified and made good; it was actively to make amends. He realized to his dismay that, absorbed in the whittling of his bow, he had forgotten what he had sworn to himself he would constantly remember – poor Linda, and his own murderous unkindness to her, and those loathsome twins, swarming like lice across the mystery of her death, insulting, with their presence, not merely his own grief and repentance, but the very gods themselves. He had sworn to remember, he had sworn unceasingly to make amends. And here was he, sitting happily over his bow-stave, singing, actually singing....

He went indoors, opened the box of mustard, and put some water to boil on the fire.

Half an hour later, three Delta-Minus landworkers from one of the Puttenham Bokanovsky Groups happened to be driving to Elstead and, at the top of the hill, were astonished to see a young man standing outside the abandoned lighthouse stripped to the waist and hitting himself with a whip of knotted cords. His back was horizontally streaked with crimson, and from weal [2] to weal ran thin trickles of blood. The driver of the lorry pulled up at the side of the road and, with his two companions, stared open-mouthed at the extraordinary spectacle. One, two, three – they counted the strokes. After the eighth, the young man interrupted his self-punishment to run to the wood's edge and there be violently sick. When he had finished, he picked up the whip and began hitting himself again. Nine, ten, eleven, twelve . . .

1. *whittling* : cutting or scraping away very thin strips.
2. *weal* : raised, inflamed mark (caused by the whip).

'Ford!' whispered the driver. And his twins were of the same opinion.

'Fordey!' they said.

Three days later, like turkey buzzards [1] settling on a corpse, the reporters came.

Dried and hardened over a slow fire of green wood, the bow was ready. The Savage was busy on his arrows. Thirty hazel sticks had been whittled and dried, tipped with sharp nails, carefully nocked.[2] He had made a raid one night on the Puttenham poultry farm, and now had feathers enough to equip a whole armoury. It was at work upon the feathering of his shafts that the first of the reporters found him. Noiseless on his pneumatic shoes, the man came up behind him.

'Good-morning, Mr Savage,' he said. 'I am the representative of *The Hourly Radio.*'

Startled as though by the bite of a snake, the Savage sprang to his feet, scattering arrows, feathers, glue-pot and brush in all directions.

'I beg your pardon,' said the reporter, with genuine compunction. 'I had no intention . . .' He touched his hat – the aluminium stove-pipe hat [3] in which he carried his wireless receiver and transmitter. 'Excuse my not taking it off,' he said. 'It's a bit heavy. Well, as I was saying, I am the representative of *The Hourly . . .*'

'What do you want?' asked the Savage, scowling.[4] The reporter returned his most ingratiating smile.

'Well, of course, our readers would be profoundly interested . . .' He put his head on one side, his smile became almost coquettish. 'Just a few words from you, Mr Savage.' And

1. *turkey buzzards* ['tɜːki 'bʌzədz]: a kind of American vulture (Cathartes aura) that feeds on dead animals (carrion).
2. *nocked* : notches, or grooves, had been made in the arrows, to receive the bowstring.
3. *stove-pipe hat* : tall cylindrical hat (usually of silk) that looks like the tube above a stove.
4. *scowling* ['skaʊlɪŋ]: with a bad-tempered expression on his face.

rapidly, with a series of ritual gestures, he uncoiled two wires connected to the portable battery buckled round his waist; plugged them simultaneously into the sides of his aluminium hat; touched a spring on the crown – and antennæ shot up into the air; touched another spring on the peak of the brim – and, like a jack-in-the-box, out jumped a microphone and hung there, quivering, six inches in front of his nose; pulled down a pair of receivers over his ears; pressed a switch on the left side of the hat – and from within came a faint waspy buzzing; turned a knob on the right – and the buzzing was interrupted by a stethoscopic wheeze and crackle,[1] by hiccoughs and sudden squeaks. 'Hullo,' he said to the microphone, 'hullo, hullo . . .' A bell suddenly rang inside his hat. 'Is that you, Edzel? Primo Mellon [2] speaking. Yes, I've got hold of him. Mr Savage will now take the microphone and say a few words. Won't you, Mr Savage?' He looked up at the Savage with another of those winning smiles of his. 'Just tell our readers why you came here. What made you leave London (hold on, Edzel!) so very suddenly. And, of course, that whip.' (The Savage started. How did they know about the whip?) 'We're all crazy to know about the whip. And then something about Civilization. You know the sort of stuff. "What I think of the Civilized Girl." Just a few words, a very few ...'

The Savage obeyed with a disconcerting literalness. Five words he uttered and no more – five words, the same as those he had said to Bernard about the Arch-Community-Songster of Canterbury.

1. *stethoscopic wheeze and crackle* : noises of interference and static on the radio waves, sounding like coughing heard through a stethoscope.

2. *Primo Mellon* : The first name commemorates Miguel Primo de Rivera (1870-1930), dictator of Spain from 1923 to 1930, and his son José Antonio Primo de Rivera (1903-36), Spanish politician and founder of Falangism. The surname is that of Andrew William Mellon (1855-1937), U.S. banker and Secretary of the Treasury from 1921 to 1932, was involved in directing and developing many industrial enterprises.

'*Háni! Sons éso tse-ná!*' And seizing the reporter by the shoulder, he spun him round (the young man revealed himself invitingly well-covered),[1] aimed and, with all the force and accuracy of a champion foot-and-mouth-baller,[2] delivered a most prodigious kick.

Eight minutes later, a new edition of The Hourly Radio was on sale in the streets of London. 'HOURLY RADIO REPORTER HAS COCCYX [3] KICKED BY MYSTERY SAVAGE,' ran the headlines on the front page. 'SENSATION IN SURREY.'

'Sensation even in London,' thought the reporter when, on his return, he read the words. And a very painful sensation, what was more. He sat down gingerly to his luncheon.

Undeterred [4] by that cautionary bruise on their colleague's coccyx, four other reporters, representing the New York *Times*, the Frankfurt *Four-Dimensional Continuum*, *The Fordian Science Monitor*, and *The Delta Mirror*,[5] called that afternoon at the lighthouse and met with receptions of progressively increasing violence.

From a safe distance and still rubbing his buttocks, 'Benighted fool!' shouted the man from *The Fordian Science Monitor*, 'why don't you take *soma*?'

'Get away!' The Savage shook his fist.

---

1. *revealed himself invitingly well-covered* : the young's man bottom invited a kick, being so plump.

2. *foot-and-mouth-baller* : presumably football, like the other games, has been made more complicated; Huxley has made it sound more like a disease (foot-and-mouth disease, which affects cattle) than a sport.

3. COCCYX ['kɒksɪks]: triangular bone at the lower end of the spinal column.

4. *Undeterred* [ˌʌndɪ'tɜːd]: not discouraged or put off (from doing something).

5. *The Fordian Science Monitor and The Delta Mirror* : *The Christian Science Monitor* is a daily newspaper published in Boston, U.S.A., the city in which the Christian Science movement was founded in 1892, with the aim of restoring the "lost element of healing" to Christianity; *The Daily Mirror*, an English newspaper founded in 1903, has always had a largely working-class readership.

The other retreated a few steps, then turned round again.
'Evil's an unreality if you take a couple of grammes.'
'*Kohakwa iyathtokyai!*' The tone was menacingly derisive.
'Pain's a delusion.'
'Oh, is it?' said the Savage and, picking up a thick hazel
switch, strode forward.

The man from *The Fordian Science Monitor* made a dash for
his helicopter.

After that the Savage was left for a time in peace. A few
helicopters came and hovered inquisitively round the tower. He
shot an arrow into the importunately nearest of them. It pierced
the aluminium floor of the cabin; there was a shrill yell, and the
machine went rocketing up into the air with all the acceleration
that its super-charger could give it. The others, in future, kept
their distance respectfully. Ignoring their tiresome humming (he
likened himself in his imagination to one of the suitors of the
Maiden of Mátsaki, unmoved and persistent among the winged
vermin), the Savage dug at what was to be his garden. After a
time the vermin evidently became bored and flew away; for
hours at a stretch the sky above his head was empty and, but for
the larks, silent.

The weather was breathlessly hot, there was thunder in the
air. He had dug all the morning and was resting, stretched out
along the floor. And suddenly the thought of Lenina was a real
presence, naked and tangible, saying 'Sweet!' and 'Put your
arms round me!' – in shoes and socks, perfumed. Impudent
strumpet! But oh, oh, her arms round his neck, the lifting of her
breasts, her mouth! Eternity was in our lips and eyes. Lenina . . .
No, no, no, no! He sprang to his feet and, half naked as he was,
ran out of the house. At the edge of the heath stood a clump of
hoary juniper bushes.[1] He flung himself against them, he
embraced, not the smooth body of his desires, but an armful of
green spikes. Sharp, with a thousand points, they pricked him.

---

1. *clump of hoary juniper bushes* ['hɔːri 'dʒuːnɪpə 'buʃɪz]: group of spiky
   evergreen shrubs ("hoary" means covered with short, white hairs;
   perhaps a play on words, because it sounds like "whore-y").

He tried to think of poor Linda, breathless and dumb, with her clutching hands and the unutterable terror in her eyes. Poor Linda whom he had sworn to remember. But it was still the presence of Lenina that haunted him. Lenina whom he had promised to forget. Even through the stab and sting of the juniper needles, his wincing [1] flesh was aware of her, unescapably real. 'Sweet, sweet . . . And if you wanted me too, why didn't you . . .'

The whip was hanging on a nail by the door, ready to hand against the arrival of reporters. In a frenzy the Savage ran back to the house, seized it, whirled it. The knotted cords bit into his flesh.

'Strumpet! Strumpet!' he shouted at every blow as though it were Lenina (and how frantically, without knowing it, he wished it were!), white, warm, scented, infamous Lenina that he was flogging thus. 'Strumpet!' And then, in a voice of despair, 'Oh, Linda, forgive me. Forgive me, God. I'm bad. I'm wicked. I'm . . . No, no, you strumpet, you strumpet!'

From his carefully constructed hide in the wood three hundred metres away, Darwin Bonaparte,[2] the Feely Corporation's most expert big-game photographer, had watched the whole proceedings. Patience and skill had been rewarded. He had spent three days sitting inside the bole of an artificial oak tree, three nights crawling on his belly through the heather, hiding microphones in gorse bushes, burying wires in the soft grey sand. Seventy-two hours of profound discomfort. But now the great moment had come – the greatest, Darwin Bonaparte had time to reflect, as he moved among his instruments, the greatest since his taking of the famous all-howling stereoscopic

1. *wincing* : reacting to pain by some involuntary movement. (Unorthodox usage: it is John who is "wincing" and who "was aware", not his flesh. The word "flesh" is a synecdoche which very effectively communicates his identification with his pain.)

2. *Darwin Bonaparte* : references to Charles Darwin (1809-82), the English naturalist whose theory of evolution by natural selection radically changed the way humans thought of themselves; and Napoleon Bonaparte (1769-1821), who ended his days imprisoned on the island of St. Helena (mentioned as a place of exile in Ch. 12).

feely of the gorillas' wedding. 'Splendid,' he said to himself, as the Savage started his astonishing performance. 'Splendid!' He kept his telescopic cameras carefully aimed – glued to their moving objective; clapped on a higher power to get a close-up of the frantic and distorted face (admirable!); switched over, for half a minute, to slow motion (an exquisitely comical effect, he promised himself); listened in, meanwhile, to the blows, the groans, the wild and raving words that were being recorded on the sound-track at the edge of his film, tried the effect of a little amplification (yes, that was decidedly better); was delighted to hear, in a momentary lull, the shrill singing of a lark; wished the Savage would turn round so that he could get a good close-up of the blood on his back – and almost instantly (what astonishing luck!) the accommodating fellow did turn round, and he was able to take a perfect close-up.

'Well, that was grand!' he said to himself when it was all over. 'Really grand!' He mopped his face. When they had put in the feely effects at the studio, it would be a wonderful film. Almost as good, thought Darwin Bonaparte, as the *Sperm Whale's Love-Life* – and that, by Ford, was saying a good deal!

Twelve days later *The Savage of Surrey* had been released and could be seen, heard and felt in every first-class feely-palace in Western Europe.

The effect of Darwin Bonaparte's film was immediate and enormous. On the afternoon which followed the evening of its release, John's rustic solitude was suddenly broken by the arrival overhead of a great swarm of helicopters.

He was digging in his garden – digging, too, in his own mind, laboriously turning up the substance of his thought. Death – and he drove in his spade once, and again, and yet again. And all our yesterdays have lighted fools the way to dusty death.[1] A convincing thunder rumbled through the words. He lifted another spadeful of earth. Why had Linda

---

1. *And all our yesterdays . . . death* : *Macbeth*, V, 5, 22-3. (John proceeds to recall some of the most memorable speeches in Shakespeare's plays, all concerned with dying.)

died? Why had she been allowed to become gradually less than human and at last . . . He shuddered. A good kissing carrion.[1] He planted his foot on his spade and stamped it fiercely into the tough ground. As flies to wanton boys are we to the gods; they kill us for their sport.[2] Thunder again; words that proclaimed themselves true – truer somehow than truth itself. And yet that same Gloucester had called them ever-gentle gods.[3] Besides, thy best of rest is sleep, and that thou oft provok'st; yet grossly fear'st thy death which is no more. No more [4] than sleep. Sleep. Perchance to dream.[5] His spade struck against a stone; he stooped to pick it up. For in that sleep of death, what dreams . . .?

A humming overhead had become a roar; and suddenly he was in shadow, there was something between the sun and him. He looked up, startled, from his digging, from his thoughts; looked up in a dazzled bewilderment, his mind still wandering in that other world of truer-than-truth, still focussed on the immensities of death and deity; looked up and saw, close above him, the swarm of hovering machines. Like locusts they came, hung poised, descended all around him on the heather. And from out of the bellies of these giant grasshoppers stepped men in white viscose-flannels, women (for the weather was hot) in acetate-shantung pyjamas or velveteen shorts and sleeveless, half-unzippered singlets – one couple from each. In a few minutes there were dozens of them, standing in a wide circle

1. *A good kissing carrion* : Hamlet, II, 2, 183. (A foul image of the decomposition of a dead dog being *kissed*, or encouraged, by the sun.)
2. *As flies . . . sport* : King Lear, IV, 1, 38-9.
3. *ever-gentle gods* : King Lear, IV, 6, 221.
4. *thy best of rest . . . no more* : Shakespeare, *Measure for Measure*, III, 1, 17-19. (Death is no different from sleep, which is the best rest we get, and certainly not to be feared.)
5. *Sleep. Perchance to dream* : Hamlet, III,1, 65. (What if we have bad dreams after death: "ay, there's the rub" [the impediment] continues Hamlet, but Huxley, with ironic wit, offers a clumsy, over-literal illustration of it by having John's spade hit an obstruction, after which he returns to the next line of Hamlet's speech.)

round the lighthouse, staring, laughing, clicking their cameras, throwing (as to an ape) peanuts, packets of sex-hormone chewing-gum, pan-glandular *petits beurres*.[1] And every moment – for across the Hog's Back the stream of traffic now flowed unceasingly – their numbers increased. As in a nightmare, the dozens became scores, the scores hundreds.

The Savage had retreated towards cover, and now, in the posture of an animal at bay, stood with his back to the wall of the lighthouse, staring from face to face in speechless horror, like a man out of his senses.

From this stupor he was aroused to a more immediate sense of reality by the impact on his cheek of a well-aimed packet of chewing-gum. A shock of startling pain – and he was broad awake, awake and fiercely angry.

'Go away!' he shouted.

The ape had spoken; there was a burst of laughter and hand-clapping. 'Good old Savage! Hurrah, hurrah!' And through the babel he heard cries of: 'Whip, whip, the whip!'

Acting on the word's suggestion, he seized the bunch of knotted cords from its nail behind the door and shook it at his tormentors.

There was a yell of ironical applause.

Menacingly he advanced towards them. A woman cried out in fear. The line wavered at its most immediately threatened point, then stiffened again, stood firm. The consciousness of being in overwhelming force had given these sightseers a courage which the Savage had not expected of them. Taken aback,[2] he halted and looked round.

'Why don't you leave me alone?' There was an almost plaintive note in his anger.

'Have a few magnesium-salted almonds!'[3] said the man who, if the Savage were to advance, would be the first to be attacked.

---

1. *petits beurres* : small biscuits made with butter.
2. *Taken aback* : disconcerted, caught by surprise.
3. *magnesium-salted almonds* : nuts coated with magnesium salts needed by the body.

He held out a packet. 'They're really very good, you know,' he added, with a rather nervous smile of propitiation. 'And the magnesium salts will help to keep you young.'

The Savage ignored his offer. 'What do you want with me?' he asked, turning from one grinning face to another. 'What do you want with me?'

'The whip,' answered a hundred voices confusedly. 'Do the whipping stunt. Let's see the whipping stunt.'

Then, in unison and on a slow, heavy rhythm, 'We – want – the whip,' shouted a group at the end of the line. 'We – want – the whip.'

Others at once took up the cry, and the phrase was repeated, parrot-fashion,[1] again and again, with an ever-growing volume of sound, until, by the seventh or eighth reiteration, no other word was being spoken. 'We – want – the whip.'

They were all crying together; and, intoxicated by the noise, the unanimity, the sense of rhythmical atonement, they might, it seemed, have gone on for hours – almost indefinitely. But at about the twenty-fifth repetition the proceedings were startlingly interrupted. Yet another helicopter had arrived from across the Hog's Back, hung poised above the crowd, then dropped within a few yards of where the Savage was standing, in the open space between the line of sightseers and the lighthouse. The roar of the air screws momentarily drowned the shouting; then, as the machine touched the ground and the engines were turned off: 'We – want – the whip; we – want – the whip,' broke out again in the same loud, insistent monotone.

The door of the helicopter opened, and out stepped, first a fair and ruddy-faced young man, then, in green velveteen shorts, white shirt, and jockey cap, a young woman.

At the sight of the young woman, the Savage started, recoiled, turned pale.

The young woman stood, smiling at him – an uncertain, imploring, almost abject smile. The seconds passed. Her lips

---

1. *parrot-fashion* : without thought, like a parrot repeating words.

moved, she was saying something; but the sound of her voice was covered by the loud reiterated refrain of the sightseers. 'We – want – the whip! We – want – the whip!'

The young woman pressed both hands to her left side, and on that peach-bright, doll-beautiful face of hers appeared a strangely incongruous expression of yearning distress. Her blue eyes seemed to grow larger, brighter; and suddenly two tears rolled down her cheeks. Inaudibly, she spoke again; then, with a quick, impassioned gesture, stretched out her arms towards the Savage, stepped forward.

'We – want – the whip ! We – want . . .'

And all of a sudden they had what they wanted.

'Strumpet!' The Savage had rushed at her like a madman.'Fitchew!'[1] Like a madman, he was slashing at her with his whip of small cords.

Terrified, she had turned to flee, had tripped and fallen in the heather. 'Henry, Henry!' she shouted. But her ruddy-faced companion had bolted out of harm's way behind the helicopter.

With a whoop of delighted excitement the line broke; there was a convergent stampede towards that magnetic centre of attraction. Pain was a fascinating horror.

'Fry, lechery, fry!'[2] Frenzied, the Savage slashed again.

Hungrily they gathered round, pushing and scrambling like swine about the trough.[3]

'Oh, the flesh!' The Savage ground his teeth. This time it was on his shoulders that the whip descended. 'Kill it, kill it!'

Drawn by the fascination of the horror of pain and, from within, impelled by that habit of co-operation, that desire for unanimity and atonement, which their conditioning had so

---

1. *'Fitchew!'* : in *Othello*, IV, 1, 150, the word is used to refer contemptuously to a woman ("a perfumed one") who plays on her sexual attractiveness; it means polecat, an animal that has scent-glands it uses when threatened. Cf. note 4, p 204.

2. *'Fry, lechery, fry!'* : *Troilus and Cressida*, V, 2, 57.

3. *trough* [trɒf]: long, narrow, open vessel or box in which animals are given their food and drink.

ineradicably implanted in them, they began to mime the frenzy of his gestures striking at one another as the Savage struck at his own rebellious flesh, or at that plump incarnation of turpitude [1] writhing in the heather at his feet.

'Kill it, kill it, kill it . . .' the Savage went on shouting.

Then suddenly somebody started singing 'Orgy-porgy,' and in a moment they had all caught up the refrain and, singing, had begun to dance. Orgy-porgy, round and round and round, beating one another in six-eight time. Orgy-porgy . . .

It was after midnight when the last of the helicopters took its flight. Stupefied by *soma*, and exhausted by a long-drawn frenzy of sensuality, the Savage lay sleeping in the heather. The sun was already high when he awoke. He lay for a moment, blinking in owlish [2] incomprehension at the light; then suddenly remembered – everything.

'Oh, my God, my God!' He covered his eyes with his hand.

That evening the swarm of helicopters that came buzzing across the Hog's Back was a dark cloud ten kilometres long. The description of last night's orgy of atonement [3] had been in all the papers.

'Savage!' called the first arrivals, as they alighted from their machine. 'Mr Savage!'

There was no answer.

The door of the lighthouse was ajar. They pushed it open and walked into a shuttered twilight. Through an archway on the further side of the room they could see the bottom of the staircase that led up to the higher floors. Just under the crown of the arch dangled [4] a pair of feet.

1. *turpitude* : depravity, wickedness.
2. *owlish* [aʊlɪʃ]: with staring, unfocused eyes, like those of an owl, a nocturnal bird of prey with large, round eyes.
3. *atonement* : reconciliation (the orgy of sex and drugs in which John had participated made him part of the lifestyle he had been rejecting).
4. *dangled* : hung down and swung. (The description of the slow rotating movement of John's feet that follows, shows us that he has committed suicide by hanging himself.)

'Mr Savage!'

Slowly, very slowly, like two unhurried compass needles, the feet turned towards the right; north, north-east, east, south-east, south, south-south-west; then paused, and, after a few seconds, turned as unhurriedly back towards the left. South-south-west, south, south-east, east . . .

Preliminary Activities

Points for discussion

Ends and Means
What do you understand by the notion of "Progress"? Have human societies always referred to such a principle? What kinds of improvement in human life does the achievement of "Progress" promise? Is it justifiable to use whatever techniques, procedures and systems that may be necessary, in order to achieve the promised improvements? Does the achievement of these ends justify the means used to achieve them?

Comparing cultures
Is it possible to compare one society and its culture with another so as to decide which is "better" than the other? What factors would need to be examined?

Who, or what, can replace a man?
Can a factory-produced individual (created by genetic engineering, artificial insemination and artificially controlled growth outside the womb) be considered human? Supposing that such factory-produced individuals have to comply with certain standards in order to be approved as human beings with the same rights as other, "natural" humans, what kind and degree of modifications could be permitted?

And a little of that human touch . . .
People often say things like "It's just human nature. . ." to do this or that: but what is "human nature"? One critic says that the world we are presented with in "Brave New World, in words and objects, is a world of facsimiles behind which certain genuine human feelings faintly persist" (Jerome Meckier, Aldous Huxley: Satire and Structure, p. 182). Try to make a shortlist of such "genuine human feelings". Are they universal? Is this a list of what is essentially human in us?

Activities while Reading

Chapter I

A map of the chapter

The following jobs are mentioned: Fertilizers (p. 20), Bottle Liners, Matriculators, Labellers, Predestinators (p. 27), oxygen-reducing mechanic (p. 31), a nurse or inoculator (p. 34). Associate each one with the following rooms: Fertilizing Room, Bottling Room, Social Predestination Room, Embryo Store, Nurseries.

At what point should the Decanting Room be inserted in the previous sequence?

Getting the sense

1. The first line of the novel describes a building of "only thirty-four storeys" as "squat": what does this tell us about this future city?

2. George Orwell's novel *Nineteen Eighty-Four* (1948) begins: "It was a bright cold day in April, and the clocks were striking thirteen."

    Compare this with the first two sentences of *Brave New World*. What similarities can you see in these two openings?

Here is the opening of a science-fiction story which deliberately reminds us of its illustrious predecessors by Orwell and Huxley:

> It was half-past love on new day in Zenith and the clocks were striking heaven. All over the city the sounds of revelry echoed upwards into the dazzling Martian night, but high on Sunset Ridge, among the mansions of the rich, Margot and Clifford Gorrell faced each other in glum silence.
>
> (From "Passport to Eternity" by J.G. Ballard, circa 1955.)

How does this differ from the other two? What effects are achieved by the intertextual allusions?

3. In the first paragraph, when the World State is mentioned, the reader is expected simply to accept that it exists; in fact, as you read you are invited to absorb new information about this imaginary world without protest (perhaps without even noticing it).

What is implied by the phrase "the World State"? (Consider in particular the historical, political, social and lingulstic implications.)

Consider what is implicitly assumed when the following are mentioned:

(i) "salary" and "bonus" (p. 22);

(ii) "the last Japanese earthquake" (p. 27);

(iii) "the elephant" (p. 32).
   Can you find any other examples of this kind?

4. Near the beginning, referring to the question of the Director's age, Huxley writes: "in this year of stability, A.F. 632, it didn't occur to you to ask it" (p. 21). Who does "you" refer to? When you read this passage you cannot yet understand why nobody wonders about the age of other people (but perhaps you guessed): make a list of other things in Chapter 1 that are puzzling and of which you expect to find explanations later (e.g. what do World Controllers do?).

5. The abbreviation A.F. is of course modelled on A.D. (anno Domini): it contrasts in a witty, ironic way with what is familiar to us now, in the twentieth century. Explain how the same satirical strategy is at work in the following cases and what effects Huxley is trying to achieve:

(i) the World State's motto;

(ii) the "squat" 34-storey buildings;

(iii) "decanted" (p. 26), "Decanting Rate" (p. 27), and "trauma of decanting" (p. 30)";

(iv) "Social Predestination Room" (p. 27; it may also be useful to look ahead at the information given on page 92, in note 3);

(v) "Unforeseen wastages promptly made good" (p. 27);

(vi) the pattern of lexical choices built up by "Hatchery", "the modern fertilizing process" (p. 23), "manufacture . . . identical twins" (p. 24), "batches", "produced" (p. 26), (individuals) "Distributed" (p. 27);

(vii) the pattern formed by "Hatchery", "viviparous" (p. 24), "like chickens drinking" (p. 28), "freemartins" (p. 30), "the normality of dogs and cows", (p. 32), "gills . . . fish" (p. 34).

Look out for more examples of this formal strategy in later chapters.

"Trauma of decanting" (p. 30). The following sentence from Sigmund Freud's *Introductory Lectures on Psychoanalysis* (published in English in 1920) can be set against the obvious irony of Huxley's neologism: "It is, of course, our conviction that the disposition to repeat the first state of anxiety [i.e. birth trauma] has been so thoroughly incorporated into the organism through a countless series of generations that a single individual cannot escape the affect [sic] of anxiety even if, like the legendary Macduff [in Shakespeare's play *Macbeth*], he 'was from his mother's womb untimely ripped' [Act 5, Scene 7] and has therefore not himself experienced the act of birth".

6. In his description of the "modern fertilizing process", the D.H.C. talks of an "operation undergone voluntarily for the good of society" (p. 22): which operation does this refer to?

7. On page 24 we read: "The principle of mass production at last applied to biology". Explain this remark. What does it imply about the way humans think of themselves? Why is the phrase "uniform batches" well chosen?

8. Think carefully about our birth rate and *Brave New World*'s "Decanting Rate" and the concepts behind them: are they really comparable? Similarly, the Embryo Store is presented as a kind of womb: think about this and make a list of differences and similarities between this "womb" and the wombs of today. Do you think the same word can be used for both?

9. What effect does Huxley achieve by having Mr. Foster talk of the human growth rate as "abnormal" compared with "the normality of dogs and cows" (p. 32)?

10. What do you think the "very interesting conditioning for Alpha-Plus Intellectuals" (p. 35) might have consisted of?

Study Questions and Writing Tasks

1. Summarise the process that is carried out at the Central London Hatchery and Conditioning Centre by writing a short description of what is done at each stage.

   (Use a sentence or two for each of the rooms listed; make use of the passive form of the verb wherever possible; use sequence markers like "First of all", "After that" and "Finally".)

2. From the first page, with the hot room and the frozen light, it is clear that the text brings into play a series of contrasts.

   Find phrases or sentences that represent the following styles:

(i)   *detailed technical language;*

(ii) *abstract, philosophical statements;*

(iii) *note-taking style;*

(iv) *chatty, informal, style.*

Match the examples of different styles in list B with the labels in list A (there are two examples for some of the labels). Put the number (1-6) of the label you have chosen in the box opposite the appropriate example.

A: Styles

(1) anecdotal style; (2) oral presentation (monologue); (3) colourful, rich descriptive style; (4) inner speech; (5) free indirect speech in abbreviated form; (6) part-taking, like a comedy routine or an advertisement.

B: *Examples*

"And in effect the sultry darkness . . . faintly stirred the air". (p. 28) ☐

"Straight from the horse's mouth", "Old, young? Thirty, fifty?" (p. 21) ☐

Mr Foster and the D.H.C. from "'Eighty-six cubic metres'" to "'we now proceed ourselves'". (p. 28) ☐

"'For of course,' said Mr. Foster . . . human invention.'" (p. 30) ☐

"The enormous room . . . down the work tables". (pp. 19-20) ☐

"Obviously no use at all. But Podsnap's Technique had immensely accelerated the process of ripening". (p. 25) ☐

"'But of course they've done much better . . . We'll beat them yet.'" (p. 26) ☐

"Mature at six; . . . the human intelligence." (p. 32) ☐

"'I shall begin at the beginning,' said the D.H.C. . . . 'sterilizes.'" (p. 21) ☐

"'If you knew the amount of overtime . . . earthquake!'" (p. 27) ☐

What stylistic feature is used in the two paragraphs after the sentence "Mr. Foster duly told them" (p. 29)? Why? What effects are created?

3. Apart from the narrator's and the Director's, which other contrasting points of view are adopted in Chapter 1? Find examples of passages that are clearly written from each of these points of view.

4. Write short paragraphs describing the role of the Director, the students, Mr Foster and Lenina.

5. Summarise Bokanovsky's Technique in a written paragraph. In a second paragraph explain briefly why it is described as "one of the major instruments of social stability".

Chapter 2

1. *Reading Comprehension*

    Decide whether the following statements are true or false. Be prepared to support your choice by referring to the relevant sentences in the text.

		T	F
a.	The roses came from all over the world.	☐	☐
b.	The D.H.C. did not want the children to destroy the books and flowers.	☐	☐
c.	It takes a long time to fix conditioned reflexes.	☐	☐
d.	People in the World State often go into the country.	☐	☐
e.	The D.H.C. tells the story of Reuben to shock his students.	☐	☐

f. Hypnopaedia was initially tested on a boy called Tommy. ☐ ☐

g. At first the value of sleep teaching was misunderstood. ☐ ☐

h. All 'castes' in Brave New World undergo hypnopaedia. ☐ ☐

i. Sleep teaching is a gradual, cumulative process with very definite effects. ☐ ☐

2. How is this chapter organised? Divide it into three sections. The first and the last section each deal with a process:

a. Prepare a summary of each process, describing how it works. (Cover the following points: How is it done? When? Why?)

b. What is the author's attitude to the process? What narrative and descriptive techniques are used by Huxley?

3. What are the main effects Huxley is trying to achieve on pp. 38-39 in his account of the experiment with the flowers and books?

4. Fill in the gaps using words from the list at the end.

Hypnopaedia provides a second stage of _____ that builds on the first stage, of "_____ conditioning", described at the beginning of the chapter. Although Class Consciousness is treated as part of an _____ programme (_____ rather than _____ education), the aim is not to raise the level of _____ of one's class position, as Marxists tried to do, but to reinforce class _____. The Director is not being _____ when he declares that for sleep teaching to work "there must be words without reason"; he believes he is simply stating a fact about the necessary reinforcing of socially appropriate "courses of _____". In twentieth-century liberal democracies such _____ of attitudes is achieved without systematic organisation, and those responsible all claim to rely on _____ rather than unreason. Nevertheless, if we recognise that what the

ACTIVITIES

D.H.C. says also applies to much of this unsystematic
_____ of social attitudes, we can appreciate Huxley's
_____ humour. The target of his satire is those people,
in the _____ world (not in that of the _____), who,
like the D.H.C., believe that irrational _____ of this kind
are "_____ and socializing forces". Such people
maintain that without these forces the social order would
be at risk, and so would their own privileged and secure
position within it.

*behaviour / prejudices / future / present / wordless /
ironic / inculcation* [twice] */ moral / moralizing /
conditioning / education / reason / intellectual /
preconceptions / knowledge / satirical*

5. One critic has written: "As *children of society in the literal
sense*, men [in the World State] no longer exist in
dialectical opposition to society but rather are identical with
it in their substance" (Theodor Adorno, "Aldous Huxley and
Utopia" in *Prisms* [London: Spearman, 1967], p. 100).
Explain the phrase in italics, with reference to the first two
chapters of *Brave New World*.

Chapter 3

Getting the sense

1. Explain how the following phrases ironically contrast
conditions in the World State with present-day conditions:
   - Centrifugal Bumble-puppy;
   - "charming" (referring to "ordinary erotic play" between
little children);
   - "'Exquisite little creature!'" (as Polly Trotsky returns to
her erotic play);

- a "viviparous mother";
- "the appalling dangers of family life";
- "you *ought* to be a little more promiscuous";
- "a splendid girl: wonderfully pneumatic";
- "horror" (at someone spending time alone);
- "I really do advise you to try her";
- "conscientious objection";
- "real" (as in "real morocco-surrogate");
- "All the advantages of Christianity".

2. *Names.*

Is Bernard Marx a suitable name for that character? Why? (Remember that Karl Marx was a Jew, a member of a persecuted race.)

John Crowne is associated with the desire for amusement and an easy life: is this appropriate to Lenina Crowne?* What could be the significance of combining this name with that of Lenin, whom she does not seem to resemble at all?

> *Crowne also wrote a play entitled *Calisto, or, The Chaste Nimph* (1675); Huxley may have wished his more erudite readers to recollect this fact and enjoy the irony.

3. The adverb "majestically" (p. 51) is used to describe the movement of the conveyors: Explain why it is appropriate in the context. Is its effect the same when it is re-used in the last paragraph of the chapter, in a sentence that also repeats a phrase from Chapter I (p. 28)?

4. Find five examples of phrases expressing the students' point of view in the first few pages of the chapter (up to "Straight from the mouth of Ford himself" on page 52). How are the students characterized?

5. What do you think a "Pregnancy Substitute" is? What exactly does it substitute? Do you think it would be effective? Would it be necessary?

6. What does the Controller mean when he says, after the passage about New Guinea savages (p. 57), that "Extremes meet"?

7. The notion of 'the simple life' is associated with a desire to maintain a tried and tested, unchanging lifestyle – a tendency to resist the social and economic forces that compel people to adopt new ways of doing things, using industrially produced and commercially distributed equipment.

Explain why "Simple Lifers" (p. 68) could not be tolerated.

8. At the end of the chapter the D.H.C. sends away the children: compare the moment in the Bible when Jesus' disciples did the same (e.g. Luke 18,16). Do you think this parallel is relevant? (In Chapter 6 we read "Our Ford loved infants".)

Study Questions and Writing Tasks

1. When the Controller says that "History is bunk" (p. 52) Huxley interrupts the narrative to focus attention on the gesture that accompanies this statement. The model is Dickens' Mr Podsnap: "Mr Podsnap had even acquired a peculiar flourish of his right arm in often clearing the world of its most difficult problems, by sweeping them behind him (and consequently sheer away)" (*Our Mutual Friend*, Book I, Ch. 11). Whose point of view seems to be indicated by the phrase "it was as though", which introduces the speculative description of the implications of Mond's action? The passage then continues with a rhetorical extravagance that recalls the style of Charles Dickens, making use of *simile*, *metaphor*, *metonymy* (a concrete instance standing for something abstract), *rhetorical questions* and *repetition*.

Find examples of these rhetorical figures.

In what way does the rhythm and repetition of "whisk" especially contribute to the effect? What effect is achieved by the phrase "those specks of antique dirt" in this context? What does this passage tell us about Huxley and his narrator's attitude to the Controller's outlook?

2.   Try to explain why the Controller's description of homelife in the past makes the students "shudder"; think about the rabbit-hole metaphor, the choice and position of adjectives and adverbs (e.g. hot, insane, maniacally, agonizing) and verbs (reeking, brooded), the use of exclamations and direct speech, and the rhythm.

In the early seventeenth century, René Descartes, the French philosopher, suggested that the living body is a machine. He got this idea from Parisian automata which worked by water pressure with pipes and valves.

3.   The Controller uses the metaphor of water bursting from a pipe (see pp. 59 and 61). Try to rewrite his argument without the extended metaphor, beginning "In order for society to be stable, . . .".

The Controller assumes that one strong emotion of pleasure or pain can be equated with twenty little emotions: but if we give, say, thirty 'pleasure-points' to eating our favourite ice-cream, how many points shall we give to the emotion of falling in love? What is the problem with these equations?

When the Controller talks of "the urge" and argues "they were forced to feel strongly" (pp. 59-60) he seems to assume that everyone has a fixed amount of possible emotion that can and must be expressed: do you agree?

4.   Make a list of at least five things you know about the Nine Years' War, covering dates, causes, weapons, countries involved.

5.   Imagine you are one of the "Simple Lifers": write a brief manifesto expressing and defending your point of view.

6.   The counterpoint structure

    a.   The different narrative sequences that alternate in this chapter are like the parallel melodies that proceed simultaneously and interact in a musical composition involving the technique of counterpoint. Using the numbering of sequences (or 'melodies') suggested in note 5 on page 51, go through the chapter writing the corresponding number in the margin next to each little section: begin on page 52 with (1) ("His fordship Mustapha Mond!" etc), then (2a) on page 53 ("'Going to the Feelies . . ." etc), and so on.

b. It is interesting to analyse the inventive ways Huxley devised for linking the various narrative strands, so that the reader can follow the separate 'melodies' in his composition. Often it is the names that help us. Sometimes the passages are connected by repetition of a word or phrase (like a reiterated theme in music) or by using cognate forms of a lexical stem (stable - stability), synomyms, or related terms (associative anaphora); as the rhythm increases the gaps between the passages in any sequence gradually disappear and the coherence across the bits of discourse becomes more obvious, while the links involve more obvious forms of syntactic cohesion, like ellipsis.

ACTIVITIES

Number of sequence	Linking item in first passage of sequence	Linking item in next passage(s) in sequence	Description of the link
1	barriers (p. 61)		synonym
3		'He's so ugly.' (p. 64)	
	'Fanny Crowne's a nice girl too' (p. 67)		ellipsis
1	'The sole result . . .' (p. 67)	'Conscientious objection on an enormous scale.' (p. 68)	
	'I do love flying.' p. 68)	'Ending is better than mending, . . .' (p. 68)	
1	historical monuments (p. 69)		metonymic (by exemplification)
3	'I've had it nearly three months.' (p. 70)		
	'There was a thing. . . (p. 70)		
	'The perfect drug.' (p. 71)	'Euphoric, narcotic, pleasantly hallucinant.' (p. 71)	
2a	proffered tube (p. 72)		substitution (by pronoun)

c. Another interesting analogy with the techniques of musical composition in this chapter is in the way Huxley introduces the theme of sleep teaching: at first a faint echo, it becomes a *leitmotif* and finally emerges as an autonomous strand of counterpoint melody. Try to identify these stages.

d. One of the advantages of the counterpoint structure is that it allows Huxley to introduce some witty and ironical juxtapositions that serve his satirical purpose. For example, Fanny's mention of Obstacle Golf is followed by Mustapha Mond's discussion of the problem of the "insurmountable obstacle" (p. 63), compromising and perhaps ridiculing the serious tone he tries to adopt. Explain the irony and comic effect of the following juxtapositions:

- 'Eight hundred Simple Lifers were mowed down by machine guns at Golders Green.' (p. 68)
  'Ending is better than mending, ending is better than mending.'

- 'And a man called Shakespeare. You've never heard of them, of course.' (p. 69)
  'It's an absolute disgrace — that bandolier of mine.'
  [Also the preceding: "old black-patent bandolier . . ."]

- '. . . a thing called God.' (p. 70)
  'It's real morocco-surrogate.'

Can you find further examples of amusing juxtapositions?

What additional advantage does the counterpoint structure reveal in the section concerning *soma* (pp. 71-72)?

Try summarising the advantages of the counterpoint structure that Huxley chose to use in this chapter.

Chapter 4

1. Which words in particular associate the low-caste lift attendant with animals?

2. A "liftman" in A.F. 632 is surely an anachronism. On the other hand, helicopters were only in experimental use when Huxley wrote the book, and the first reliable models were produced in Germany in 1939. What other anticipations of future inventions and constructions are there in §1 of this chapter?

3. Looking at the sky, Bernard, moved, says "'Isn't it beautiful!'" (p. 77). Explain the satirical effect created by Lenina's response.

SATIRE: Satire itself is not a technique but a purpose, an effect that a writer intends to produce. It can be achieved by many different techniques, all of which play on the difference between a known model and another permutation or variant of it. Often the model is a stereotype or the image that some social group has of itself (e.g. university students as intelligent, interested in knowledge and well-read), which the writer contrasts with a description which is presented as corresponding better to reality or as being more plausible (e.g. an account of university students spending all their time in coffee bars and never reading more than the necessary minimum). It is most important to remember that the first of these two models is *not* the one described in detail in the satirical text: it is assumed to be a well-known cultural model. However, the text will have to ensure that the reader understands that the description given (i.e. students as the writer wants us to see them) is supposed to be compared and contrasted with some given, or standard view. Generally-speaking, satirical texts will make sure that the reader is reminded of this contrast: they will include indications of the target of the satire.

When analysing satire, therefore, it is advisable to try to distinguish, as clearly as possible, these three aspects:
– *the target*: what exactly is the author attacking or making fun of?
– *the technique(s)*: look for signs of irony, parody, exaggeration, distortion, over-extension.
– *the satirical point*: what is the implied 'message'?

4. The Red Rocket (p. 79) arrives seven minutes late and this is viewed as "scandalously unpunctual", a remark that contributes to our image of Henry and our knowledge about this future world; it can also be seen as ironically funny and as a parody (of present-day attitudes) that serves a satirical purpose: explain these levels of meaning.

5. Making reference to the three aspects described above, explain the satire in the description of newspapers and other mass media (p. 83).

6. When you first encountered Helmholtz Watson in this chapter did you think he was going to play an important part in the novel? Why?

7. In what ways does Watson's personality seem to be contradictory?

Study Questions and Writing Tasks

1. *Point of view.*

The Red Rocket (p. 79) is introduced first as "a small scarlet insect": whose point of view is this? Why is it an especially well-chosen metaphor in the context?

How is the reader made to share Bernard's point of view in §2 and what effect does it have on the reader's relationship to that character? Pay close attention to: the end of the second paragraph (where the word "wretched" is focused on); the word "hideous" in the third paragraph; interrogatives and exclamatives in his 'inner speech'.

2. *Imagery.*

There is extensive use of natural imagery in Chapter Four, §1. In the previous question we saw that the natural image of an insect was used metaphorically to describe a mechanised world. Find at least five other examples in this section and comment on their function and effect.

Chapter 5

1. What is implied by the use of the name Calvin Stopes?

2. Which "Bottle" is intended in the song? What does this suggest?

3. Why do you think the "Aphroditaeum" club is so named?

4. What does the Fordson Community Singery correspond to in our world?

5. The orgy culminates in a red "foetal darkness", as if, as in the Cabaret song, they longed to return to the Conditioning Room: what does this mean? How does it fit in with what we learn of character development in this new society?

Study Questions and Writing Tasks

1. One of the best-known poems in English literature begins:

> The curfew tolls the knell of parting day,
> The lowing herd wind slowly o'er the lea
> The ploughman homeward plods his weary way
> And leaves the world to darkness and to me.
> Now fades the glimmering landscape on the sight,
> And all the air a solemn stillness holds,
> Save where the beetle wheels his droning flight,
> And drowsy tinklings lull the distant folds;

These lines are from the "Elegy Written in a Country Churchyard" (1751), by Thomas Gray (1716-1771), who is buried in the churchyard at Stoke Poges, which is generally taken to be the setting for this poem. Look at the opening two paragraphs of Chapter 5: what corresponds to Gray's "curfew", "lowing herd" and the "droning" of the beetle? What in particular does Huxley add that has no correspondent in Gray's idyllic scene? Is this just a clever game Huxley has chosen to play, or do these allusions add something to the effect of the text? (Remember that this is a chapter that focuses exclusively on the immediate experience of Lenina and Bernard, apart from one short paragraph of Lenina's memories on p. 91).

2. Huxley uses the same technique for comic, satirical effect three times in this chapter. Look at the note for "bowels of compassion" (p. 98) and decide which technique is common to the following examples: "The crying and clashing of the harmonies were an obsession in *the melted bowels*" (p. 99); "the feet of the Greater Being . . . down the invisible stairs"

(p. 100); "it was as though she [Clara Deterding] were having her throat cut" (p. 101). Try to explain it (and give it a suitable name). What effect is Huxley trying to achieve?

3. What elements of satire can you find in this chapter and the previous one? (Consider, amongst other things, the characterization of Benito Hoover and of Lenina, the discussion of the Slough Crematorium, the Solidarity Service.)

4. It is instructive to compare the first part of Chapter 5 with Act 5, Scene 1 of Shakespeare's *Hamlet* (the churchyard scene). Compare Hamlet's famous speech when he takes the skull of the old court jester (beginning "Alas, poor Yorick!" [line 185]), with Henry's speculations on the squirt of hot gas over the Crematorium. This will help you appreciate Huxley's satirical wit.

Chapter 6

1. To what extent are the first three words the key to the whole of §1?

2. What, for Lenina, seem to be the two most important considerations in choosing a holiday location?

3. Explain the satire in: Lenina discussing Bernard with Henry "one evening when they were in bed together" (p. 105); "Semi-Demi-Finals of the Women's Heavyweight Wrestling Championship" (p. 106); " 'I am free. Free to have the most wonderful time.' " (p. 108).

4. Why was it that Bernard "absolutely refused" the ice-cream "in spite of his misery" (p. 106)? Why does he say " 'I'd rather be myself' "?

5. Why is Bernard contemptuous when Lenina says " 'Everybody's happy nowadays' " (p. 108)?

6. Is the change significant in the modified saying, "Never put off till tomorrow the fun you can have today" (p. 110)?

7. The exchanges between Bernard and Lenina are really a series of misunderstandings and non-communication: find examples of this (it happens perhaps ten times) and explain what goes wrong in each case.

8. What do you think Bernard means when he says they went to bed together "like infants" (p. 111)? Does this distinction between self-control (adult) and self-indulgence (immature) offer a valid key to the book's meaning, or is it simply more evidence of Bernard's bitterness? (See also the important piece of information given on page 114 about Alphas.)

9. Why does Bernard address the Director "as airily as possible" (p. 111)?

10. Listening to the Director's account of how he lost the girl in New Mexico, Bernard expresses sympathy for his "terrible shock", but does so "almost enviously" (p. 113): explain why, and how Huxley is using irony here.

11. Why is it appropriate to describe Huxley's use of the term "solecism" (in Bernard's thoughts, on page 112) as an instance of cataphora (a characteristic stylistic feature of Huxley's prose)?

12. Why, do you think, has "caffeine solution" (p. 116) replaced coffee?

13. Why does Bernard want Lenina to come to the Reservation with him?

14. Paraphrase the rhyme "Was and will make me ill, I take a gramme and only am" (p. 119) to make the meaning clear.

ACTIVITIES

Study Questions and Writing Tasks

1. Can you re-write the proverb, "When the individual feels, the
    community reels", without the metaphor, bringing out its
    significance for the new society?

2. Divide up the information about the Savage Reservations
    into three categories: (a) the predictable; (b) the surprising;
    (c) the most important new facts. (Which other significant
    fact about the Reservations had already been given at the
    start of the Chapter?) What techniques does Huxley adopt
    to let the reader know about the Reservations and to make
    the information more convincing? How does Huxley make
    this giving of information more interesting? Had he used
    these techniques in previous chapters?

3. List the main events of the plot in Chapters 4, 5, and 6.

4. Read the following excerpts from *The Land of Cockaygne*, a
    picture of an earthly paradise, written in about 1315. It
    belongs to a long tradition of popular images of bliss on
    earth, and, as the editor of this version notes, "There is
    nothing refined and spiritual in this poor-man's satirical,
    anti-clerical presentation of the Paradise enjoyed by the
    monks who live on the fat of the land in jeweled luxury,
    without serfdom or toil, passing their time in eating,
    drinking, flying about, and tumbling the nuns" (J.B. Trapp in
    The Oxford Anthology of English Literature, Vol. 1 [Oxford
    University Press, 1973], p.477). What similarities can you
    see between this picture and the description of the Santa
    Fé hotel (p. 115)?

> Far in the sea, to the west of Spain,
> Is a country called Cockaygne.
> There's no land not anywhere,
> In goods or riches to compare.
>
> In Cockaygne there's meat and drink,
> Without trouble, fuss and swink [toil].
> The food is fine, the drink is clear
> At noon, at snack-time, at supper.

There are many sweetest sights,
All is day, there are no nights;
(.....)
But all is play and joy and glee
Happy he that there may be.

There are rivers broad and fine
Of oil and honey, milk and wine;
Water serves there for no thing
But looking at or washing in.
There are fruits of many sorts,
Endless pleasures, joys and sports.

[Paraphrase by J.B Trapp, on the basis of the text in R.H. Robbins, *Historical Poems of the 15th and 16th Centuries* (1959), in *The Oxford Anthology*, Vol. 1, pp. 487-88.]

5. You learn a lot about a society from its favourite drug: is this true in the case of soma? Write a short paragraph developing this theme.

Chapter 7

1. Lenina comprehends the new experience in terms of what is familiar to her: where do we see this happening?

2. It is interesting to know that in the manuscript of the novel, when the shocked Lenina looked for *soma* as an escape from the horrors around her, "Huxley had Bernard explain to her why his pockets were empty: 'Why should I want to take a holiday from my holiday?' ". (As quoted in Watt, "The Manuscript Revisions" [see the Bibliography], p. 376). Huxley crossed out this sentence: what is the effect of his change?

3. Using your own words, explain why John *wanted* to be hit with the whip (p. 131).

4. Comment on the irony of Linda's complaint: " 'This beastly wool isn't like acetate. It lasts and lasts' " (p. 135).

5. Linda says "Mending's anti-social", which refers to existence in the World State: explain what "anti-social" means there. A little later in the last paragraph of Chapter 7 she complains that the Indians think she is "anti-social" if she has sex with several people "in the ordinary way" (i.e. as people normally do): how far is it appropriate to use the same term in both cases? Is it simply inappropriate? Do you think this is a case of an ironic contrast?

6. Linda, referring to John's attempt to kill Popé, says, "Being mad's infectious" (p. 136): translate this into the more scientific language that a social anthropologist might use to make the same point.

7. What makes the last lines of Chapter 7 amusing? (It is, after all, a very clear satirical attack on the human consequences of the extreme specialisation that characterises complex societies, where there is a high degree of what sociologists today call "functional differentiation"). Why is it funny that Linda lumps together those two children's questions?

Study Questions and Writing Tasks

1. The opening narrative, describing the approach to Malpais, is very convincing, partly because it involves all the senses and makes use of effective figurative language. Take a sheet of paper and draw a five-pointed star on it like this:

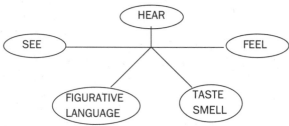

Now, go through the first five or six paragraphs (up to when Lenina says "I don't like it"), placing all the relevant items in the appropriate places in the diagram. The first sentence, for example, has words or phrases for "figurative language" (simile, metaphor), and for "see" (the "lion-coloured dust").

2. How does Huxley arrange the plot and incidents so that the encounter with the Indians will have the maximum impact on Bernard and, particularly, on Lenina? How does he keep the reader interested? (Think about how the various novelties are introduced, the surprises, the different discourse styles, shifts in point of view and so on).

3. The account of the first sight of Linda is certainly given from Lenina's point of view. This is apparent in the first sentence of the section ("The squalor of that little house . . . !"). Go through the passage (down to "Oh, my dear, my dear") identifying all the words that reflect Lenina's attitude. Summarize the paragraph in one or two sentences, beginning "The woman that Lenina saw . . .".

Chapter Eight

1. Comment on the episode in Chapter 8 (pp. 140-1) in which Linda slaps the child John after she has been beaten (from "'Oh, don't cry, Linda'".), accounting for Linda's actions in psychological terms.

2. John is dissatisfied with Linda's answers to his questions: "The old men of the pueblo had much more definite answers" (p. 144). Look at this in context: do you read it as satire involving an ironic comment on tribal myths, or as a critical comment on the secularising trend in modern culture? Or perhaps it is both?

3. Explain in your own words why John was so attracted by the passages in Shakespeare that are quoted.

4. Compare the paragraph in which the young John stabs Popé (pp. 146-7), with the earlier passage in which Linda hits him and then kisses him (pp. 140-1): what do they have in common? Huxley makes us share the child's point of view when he writes "oh, the blood!": why is this particularly effective? Notice other places where we experience this event through John's feelings (there are at least three apart from the phrases referring explicitly to his experience). Account for Popé's reaction ("Ahaiyuta" is the name of a god in Zuñi legend: why does he use this name here?) and try to say why Huxley has introduced this episode.

5. What do Bernard and John have in common? Refer to passages where specific similarities emerge.

Study Questions and Writing Tasks

1. List what we learn about John's past in Chapters 7 and 8, selecting the facts that seem particularly significant.

2. Look carefully at the second section on pages 137-138 (from "It was very hot" to "She didn't answer"). Identify the words and phrases that accentuate the fact that the narrator perceives the world from a child's point of view, helping the reader to imaginatively share the experience.

3. "Everybody belongs to every one else": this slogan, which was introduced in Chapter 3 (pp. 58, 61 and 65), and reiterated in Chapter 7 (p. 136) and again here (p. 141), has been described as "a synthetic myth mediating a hidden emotional conflict inherent in a society where it is evident that nobody belongs to anybody or anything" (Peter Larsen, "Synthetic Myths . . .", p. 506). Larsen further explains that "the synthetic myth is typically geared for reiteration, and does not provide intellectual, but only moral knowledge" and he divides those in *Brave New World* into "five groups: jingles, rewritten nursery rhymes, rewritten proverbs and pseudostatements" (p. 507). By "pseudostatements" he means statements that are accepted as "axiomatic, self-evident, utterly indisputable" (as the text says with reference to the proverbs: BNW, p. 58), but which cannot in fact be proven either true or false because it is impossible "to establish the conditions under which truth or falsity can be determined" (Larsen, p. 508) — for example "progress is lovely" (BNW, p. 116). Find a couple of examples of each of the five groups.

What do you think of Larsen's contention that the jingles "are only marginally different from advertising slogans in our society" (p. 507)? He cites as examples "Things go better with Coke" and "The right one, the bright one: Martini": "Once a slogan has been associated with a product, it tends to become even shorter. Martini's slogan has been reduced to 'the right one'. 'Martini' and 'the right one' become synthetic myths which disguise the processes of their mediation" (p. 507). Do you agree? Can you think of further examples of your own? Try to explain in your own words the following point made by Peter Larsen, illustrating your argument with reference to your own examples: "Any specific oppositions which might be mediated by consuming e.g. Martini have disappeared" (p. 507).

Chapter Nine

1. Compare the two conversations on page 154. How does Huxley indicate the way that the relative positions and presuppositions of the speakers affect the way they address each other? Do Bernard's stammering (with the Controller) and interrupting (with the Warden) have any communicative function? In other words, how do they reveal the interpersonal aspect of the exchanges, at least from Bernard's point of view?

2. We know more about Lenina than John does: how is this crucial to the effects created in Chapter 9 and the last page of Chapter 8? Give specific examples, paying attention especially to the Shakespeare quotations. Does this mean that John is simply an idealistic fool to be laughed at? If not, why not?

Chapter Ten

1. How does Huxley indicate immediately to the reader, perhaps unfamiliar with the districts of London, that the Bloomsbury Centre is the Central London Centre by another name?

2. What is the main function of the first four paragraphs? The most noticeable new elements are, on one side, the insistence on the "buzz" of work in that "hive" of activity, and, on the other . . . what? See the fourth paragraph and identify all the words that bring out this other aspect, which had not been emphasised in the first chapters. Why is it foregrounded now?

3. In what way is the reprimanding of Bernard like a "show trial" in miniature? Given this similarity, what is the target of Huxley's satire here? Which phrases in particular indicate the target to the reader?

4. Why, in your opinion, does the Director refer to Bernard's opinions about sport and soma as "heretical views" (p. 160)? Explain the orthodox view.

5. Why is it ironic that Bernard's revenge on the Director should take place in the Fertilizing Room? How does Huxley increase the drama of the confrontation?

6. Which entry has the greater dramatic impact, that of Linda or that of John? Why?

Follow-up Activity

This chapter recounts a very dramatic episode. Go through it, selecting a minimal number of significant phrases that can be memorised and recited as the basis of a brief re-enactment of the action with four main characters and a crowd of onlookers (who will have to laugh or be silent at the appropriate moments).

Chapter Eleven

1. What changes do we see in Bernard in this chapter?

2. Is John impressed by what he is told about the Bombay Green Rocket (p. 169)? How does Huxley let us know?

3. According to Bernard's report, John, the Savage, finds "civilized infantility too easy or, as he puts it, not expensive enough" (p. 169): explain what you think he means in your own words.

4. Why does Mond start to laugh at Bernard's report? Which is the word that first indicates this new response?

5. In what sense was it "*some malice* of his memory" that made John repeat Miranda's "brave new world" speech at one point (on page 171)?

6. Comment on Huxley's witty inversion of 'normal' views, when he has Bernard first note that "early conditioning" can "run counter [i.e. go in the opposite direction] to natural impulses" (p. 171), only to explain what he means in a way that will probably upset most readers expectations (and make them smile at Huxley's joke).

7. Huxley's choice of the epithet "venerable piles" for Eton (p. 171) is intentionally incongruous and humorous, as is the use of the adjective "quaint" (see note 2, p. 164) for the "chrome-steel statue of Our Ford" (p.171). Vita-glass, in particular, was a modern material in the thirties and its use was considered hygienic, thanks to propaganda about the role of the sun in preventing rickets; this is why, in the gently ironic lines of John Betjeman's poem "The Dear Old Village", we read, "And many a cultivated hour they pass / In a fine school with walls of vita-glass". Comment on Huxley's humorous effects in these lexical choices.

8. Comment on this passage from the article by June Deery (cited in the *Bibliography*):

> . . . we can assume that numerous upper-class females exist somewhere in this society – there is nothing which precludes this – but in Huxley's account we get only a brief glance of one of them – the headmistress at Eton. Even here we encounter her when she is in a position of need relative to the Alpha-Plus male who approaches her, and we note that her superior is a male Provost. The name of this upper-class female is, incidentally, 'Miss' Keate, surely an anachronistic form of address in a society where there is no marriage. Perhaps Huxley has forgotten this in his desire to recreate the stereotype of the spinsterish headmistress, the woman who achieves her position only by forfeiting her 'true femininity'. (p. 262)

9. What important new fact do we discover about the Savage Reservations?

10. In Dr. Gaffney's account of their library (p. 174), identify the technique used for humorous effect. If this passage is satirical, what is the target of the satire and the implicit criticism being made?

11. Lenina at one point says "they all want to know . . . what it's like to make love to a Savage" (p. 176): if you had been writing the novel, would you have retained our expression "make love" in this context? Why/why not?

12. The feely, *Three Weeks in a Helicopter*, is intended to seem ridiculous and to parody the novel *Three Weeks* (see the note on page 178), which had become notorious for its love scenes, described with lavish excess, that take place on a tiger-skin (cf. Lenina's mention of a "bear-skin rug" on page 53); its readers were encouraged to feel morally superior to the lovers (who are punished at the end), while no doubt the main reason why most people read the book was to participate, emotionally, in the very eroticism they denounced. Can you now explain the satirical irony of the ending of the feely?

There is also satire at the expense of those cultural tendencies that Huxley parodied and exaggerated in the *Brave New World* society. Relate the following phrases in particular to this overall satirical purpose: "He developed for the Beta blonde an <u>exclusive and maniacal</u> passion." / "a wildly <u>anti-social</u> *tête-à-tête*" / ended happily and <u>decorously</u> with the Beta blonde becoming the mistress of all her three rescuers". What techniques are mainly used here?

Huxley brings into play stereotypes that can be described as racist and sexist: does this mean *Brave New World* is a racist and sexist book? What other examples of racist or sexist presuppositions have you noticed so far?

13. In the last two paragraphs there is a deliberate and careful parallelism between John's actions and those of Lenina, "took out" matching "pulled out" and so on. What do you think Huxley is implying?

14. How, in this chapter and the previous one, does Huxley prepare the reader for John's behaviour at the beginning of Chapter 12? Are we supposed to be surprised?

Study Questions and Writing Tasks

1. Chapter 11 consists of: (1) linking narration; (2) direct speech passages, illustrating relationships and incidents; (3) Mond's reading of Bernard's report. The linking narration, although generally deriving from an omniscient, external viewpoint, continually drifts from this detached point of view to that of certain of the characters, which may also be illustrated by direct quoting of speech or writing, as in (2) and (3). Go through the chapter, carefully noting where the narrative has adopted the point of view of one of the characters within the storyworld (an internal point of view). Particularly interesting and effective is the oscillation between the point of view of Lenina and that of John in the final section at the "feelies".

2. Identify the single passage in the omniscient narration in which another external point of view seems to have been adopted: that of a technician with 'inside knowledge' of the technological processes in the society. Whose 'voice' are we presumably listening to in this passage of free indirect speech?

Chapter Twelve

1. In today's world, the Archbishop of Canterbury (in Kent), is the head of the Church of England. He is also known as the Primate of All England and is a very important public and religious figure. Huxley's "Arch-Community-Songster" is clearly modelled on this figure. Make a list of features in the first part of the chapter that make this identification (with an uncharitable stereotype) obvious. Does he seem to belong more to our society or to theirs?

2. Why exactly does Lenina feel "a sense of dreadful emptiness" (p. 184) when Bernard announces that John is not coming? Was the feeling new to her? Which other unusual feeling had already been mentioned?

3. Is it significant that Lenina "had lingered for a moment to look at the moon" (p. 186)?

4. What specifically was it that made the 'New Theory of Biology' unpublishable? In what way was this notion "dangerous and potentially subversive"? What happens to inventive, clever people in the World State?

5. Helmholtz and the Savage like each other at once (after their first meeting): why is this? How does Huxley show us the limitations of Helmholtz's understanding?

6. When Huxley composed Helmholtz's poetry, what considerations do you think he had in mind? Is it accidental that it is not very appealing?

7. According to La Rochefoucauld, "In the distress of our best friends we always find something that does not displease us". Perhaps Huxley had this in mind when he wrote the sentence, "One of the principal functions of a friend is to suffer (in a milder and symbolic form) the punishments that we should like, but are unable, to inflict on our enemies" (p. 189). Whose opinion is this? Do you agree? Are you expected to agree? Why is this comment introduced?

8. What do you think Helmholtz might mean when he calls for "some other kind of madness and violence" (p. 194)? Why do you think the chapter closes on this comment?

Study Questions and Writing Tasks

1. Make a list of the new aspects of Bernard's character that are revealed in this chapter and write a 'character study': briefly describe his past and his aspirations, but discuss in greater detail how both the good and bad sides of his personality have been accentuated by circumstances, giving specific examples to demonstrate the changes that occur.

2. Write a short paragraph explaining, in your own words, why Helmholtz finds *Romeo and Juliet* so funny.

Chapter Thirteen

1. The little paragraph about the "promising young Alpha-Minus administrator" in Africa who will die of sleeping-sickness as a result of Lenina's moment of distraction (p. 196) gives us several bits of information about this imaginary world: make a list of them. Which contrast or disproportion is this aside intended to demonstrate? Which elements in particular play a part in indicating this?

2. Why was Lenina "genuinely shocked" (p. 200) at John's account of a marriage vow? Why does Huxley make a point of telling us this?

3. Which "unspoken hint" (p. 201) does John, for a moment, believe Lenina has understood? Why would this have been impossible for her?

4. What is implied by Huxley's choice of the terms "advanced", "retreated", "intruding" and "brought to bay" (p. 202), and later, "striding up and down, marching, marching" (p. 204), and "parleying" (p. 206)?

Study Questions and Writing Tasks

1. Taking as your model the paragraph examined in the first question above, write a comparable sentence or two about similar cases of criminal irresponsibility. For example, a lorry driver listening to the radio or lighting a cigarette as he thunders at speed through a built-up area where children play.

2. Lenina starts a number of sentences without finishing them: complete them for her. (See pages 198, 199, 201, 203).

3. Examine the quotations from Shakespeare in this chapter: what distinguishes the first ones from the last ones? Between these two categories are some that address another theme, which leads John from the tone of the first quotations to that of the last ones: what is the theme that these in-between quotations share? More generally, what do most of the quotations have in common? In what way are they crucial in explaining John's reactions to Lenina's attempted seduction?

4. Reconstruct the telephone conversation at the end of Chapter 13, filling in the missing part.

Chapters Fourteen and Fifteen

1. A "Hospital for the Dying" with a "Galloping Senility" ward: comment on the satire brought into play in these names.

2. What does the nurse mean when she says that "Number 3 . . . Might go off any minute now" (p. 209)?

3. While John is at Linda's bedside, he calls to mind an image he still has of the "beautiful Other Place" as "a paradise of goodness and loveliness": why is it appropriate to introduce this elegaic tone here, lamenting the loss of innocence? Which recent incident in the story marked the culmination of the defilement of John's memory "by contact with the reality"? What seems to be implied by the refusal of these memories to reappear (pp. 212-3) and by the resurgence of bad memories of his own past life?

4. Which incident does Linda apparently relive when John arouses her from "her *soma*-holiday with Popé" (p. 213)?

5. What was the number of Linda's bed?

6. Huxley returns to the notion of defilement when he has John see the twins as maggots that "swarmed defilingly over the mystery of Linda's death" (p. 217). In what way does this observation clarify the deeper meaning of the death scene in the narrative of John's character-development? (The word "defile" will recur definitively and very effectively at the start of Chapter 18).

7. Once again John finds himself involuntarily remembering the "brave new world" speech from *The Tempest*, as he had in the electrical equipment factory (p. 171): what do the two situations have in common? What is it that particularly disturbs John? In what way is his reaction a vivid dramatisation of one of the philosophical themes being explored in the novel?

8. John, in a rage, shouts at the Deltas " 'I'll make you be free whether you want to or not' " (p. 220); Huxley perhaps intended this as a sarcastic allusion to the contradictions in the thought of Jean-Jacques Rousseau (see note 1, p. 104) since, as Peter Firchow has pointed out, "This is an unmistakable allusion to the famous/infamous Rousseauean doctrine that there can be no slaves, not even willing ones, for such perverse creatures would have to be 'forced to be free'" (*End of Utopia*, p.90). Comment on the irony of the Savage's statement in relation to (1) John's original intentions; (2) the concept of freedom in the World State; (3) the imposition of utopian aims in general. The whole paragraph reflects John's point of view: which other words and phrases in particular reveal his contemptuous attitude?

9. The proverb "God helps those who help themselves" is normally intended as a reminder about the dangers of apathy and inactivity, but on page 221 Watson ironically takes it too seriously: what meaning does he apparently give it?

10. What elements of satire are there in the account of how the police deal with these troublemakers?

Study Questions and Writing Tasks

1. Illustrate how the theme of conflict and non-communication runs through Chapter 14. Exactly what oppositions are at work?

2. The episode in the Hospital for the Dying involves a conflict between two very different ways of thinking about death: briefly define those two attitudes and then show how Huxley exploits the possibilities of the situation to bring out the contrast and intensify the drama.

Chapter Sixteen

1. How are Bernard and Helmholtz contrasted at the start of the chapter?

2. It could be said that the presence of the "massive volume" by "Our Ford", *My Life and Work*, is in conflict with the principles of the society: do you agree?

3. Why is John caught by surprise when he meets the Controller? Why is his surprise still further increased when they start to talk?

4. Why don't the Controllers want anything old in their "brave new world"?

5. When John exclaims "Goats and monkeys!" (see the note to p. 226), the Controller murmurs "Nice tame animals, anyhow": what do you think he means by this?

6. What is the main difficulty involved in Helmholtz's job?

7. What do you suppose the Controller means when he talks of (1) "over-compensations for misery" (p. 228) and (2) the notion that everyone "goes through life inside a bottle" (p. 229)? (In both cases it seems likely that Huxley is using Mond as a mouthpiece for his own views).

8. In the Controller's metaphor of the iceberg (p. 230), what does "the water line" represent?

9. Can you summarise the Controller's argument against developing the full potential of all members of society? What difference does it make if we bring into consideration also the use of automation, robots and computerisation?

10. What does Mustapha Mond mean by "real science" and why is it like "unorthodox cooking"?

11. If "truth" and "beauty" are two of the key terms in this chapter, what is the other? What is the significance of the Nine Years' War in relation to these three?

Study Questions and Writing Tasks

1. Write a short explanation of why Bokanovsky Groups are "the foundation on which everything else is built" (p. 228).

2. Referring to any of the historical events described by Mond, write six conditional sentences about what *would have* happened if some factor *had been* different.

    e.g. If other forms of activity had been available after work during the Ireland experiment, there would not have been unrest and workers would not have consumed so much *soma*.

Chapter Seventeen

1. What is the purpose of Chapter 17? Why is this material introduced at this point, just before the final chapter? What is the key word, introduced in the first sentence, that links the various quotations?

2. Does it appear that Mond has properly understood the passages he quotes, particularly from Maine de Biran?

3. Cicero refers to the argument of Chrysippus that "as nature shows phenomena which are beyond the capacity of men, there must be in the universe a power greater than Man".* Perhaps John had in mind arguments of this kind when he suggested that it is natural to feel there is a God (p. 240): what do you think of the Controller's response? Is it a satisfactory and appropriate answer?

    *The Nature of the Gods, translated by Horace C.P. McGregor, Penguin Books, 1972, p. 199.

4. What is your reaction to the Controller's statement that, in modern times, God "manifests himself as an absence"? Does he explain why God is not compatible with machinery and universal happiness? Can you try and make his argument for him?

5. In assessing the happiness of the individual, Mond says "you've got to stick to one set of postulates" (p. 242). What do you understand by this? Do you agree, or can the values of one society be used to judge another? (Consistently with this position, Mond never claims that his is a perfect society, although critics often overlook this; the most he claims is that it is "properly organized").

6. Explain the connection between "industrial civilization" and "self-indulgence" (p. 243) that the Controller asserts exists. Do you agree?

7. The Controller asserts that "There's no such thing as a divided allegiance" (p. 243): is this true, judging by what we've seen so far of individuals in this society?

8. "'Isn't there something in living dangerously?'" asks John (p. 245): what comment would you make on the reply he gets from Mond?

9. Does the final formulation of the choice between the Savage's position and that of the Controller accurately reflect the issues they have touched on? Is the real nature of the choice to do with "claiming the right to be unhappy" or does this formulation reflect the limited comprehension each has?

10. In *Brave New World Revisited* Huxley writes:

> Any bird that has learned how to grub up a good living without being compelled to use its wings will soon renounce the privilege of flight and remain forever grounded. Something analogous is true of human beings. If the bread is supplied regularly and copiously three times a day, many of them will be perfectly content to live by bread alone . . . (Chapter 12; Grafton Books paperback edition, p. 186).

Having read Chapter 17, can you explain how this analogy relates to *Brave New World*?

Chapter Eighteen

1. What causes the "unpleasant and characteristic sound" that opens the chapter?

2. Do you think the Controller gave the real reason why the Savage could not go to the islands with the others?

3. We are told that after his "purifications" John "felt he had earned the right to inhabit the lighthouse" (p. 250): which statements of his in previous chapters should have had led us to expect sentiments of this kind at this point?

4. Why does the Savage resolve not to eat the "pan-glandular biscuits" he had brought, "even if he were starving" (p. 252)? Who is responsible for the further comment "It would also teach him": the narrator or John himself? What is its significance?

5. The sentence on page 253 recapitulating John's reasons for coming to the lighthouse ("It was to escape . . . ") makes its clear why the word earlier used to describe his chosen place of retreat was particularly suitable: what was the word?

6. Why do you think Huxley uses the simile of turkey buzzards to describe the reporters?

7. Thinking of his mother (on pages 259-60), John remembers from *Hamlet* the phrase "good kissing carrion"; the word "carrion" here means the flesh of a dead animal, but in Shakespeare it can also be applied with contempt to living flesh given up to sexual pleasure. Could this be relevant here?

8. Why is the final episode described as an "orgy of atonement" (p. 264)?

9. Is it accidental or is it inevitable that John's experience of solitude finishes tragically? Is the ending tragic in your opinion? Are there any comic elements?

10. What elements of satire are there in the final section, from the point when "the first of the reporters found him" (p. 254)?

Writing Tasks

1. To what extent is the ending a satisfactory conclusion to the novel? Or is it really only the conclusion of John's personal story?

2. Try to explain concisely (in a few sentences) why it is that John kills himself at this point.

Reviewing Activities and Follow-up Work

1. Try to complete this chronological chart, which is based on
   that in Robert S. Baker, *The Dark Historic Page*, pp. 138-39
   (see *Bibliography*).

A.F. 141	Outbreak of .... followed by ....
....	Beginning of "World Control". The "conscription of ...." followed by a period of social restiveness and instability.
	The rise of "........................... objection and [a] .... movement".
	The .... massacre of "................... ...."
	The British Museum Massacre.
	Abandonment of force by the ....
	Period of social re-education; intensive propaganda against .... reproduction; a "campaign against .... "
	Museums ....
	Suppression of all .... before A.F. 150.
A.F. 178	Government subsidization of special programmes in .... and ....
	Stabilization of the World State.
A.F. 473	....
....	Civil war in Cyprus. .... Alphas killed.
A.F. 482 (approx.)	The .... Experiment (increased .... time and .... hours of work per day).
....	The present of *Brave New World*.

2. Write a brief summary of Aldous Huxley's message in *Brave New World*, relating it to the epigraph by Berdiaeff (p. 3): focus on the question of why, according to Huxley, people will not want a utopia when they can have one.

3. **a.** One critic characterises the main characters in the novel using the following phrases: "the eager-beaver management type" (two examples, one of them "in maturer form"); "the popular girl . . . fashionable and desirable, but not quite conforming to the official sexual code"; a "more conventional" girl, "given to pious platitudes and 'moral' exhortations"; "the misfit" (adapted from Peter Firchow, *The End of Utopia*, p. 81). Identify each of them.

b. Using the following chart, the characters can be reconsidered. You have to put together lists of significant facts about each of the characters in turn; then divide the information into the four categories.

BNW CHARACTERS

A.
ARENA
(public knowledge)

What s/he knows about him/herself	What others know about him/her

Bernard works in the Psychology Bureau (p. 51)

B.
FAÇADE
(private knowledge)

What s/he knows about him/herself	What others do **not** know about him/her

He wants to kill some of those around him (p. 72)

C.
BLINDSPOT
(others' knowledge)

What s/he does **not** know about him/herself	What others know about him/her

He is a coward (p. 221)

D.
UNKNOWN
(unrecognised factors)

What s/he **not** know about him/herself	What others do **not** know about him/her

He longs for strong experiences (p. 1113)

4. *Language.*

In *Brave New World* "having" tends to mean "having sex with"; what other examples of semantic shift and of new coinages can you find? Why do you think Huxley has, on the whole, included so few (compared with many science-fiction stories or with George Orwell's *Nineteen Eighty-Four*, with its "Newspeak")?

5. The classic descriptions of utopias in the English tradition, from Thomas More's *Utopia* (1516), through Jonathan Swift's *Gulliver's Travels* (1726), to Bulwer Lytton's *The Coming Race* (1871) or William Morris's *News from Nowhere* (1890) are invariably presented as the narrative of a returned traveller. For example, More's Raphael Hythloday has travelled to unknown lands and gains respect by "speaking as shrewdly about the manners and governments of each place he had visited briefly as though he had lived there all his life" (Book 1). After reading the following excerpts, which are included for comparison, write a short account of how Huxley in the first three chapters of *Brave New World* has solved the problem of informing the reader about how his imaginary society is organised. (Think about the role of the students in particular.)

(i) ". . . I happened to see Peter talking with a stranger, ... When Peter saw me he approached and greeted me. As I was about to return his greeting, he drew me aside and, indicating the stranger, said, 'Do you see that man? I was just on the point of bringing him to you. (...) for there is no man alive today who can tell you so much about strange peoples and unexplored lands; and I know that you are always greedy for such information.' (...)

When Peter had told me this, I thanked him for his kindness in introducing me to a man whose conversation he hoped I would enjoy, and then I turned toward Raphael. After greeting one another and exchanging the usual civilities of strangers upon their first meeting, we all went to my house. There in the garden we sat down on bench covered with grassy turf to talk together. (...)

Now I intend to relate only what he told us about the manners and institutions of the Utopians, ..."

(Thomas More, *Utopia*, Book 1, translation by Robert M. Adams)

(ii) "I desired leave of this Prince to see the curiosities of the island [of Laputa], which he was graciously pleased to grant, and ordered my tutor to attend me. I chiefly wanted to know to what cause in art or in nature it owed its several motions, whereof I will now give a philosophical account to the reader." (Part III, Ch. 3)

"I had the favour of being admitted to several Houyhnhnms, who came to visit or dine with my master; where his Honour graciously suffered me to wait in the room, and listen to their discourse. (...) By conversing with the Houyhnhnms, and looking upon them with delight, I fell to imitate their gait and gesture, ..." (Part IV, Ch.10)

(Jonathan Swift, *Gulliver's Travels*)*

*See also: W.K. Thomas, *"Brave New World* and the Houyhnhnms", *Revue de l'Université d'Ottawa*, Vol.37 (1967), pp.688-96.

(iii) "'Frankly, my dear Guest, you will do me a great service if you are come to set my old tongue wagging. (...) Am I to consider you as an inquirer who knows a little of our modern ways of life, or as one who comes from some place where the very foundations of life are different from ours — do you know anything or nothing about us?'

He looked at me keenly and with growing wonder in his eyes as he spoke; and I answered in a low voice:

'I know only so much of your modern life as I could gather from using my eyes on the way here from Hammersmith, and from asking some questions of Richard Hammond, most of which he could hardly understand.'

The old man smiled at this. 'Then,' said he, 'I am to speak to you as -'

'As if I were a being from another planet,' said I."

(William Morris, *News from Nowhere*, Ch. 9)

6. If you can find the science-fiction novel *Childhood's End* (1954) [*Le guide del tramonto* in Italian] by Arthur C. Clarke, you can compare the Cyprus experiment in *Brave New World* with the Athens Colony described in Chapters 15ff of Clarke's book. This is a more optimistic look at an experiment in social engineering involving a community of exceptional individuals on an island.

7. Huxley refers in *Brave New World Revisited*, Chapter 12, to the parable of the Grand Inquisitor given in *The Brothers Karamazov* by Feodor Dostoyevsky (1821-81), which is a model for the Controller's contentions in Chapter 17 and in reference to the Cyprus experiment described in Chapter 16; you will find it interesting and useful to read the relevant chapter of Dostoyevsky's novel and make comparisons with *Brave New World.*

8. Find out what Sigmund Freud said that could be described as revealing "the appalling dangers of family life" (Chapter 3); of particular relevance to *Brave New World* are Freud's studies of the Oedipus complex, of sexuality in children and of the damaging consequences of repression.

9. The anthropologist Bronislaw Malinowski had, in 1914-18, carried out fieldwork on the South Pacific islands mentioned in *Brave New World*, and his findings had become the subject of public interest thanks to his books, *Argonauts of the Western Pacific* (1922) and *Sex and Repression in Savage Society* (1927). In Chapter 3, the World Controller presents a wistful, idealising image of the world they describe: compare this picture with the accounts given by anthropologists such as Malinowski or Margaret Mead (especially her *Coming of Age in Samoa* [1932] and the section on sex and temperament in her 1935 book, *Three Primitive Societies*). In a letter of 28th November 1930, Huxley recommends Malinowski's *Sexual Life of Savages* and a book entitled *Growing up in New Guinea* which 'he thinks' is by Margaret Mead, commenting that it is "an account of savages more puritanical than New England Calvinists in the 17th century!" (*Letters*, pp. 343-4).

10. J.G. Ballard's short story "Passport to Eternity" (in his collection *The Venus Hunters*, 1980), which is quoted in the activities for Chapter One, makes interesting reading alongside *BNW*. It extends Huxley's parody of the idea of dream-holidays (three grammes "for a dark eternity on the moon") and presents a satirical portrait that can be compared to that in *Brave New World.*